FUNCTIONAL LINKAGE IN BIOMOLECULAR SYSTEMS

Functional Linkage in Biomolecular Systems

Edited by

Francis O. Schmitt
Diana M. Schneider

Neurosciences Research Program
Massachusetts Institute of Technology
Boston, Massachusetts

Donald M. Crothers
Yale University
New Haven, Connecticut

with the organizing and editorial assistance of

Parvati Dev
Neurosciences Research Program
Massachusetts Institute of Technology
Boston, Massachusetts

Frederick E. Samson, Jr.
Ralph Smith Center for Mental
Retardation
University of Kansas Medical Center
Kansas City, Kansas

1975

Raven Press, Publishers ▪ New York

Made in the United States of America

International Standard Book Number
0–89004–006–0
Library of Congress Catalog Card Number
74–144–79

ISBN outside North and South America only: 0–7204–7535–x

To Barbara

For encouragement, patience, and understanding always

Frank

Acknowledgment of Sponsorship and Support

Grateful acknowledgment for support of the conference is made to the following donors: the Camille and Henry Dreyfus Foundation, the Green Foundation, National Institutes of Health Research Support Grant (Massachusetts Institute of Technology), the Vingo Trust II, the Volkswagen Foundation, and A. Zaffaroni.

Sponsored by the Massachusetts Institute of Technology, the Neurosciences Research Program is supported in part by the National Aeronautics and Space Administration; the U.S. Public Health Service; National Institute of Mental Health Grant No. MH23132; National Institute of Neurological Diseases and Stroke Grant No. NS09937; the National Science Foundation; the Office of Naval Research; the Grant Foundation; Neurosciences Research Foundation; the Rogosin Foundation; and the Alfred P. Sloan Foundation.

Foreword

This volume is based on a week-long conference held August 2–7, 1973 in Pebble Beach, California, organized and sponsored by the Neurosciences Research Program (NRP). It represents a major departure from previous NRP conferences, in that it was concerned with the role in neuroscience of a single broad physicochemical principle—that of functional linkage in biomolecular systems.

The conference was organized as a series of 13 topics, each represented by several leading investigators in the respective fields. This volume essentially follows the conference format. To focus maximally on the broad concept of functional linkage, the volume was prepared by the editors following the conference, in the style used in the *NRP Bulletin;* it is not a collection of papers submitted by the participants. One of us (D.S.) organized the transcriptual material into chapters. These were submitted to participants for approval and updatings and the revised material was then integrated by the editors into the final manuscript.

The editors wish to extend their gratitude to the NRP staff, without which this volume and the conference on which it was based could not have come about.

F. O. Schmitt
D. M. Schneider
D. M. Crothers
August, 1974

Contents

Participants

Gerold Adam
Dozent, Fachbereich Biologie
Universität Konstanz
775 Konstanz,
Federal Republic of Germany

W. Ross Adey
Professor of Anatomy and Physiology
Brain Research Institute
University of California
Los Angeles, California 90024

Julius Adler
Professor, Departments of
Biochemistry and Genetics
University of Wisconsin
Madison, Wisconsin 53706

Daniel E. Atkinson
Professor of Chemistry
Chemistry Department
University of California
Los Angeles, California 90024

Lloyd M. Beidler
Professor, Department of Biological Science
Florida State University
Tallahassee, Florida 32306

Howard C. Berg
Associate Professor
Department of Molecular,
Cellular and Developmental Biology
University of Colorado
Boulder, Colorado 80302

Floyd E. Bloom
Chief, Laboratory of Neuropharmacology
Division of Special Mental Health Research
National Institute of Mental Health
St. Elizabeth's Hospital
Washington, D.C. 20032

Robert Blumenthal
Laboratory of Theoretical Biology
National Cancer Institute
National Institutes of Health
Bethesda, Maryland 20014

William E. Bunney, Jr.
Director, Division of Narcotic
Addiction and Drug Abuse
National Institute of Mental Health
Rockville, Maryland 20852

Melvin Calvin
Director, Laboratory of Chemical
Biodynamics
University of California
Berkeley, California 94720

Carolyn Cohen
Professor of Biology
Member, Rosenstiel Basic Medical Science
Center
Brandeis University
Waltham, Massachusetts 02154

Richard Cone
Professor of Biophysics
Department of Biophysics
Johns Hopkins University
Baltimore, Maryland 21218

Jack D. Cowan
Professor and Chairman
Department of Theoretical Biology
University of Chicago
Chicago, Illinois 60637

Donald M. Crothers
Professor of Chemistry, Molecular
Biophysics, and Biochemistry
Department of Chemistry
Yale University
New Haven, Connecticut 06520

Vincent G. Dethier
Professor of Biology
Department of Biology
Princeton University
Princeton, New Jersey 08540

Parvati Dev
Staff Scientist
Neurosciences Research Program
Massachusetts Institute of Technology
165 Allandale Street
Jamaica Plain Station
Boston, Massachusetts 02130

Jared M. Diamond
Professor of Physiology
Physiology Department
University of California Medical Center
Los Angeles, California 90024

Edward A. Dratz
Assistant Professor of Chemistry and
  Biochemistry
Natural Sciences II
University of California
Santa Cruz, California 95060

Mac V. Edds, Jr.
Dean of Natural Sciences and Mathematics
South College
University of Massachusetts
Amherst, Massachusetts 01002

Gerald M. Edelman
Professor, The Rockefeller University
New York, New York 10021

Stuart J. Edelstein
Assistant Professor of Biochemistry
Section of Biochemistry,
  Molecular and Cell Biology
Cornell University
Ithaca, New York 14850

Manfred Eigen
Director, Max Planck Institute
  for Biophysical Chemistry
Göttingen, Federal Republic of Germany

C. Fred Fox
Professor of Molecular Biology in
  Bacteriology
Department of Bacteriology
University of California
Los Angeles, California 91403

Guido Guidotti
Professor of Biochemistry
Harvard University
The Biological Laboratories
Cambridge, Massachusetts 02138

Gordon G. Hammes
Professor and Chairman
Chemistry Department
Cornell University
Ithaca, New York 14850

Terrell L. Hill
Senior Research Chemist
Laboratory of Molecular Biology
National Institutes of Health
Bethesda, Maryland 20014

Hugh E. Huxley
Medical Research Council Laboratory
  of Molecular Biology
Hills Road
Cambridge, England

Karl-Ernst Kaissling
Wissenchaftliches Mitglied der
  Max-Planck-Gesellschaft
Dozent, Max-Planck-Institut für
  Verhaltensphysiologie
8131 Seewiesen,
  Federal Republic of Germany

Lynn C. Klotz
Assistant Professor
Department of Biochemistry and
  Molecular Biology
Harvard University
Cambridge, Massachusetts 02138

Juan Igal Korenbrot
Lecturer, Physiology Department
University of California
School of Medicine
Los Angeles, California 90024

Daniel E. Koshland, Jr.
Professor of Biochemistry
Department of Biochemistry
University of California
Berkeley, California 94720

Albert L. Lehninger
DeLamar Professor and Director of the
  Department of Physiological Chemistry
The Johns Hopkins University
  School of Medicine
Baltimore, Maryland 21205

Harden M. McConnell
Professor of Chemistry
Department of Chemistry
Stanford University
Stanford, California 94305

Donald M. MacKay
Professor of Communications
University of Keele
Staffordshire ST5 5BG, England

James C. Metcalfe
National Institute for Medical Research
Mill Hill
London NW7 1AA, England

Garth L. Nicolson
Director, Electron Microscopy Laboratory
The Salk Institute
San Diego, California 92112

Marshall W. Nirenberg
Chief, Laboratory of Biochemical Genetics
National Heart and Lung Institute
National Institutes of Health
Bethesda, Maryland 20014

Gustav J. V. Nossal
Director and Professor of Medical Biology
The Walter and Eliza Hall Institute
  of Medical Research
Royal Melbourne Hospital
Melbourne, Victoria 3050, Australia

Lars Onsager
Professor, Center for Theoretical Studies
University of Miami
Coral Gables, Florida 33124

Michael A. Raftery
Professor of Chemical Biology
Division of Chemistry and
  Chemical Engineering
California Institute of Technology
Pasadena, California 91109

David A. Rees
Unilever Research
Colworth/Welwyn Laboratory
Colworth House
Sharnbrook
Bedford, England

Werner E. Reichardt
Director, Max-Planck-Institut für
  biologische Kybernetik
Spemannstrasse 38
74 Tübingen,
  Federal Republic of Germany

Martin Rodbell
Section Chief
Section on Membrane Regulation
NIAMDD, National Institutes of Health
Bethesda, Maryland 20014

Lawrence I. Rothfield
Professor and Chairman
Department of Microbiology
University of Connecticut
School of Medicine
Farmington, Connecticut 06032

Arnold E. Ruoho
Helen Hay Whitney Post Doctoral Fellow
Department of Biology
University of California at San Diego
La Jolla, California 92037

Frederick E. Samson, Jr.
Staff Scientist
Neurosciences Research Program
Massachusetts Institute of Technology
165 Allandale Street
Boston, Massachusetts 02130

Francis O. Schmitt
Chairman, Neurosciences Research Program
Institute Professor Emeritus
Massachusetts Institute of Technology
165 Allandale Street
Boston, Massachusetts 02130

Diana M. Schneider
Staff Scientist
Neurosciences Research Program
Massachusetts Institute of Technology
165 Allandale Street
Boston, Massachusetts 02130

Gerhard Schwarz
Professor of Biophysical Chemistry
Biocenter of the University of Basel
Department of Biophysical Chemistry
Klingelbergstrasse 70
CH4056 Basel, Switzerland

George R. Siggins
Research Physiologist
Laboratory of Neuropharmacology
National Institute of Mental Health
St. Elizabeth's Hospital
Washington, D.C. 20032

S. Jonathan Singer
Professor of Biology
Department of Biology
University of California at San Diego
La Jolla, California 92037

Hermann Träuble
Karl-Friedrich-Bonhoeffer-Institut
Max-Planck-Institut für
  Biophysikalische Chemie
D 3400 Göttingen-Nikolausberg,
  Federal Republic of Germany

Jonathan W. Uhr
Professor and Chairman of Microbiology
University of Texas Southwestern
  Medical School
Dallas, Texas 75235

Laurens L. M. van Deenen
Professor of Biochemistry
Department of Biochemistry
University of Utrecht
Vondellaan 26
Utrecht, The Netherlands

Donal A. Walsh
Professor of Biological Chemistry
Department of Biological Chemistry
University of California School of Medicine
Davis, California 95616

Annemarie Weber
Professor of Biochemistry
Department of Biochemistry
University of Pennsylvania
School of Medicine
Philadelphia, Pennsylvania 19104

Frederic G. Worden
Executive Director
Neurosciences Research Program
Professor of Psychiatry
Massachusetts Institute of Technology
165 Allandale Street
Boston, Massachusetts 02130

Jeffries Wyman
Guest Professor
University of Rome
Institute of Biochemistry and
*   Instituto Regina Elena*
Rome, Italy

Yehoshua Y. Zeevi
Vinton Hayes Fellow
Division of Engineering and Applied Physics
Harvard University
Cambridge, Massachusetts 02138

Bruno H. Zimm
Professor of Chemistry
Department of Chemistry
University of California at San Diego
La Jolla, California 92037

NRP ASSOCIATES AND THEIR INSTITUTIONAL AFFILIATIONS

W. Ross Adey
Brain Research Institute
University of California at Los Angeles

Floyd E. Bloom
St. Elizabeth's Hospital
National Institute of Mental Health

David Bodian
The Johns Hopkins University
School of Medicine

Theodore H. Bullock
University of California at San Diego
School of Medicine

Leo De Maeyer
Max Planck Institute
* for Biophysical Chemistry*
Göttingen, West Germany

Mac V. Edds, Jr.
University of Massachusetts at Amherst

Gerald M. Edelman
The Rockefeller University

Manfred Eigen
Max Planck Institute
* for Biophysical Chemistry*
Göttingen, West Germany

Humberto Fernández-Moran
Division of Biological Sciences
The University of Chicago

Robert Galambos
University of California at San Diego
School of Medicine

David Hubel
Harvard Medical School

Holger V. Hydén
Institute of Neurobiology
University of Göteborg, Sweden

Ephraim Katzir-Katchalski
The Weizmann Institute of Science, Israel

Seymour S. Kety
Massachusetts General Hospital
Harvard Medical School

Albert L. Lehninger
The Johns Hopkins University
School of Medicine

Robert B. Livingston
University of California at San Diego
School of Medicine

Functional Linkage in Biomolecular Systems, edited by
F. O. Schmitt, D. M. Schneider, and D. M. Crothers.
Raven Press, New York © 1975.

Introduction: The Role of Functional Linkage in Molecular Neurobiology

HISTORICAL PERSPECTIVES

The concept of functional linkage in biomolecular systems resulted from the fusion of several streams of scientific thought. In biology, epoch-making advances culminated in the great revolution of molecular biology; in this volume we are particularly concerned with concepts involving the highly dynamic, "cooperative" interactions within and between certain macromolecules and with their neurobiological consequences. In physics and chemistry, developments during the same period in the areas of thermodynamics, kinetics, statistical mechanics, and instrumentation provided theoretical and technical bases for understanding these dynamic intramolecular and intermolecular interactions or linkage properties that molecular biologists have demonstrated to be fundamental to life processes.

The nervous system is highly dependent on fast biophysical and biochemical processes that are electrochemical and chemo-electrical in nature. Neuroscience is therefore the branch of life science in which the concepts of functional linkage are of most direct and immediate application.

The concepts and processes dealt with in this book developed gradually over a period of a half-century, beginning in the mid-1920s, by which time the microscopic anatomy of brain tracts had been extensively characterized. The neuron doctrine, formulated earlier in the last century, had been developed to a point where the function of the nervous system was visualized as resulting from series and parallel interactions of nets of neurons in which an impulse arriving at a dendritic terminal was transmitted down the axon to synaptic terminals; neurons were thus viewed as contiguous, but not continuous as reticularist theory had claimed. In the late nineteenth century and early years of the twentieth, neurophysiology was dominated by Sherrington (see Swazey, 1969). His investigations and publications on the integrative action of the nervous system led to a concept of the interaction, via nerve impulses, of numerous neuronal centers in various parts of the central nervous system. Since the work of DuBois-Reymond (1848), these impulses were known to be based on bioelectrical properties; the propagating impulse was successfully modeled with an iron-wire model by Lillie (1923). Three decades later the basis of the nerve impulse was explained in the ionic diffusion theory of Hodgkin and Huxley (1952).

The application of the techniques of electronic amplification and oscilloscopic recording, initiated by Erlanger and Gasser (1937), introduced a new era, since it was now possible to record with temporal fidelity even the fastest (ca. 10^{-4} sec) bioelectric events in the nervous system. This permitted the mapping of action waves (fast spike potentials and slower afterpotentials) over axons, synapses, and extensive neuronal nets. Slower electrical phenomena of the whole brain (EEG) were also discovered during this period. The ability to record from microelectrodes placed inside neuronal cell bodies (unit recording) introduced a still more dynamic phase of neurophysiology, in which function could be referred to individual neurons. The time was now ripe for the development of molecular neurobiology and the application of the concepts of functional linkage that had been developing simultaneously in physics and chemistry.

However, let us first trace the origins of dynamic neurochemical concepts. For convenience these may also be traced to the starting point of our narrative, half a century ago, in the work of Loewi and Dale, which led to the acceptance of the concept that the nerve impulse is conducted across the synaptic gap between axon terminals and the postsynaptic membrane by chemical mediators or *transmitters,* not by electrical means, as had until then been supposed.

The search was now on for substances that could survive the rigid requirements for qualification as "Grade-A-Certified" excitatory or inhibitory neurotransmitters. Seven such substances have so far been identified, and others wait to be fully tested and accredited. The role of transmitters such as norepinephrine in complex behavioral patterns, such as affective behavior, soon became evident, and the now thriving fields of molecular pharmacology and psychopharmacology were established. Neurotransmitters can produce fast and biologically significant changes when present in extremely low concentrations, in the range of 10^{-8} to 10^{-12} M. How is such action accomplished?

Also beginning roughly in the mid-1920s were investigations with X-ray diffraction and polarization optics that, together with the development of high-resolution electron microscopy in the 1940s, induced revolutionary advances in our knowledge of tissue and molecular ultrastructure. Technical developments led to the widespread use of apparatus such as the ultracentrifuge and other equipment for characterizing macromolecules and ushered in the period of molecular biology, whose most spectacularly successful achievement was molecular genetics. Molecular neurobiology, which had developed substantial impetus during the rise of molecular biology, profited by the great increase in the popularity of neuroscience and mounted to a sustained crescendo in the late 1960s.

From the biological side, the stage was now set for the profitable investigation of the role of functional linkage in biomolecular systems.

THE CONCEPT OF FUNCTIONAL LINKAGE

In parallel with the revolution in molecular biology, biophysical chemists developed the concepts and techniques necessary for studying the functional linkage between intra- and intermolecular parameters and applied these principles and techniques to cell physiology. Included in this category, for convenience if not rigorous conceptual usage, are the concepts of co-operativity, allosteric interaction, transductive coupling, and amplification. Many vital processes of the cell depend on such functional linkages: the action of many enzymes and enzyme systems, hormonal effects, metabolic and homeostatic control mechanisms, gene expression, biosynthetic mechanisms, the conversion of metabolic chemical energy into mechanical, electrical, osmotic, and other forms of work, and the transduction from one energy modality to another, as in sensory transduction.

The application of these concepts converted the highly descriptive, relatively static field of neurochemistry, founded by Thudichum (see Drabkin, 1958), into a new science whose *leitmotiv* is molecular dynamism. Like the revolution in neurophysiology that was initiated by the introduction of electronic amplifiers and oscilloscopes, the consideration of fast reactions (10^{-7} to 10^{-9} sec) within and between macromolecules opened up the possibility of new insights into the mechanisms of brain and mind.

The theme that runs through many of the phenomena of functional linkage is that of *cooperativity,* a term that refers to the ways in which the components of a macromolecule, a system of macromolecules, or, in the most general case, of any system of components, act together so as to switch from one stable state of a molecule to another. Frequently involved are phase transitions (as in helix-coil transitions), hysteresis, and a one-to-many input-output relationship.

A sigmoidal relationship is frequently shown between the input parameter and the output response of a cooperative system. Sigmoidicity alone is neither necessary nor sufficient evidence that a process is cooperative; it is important to determine whether the parameters can vary independently or whether they tend to change in a concerted manner. Suppose that a protein contains several subunits, and binding to one subunit has no effect on the affinity of other subunits for the ligand. It is then proper to say that binding is noncooperative with respect to interactions between the subunits, or between the ligands, since they act independently. However, if this non-cooperative ligand binding converts a subunit from one conformational structure to another, then the reaction can be said to be cooperative *with respect to the interactions between the protein dihedral angles,* since these change in a concerted way. In summary, one must always specify the parts considered to be the elemental units of the system in connection with any statement about the cooperativity of a reaction.

Allosteric interactions in proteins and their role in the control of cellular metabolism by conformational changes represent one type of functional linkage. Enzymes frequently contain two kinds of sites, those that activate or inactivate the enzyme and those that exert the specific catalytic action. The influence of binding at the control site on the activity of the catalytic site is said to be an allosteric interaction (Greek, *allo* = other, *stereo* =

space). Various combinations of positive and negative feedback by products of the enzyme action and other metabolites can exert control to produce a homeostatic kinetic process. Allosteric interactions may also occur between subunits of structures such as membrane receptors, adjacent enzymes, and macromolecular assemblies. The first enzyme in a self-regulating enzyme system is frequently inhibited by products of the action of the last enzyme in the pathway. The first enzyme in the pathway is called a regulatory or *allosteric* enzyme. The known allosteric enzymes have more than one, sometimes many, polypeptide chains. Such systems have an atypical dependence of reaction velocity on substrate concentration, and hyperbolic Michaelis-Menten kinetic relationships do not apply.

Another type of functional linkage is *transmodal transduction*. In the most general case, that in which the chemical free energy available in molecules such as ATP or cyclic AMP is coupled to the macromolecular machinery of tissues to do various kinds of work, the "high-energy" molecule must be covalently linked with the effector lattice of the cell. The best-known example of such transmodal energy conversion is muscle contractility. In this process, cooperative interactions of Ca^{2+} with troponin and of one tropomyosin molecule with seven actin subunits has been demonstrated (see Chapter 14), as has the transductive process proper, in which heavy meromyosin interacts via nucleotide triphosphate with actin and its complex with tropomyosin and troponin. As our knowledge has grown concerning receptors and their coupling with the systems that link the molecular complex of the receptor (for vision, audition, smell, taste, etc.) to the cellular systems that transduce sensory inputs to action potentials in sensory nerves, an appreciation has developed concerning the importance of functional linkage in the process. These matters are discussed in Chapters 1, 10, 11, 12, and 13.

Another form of functional linkage is that in which a signal gives rise to an amplified response, frequently larger than the input signal by orders of magnitude. One example of such *amplification* is the relatively large change in cyclic AMP concentration induced by small amounts of hormones such as glucagon (Chapter 9). More complex phenomena that include amplification are the immune response (Chapter 8) and the dramatic alteration of swimming behavior in chemotactic bacteria produced by a small concentration gradient of an attractant (Chapter 13). Amplification in biochemical systems can be achieved by controlling the activity of enzymatic catalysts. There are a number of well-documented cases of enzymes whose activity is controlled by ligands; this topic is considered at length in Chapter 2. Cooperativity plays an important role in amplification. An enzyme whose subunits interact cooperatively can be converted from an inactive to an active form over a narrow range of ligand concentration, thus increasing the amplifier gain. In such cases, the "amplified" response may not be chemically identical to the stimulus, or even in the same modality, but the output is much larger quantitatively than the input, in terms of energy or the potential to do work. This concept is of practical utility, if not theoretical rectitude. One case of amplification in the strictest sense is electrosensing in certain fish, in which extremely weak electrical signals are converted into action potentials in sensory nerves.

Cooperativity plays an important role in the transductive coupling of different energy modes. An example considered in Chapter 1 is the transduction of chemical to mechanical energy through a cooperative helix-coil transition in which cooperativity influences the rate of the process. The most spectacular example of transductive coupling in neurobiology is in sensory transduction, in which the activity of the receptor cell can be altered by the absorption of one photon (in vision) or of one molecule of pheromone attractant (in olfaction).

THE DEVELOPMENT OF CONCEPTS OF FUNCTIONAL LINKAGE

The earliest biochemical observations of phenomena much later to be termed cooperative were those of Christian Bohr (Bohr, 1903a,b; Bohr, Hasselbalch, and Krogh, 1904), the father of Niels Bohr, who discovered that O_2 is dissociated from hemoglobin as the CO_2 tension is increased. Another way of defining the "Bohr effect," formulated much later, is that the binding of oxygen by hemoglobin results in the discharge of protons. Ten years later, Haldane and his collaborators (Christiansen, Douglas and Haldane, 1914) demonstrated the converse effect, that oxygenation of hemoglobin drives off CO_2. Bohr had sought for the reciprocal effect, but failed to find it, although it could have been predicted mathematically.

The discovery of the adaptation of the chemical structure of hemoglobin to its function is delightfully and authoritatively told by Edsall (1972).[1] He relates how Bohr, in collaboration with Hasselbalch and Krogh (1904), critically analyzed the curves of O_2 binding by hemoglobin and concluded that their sigmoid shape (as compared with the hyperbolic shape that was expected from the mass action law for a single binding site) was not due to error. The controversy provoked much work to explain why the curve was not hyperbolic. Bohr's data showed that, after the first oxygen molecule was bound, succeeding ones bound to hemoglobin more easily. Unfortunately, he held to the view that hemoglobin solutions contain a heterogeneity of hemoglobin molecules and that this was responsible for the sigmoid curves; thus he missed intramolecular cooperativity.

During this period of uncertainty about the molecular status of hemoglobin, A. V. Hill (1910) derived a mathematical approximation which, a half-century later, is proving valuable as a measure of cooperativity between

---

[1] The editors thank Prof. J. T. Edsall for his helpful criticism in the preparation of this chapter.

ligand-binding sites. Hill proposed that the hemoglobin monomers, each with a single heme group, could aggregate reversibly to varying extents, and that the aggregates would bind oxygen in a fashion that we now term "cooperative." He expressed the percent saturation function y of hemoglobin as

$$y = \frac{100Kx^n}{1 + Kx^n}$$

where K is a constant and x represents the activity (concentration or partial pressure of the ligand); n, the Hill coefficient as it has come to be known, was originally conceived by Hill to be a measure of the degree of aggregation of hemoglobin. Subsequently, Wyman (1948, 1963) showed that the Hill coefficient, under certain conditions, measures the free energy of interaction between sites.

Adair, who, according to Edsall, was unique among the biochemists of his time in that he studied Gibbsian thermodynamics, used improved osmotic measurements to establish that hemoglobin is a tetramer weighing 67,000 daltons (Adair, 1925). He formulated a general equation for ligand binding of hemoglobin in terms of four successive binding constants. If these constants progressively increase as more oxygen is bound, the process will be cooperative. Adair's work had far-reaching significance not only for the study of oxygen carrying by hemoglobin, but also for the study of many enzymes.

Cooperativity theory really became established as a powerful concept from the landmark papers of Wyman (1948) and Wyman and Allen (1951), who proposed that cooperative ligand interaction has its origin in conformational changes, that is, in fast alterations in the three-dimensional tertiary structure of the protein molecule. The section of Wyman's paper on "linked functions" was remarkably perceptive. The thesis of cooperativity through conformational change in hemoglobin was confirmed by the crystallographic work of Perutz, Rossmann, Cullis, Muirhead, Will, and North (1960), who showed that the distance between the four heme groups is too great for direct interaction; the interaction must therefore be indirect, presumably through conformational changes. This was confirmed by the finding that the distances between the heme groups in hemoglobin are shifted substantially by oxygen binding.

During the next decade, the concept of cooperativity and the broader one of functional linkage received important and insightful contributions from the work of Novick and Szilard (1954), Umbarger (1956), Yates and Pardee (1956), and others concerning feedback (end-product) inhibition of bacterial biosynthetic pathways. Koshland (1958) suggested that binding to substrate involves an induced fit, produced by alteration of the conformation of the catalytic site.

However, it was not until 1963 that the word "allosteric" was used, in a paper by Monod, Changeux, and Jacob that further developed the concept of the control of enzymic—hence of cellular—activity through protein conformational changes. In their model, proteins were assumed to have two nonoverlapping receptor sites: a catalytically active site that binds and reacts with substrate, and an *allosteric* site that specifically and reversibly binds an allosteric effector. Binding of the latter produces a reversible alteration in the conformation of the protein—an allosteric transition—that changes the active site and certain kinetic parameters characteristic of the enzyme. These investigators concluded that there need be no direct interaction between the substrate and the metabolic ligand that activates the allosteric protein; the effect is due entirely to reversible conformational changes induced when the effector ligand is bound by the allosteric protein.

This conclusion had been foreshadowed by the theoretical work of Wyman 15 years earlier and was further enlarged by his later work in collaboration with Monod and Changeux (Monod, Wyman, and Changeux, 1965). Their main purpose was to develop and justify the idea that a general and simple relationship between symmetry and function may explain the emergence, evolution, and properties of oligomeric proteins as molecular "amplifiers" of random and structural accidents or of highly specific organized, metabolic interactions. In a systematic and remarkably lucid survey, they listed the general properties of allosteric proteins: They are oligomers with several identical structures; allosteric interactions involve quaternary conformational changes; and homotropic interactions, that is, between identical ligands, according to their model, are always cooperative, while heterotropic interactions, that is, between different ligands, may be either cooperative or antagonistic. This ability to mediate cooperative interactions between stereospecific ligands is the physiologically most important property of allosteric proteins. Protein monomers ("protomers") recognize and associate with like monomers with extreme specificity; specific association occurs even at high dilution and in the presence of other proteins, that is, in crude extracts. The authors concluded that cooperativity is a decisive factor in the emergence and selective maintenance of symmetrical oligomeric proteins.

The model of Monod et al. (1965) assumed that allosteric proteins exist in only two states, T (tensed) and R (relaxed), the latter having a much higher affinity for ligand than the former. Thus, all the subunits of the oligomeric protein had to change their conformation simultaneously in the $T \rightleftharpoons R$ transition. An alternative theory was developed by Koshland, Nemethy, and Filmer (1966), who proposed that each subunit of the oligomer could undergo a conformational transition, induced by the binding of ligand. This could then induce conformational changes in neighboring subunits. However, the transition was not all or none, as in the theory of Monod, Wyman, and Changeux. Either of the two theories was capable of explaining many of the experimental data on cooperativity. Tests to distinguish the two theories from each other, or indeed from other possible interpretations, required new approaches, involving rapid kinetic methods and other techniques.

In addition to thermodynamics, the approach of statistical mechanics was of great importance for the theoretical development of the functional linkage concept. This approach had its basis in physics rather than in chemistry. Of particular historical interest in this field is the theoretical work of Ising (1925), who developed a nearest-neighbor interaction theory for transformations in one-dimensional ferromagnets. The Ising model, which exemplifies the simplest system of interacting particles that retains features of physical reality, raises the fundamental question of whether the formulations of statistical mechanics can predict phase transitions and, if so, how. For almost half a century, various forms of Ising models have formed the basis for theoretical constructs concerning interaction coupling, the aim being to express the partition function in a tractable form, thus facilitating the derivation of exact analytical expressions for thermodynamic quantities. A good review of the theory of the Ising model was provided by Newell and Montroll (1953).

The work of Schellman (1955) foreshadowed the application of statistical mechanical methods to helix-coil transitions. Using the heat and the entropy of adding a segment to the helix as basic parameters, he considered special nucleating end effects. In his simple theory, helix-coil transitions are sharp and dependent on chain length. A major advance in the statistical mechanical development of linkage theory was made by Zimm and Bragg (1959), who showed that helix-coil phase transitions in polypeptide chains are sharp, and are produced by changes of only a few degrees in temperature or a few percent of solvent concentration. The formation of the first turn of a helix is difficult and involves a large decrease of entropy. But once formed, this turn serves as a template for others; such nucleation is typical of sharp transitions. The finite chain problem was attacked with the matrix method, developed by Kramers and Wannier (1941a,b), which considers interactions between distant segments as well as nearest neighbors. In the 15 years since the work of Zimm and Bragg, there have been many applications of theories of cooperativity and other linkage phenomena to systems of biological interest, including polypeptides, nucleic acids, polysaccharides, and lipids.

These developments in concepts of functional linkage were aided by great advances in determining the kinetics of fast reactions. These were discussed at length at an International Colloquium for Fast Reactions in Solutions (see Eigen, 1960), with contributions representing every type of related technique then available. Developments proceeded along two lines, from biochemistry and from physics.

From the biochemical approach, the work of Hartridge and Roughton (1923; see also Roughton, 1960) pioneered the measurement of reaction velocities in the millisecond-to-second range, in contrast to previous methods, which had been limited to processes taking minutes or hours. Their apparatus permitted the rapid mixing of reactants in a restricted space, the composition of the streaming fluid being determined by fast—for example, spectroscopic—methods at varying distances from the mixing chamber or, in work done many years later, after sudden stoppage of the fluid after mixing (hence the appellation "stopflow" method). Types of chemical reactions amenable to study by rapid flow technique were reviewed by Chance (1960).

On the physical side, early formulations concerned the relaxation kinetics of reactions in gases (Einstein, 1920; Meixner, 1943a,b). The development of various relaxation techniques, especially those of Eigen and DeMaeyer (1963), permitted measuring the kinetics of fast (to 10^{-7} sec) and very fast (to 10^{-9} sec) reactions, whose rates are close to those for diffusion-controlled kinetics (10^{-10} sec). Additional methods for measuring fast reactions include those of flash photolysis (see particularly Porter, 1963), photochemistry, fluorescence, and electrochemistry, as well as the related methods of electron spin resonance and nuclear magnetic resonance. For a survey of these methods see Caldin (1964).

The availability of methods for measuring fast state transitions made it possible to investigate cooperative, allosteric, transductive, and other types of functional linkage. It became obvious that the attack on major problems of molecular neurobiology, involving bioelectric events in the range of 10^{-3} to 10^{-6} sec, would receive powerful support from biophysical chemists, particularly those concerned with fast reactions; conversely, problems of neuroscience, looming ever larger in importance among the problems of life science, indeed of all science, might greatly interest these same biophysical chemists. These factors were crucial in the decision in 1962 to organize a multidisciplinary, multiuniversity attack on basic problems of neuroscience. The Neurosciences Research Program (NRP), sponsored by the Massachusetts Institute of Technology, was founded from the impetus of the developments recounted above. Manfred Eigen and Leo DeMaeyer, leading investigators in the field of fast reactions, helped to organize the NRP and were among its charter members.

THE APPLICATION OF FUNCTIONAL LINKAGE CONCEPTS TO MOLECULAR NEUROBIOLOGY

It may be useful at this point to list some of the major problems of molecular neurobiology in which functional linkage is a key factor. Their treatment in the three NRP Intensive Study Programs (Quarton, Melnechuk, and Schmitt, 1967; Schmitt, 1970; Schmitt and Worden, 1974), and in the Work Sessions reported in the *NRP Bulletin,* as well as in the rapidly growing literature of neuroscience, made it reasonable to organize a conference on the subject of functional linkage.

Membrane processes are of primary interest and are currently being investigated from the viewpoint of molecular organization and composition, including the chemical characterization of membrane-borne molecular machines (channels, ionophores, and other mediators of excitability, pumps, permeases, receptors, adenylate cyclase, and other enzymes), and with regard to the dynamic interactions and coupling that subserve brain function. Bilayer systems and similar models have proved extremely valuable in analyzing functional linkage.

The synapse presents important opportunities and challenges, particularly with regard to its ultrastructure and the dynamics of transmitter action: Functional linkage is involved in the release and reabsorption of transmitter, receptor binding of the transmitter ligand, and the resulting excitation or inhibition of postsynaptic neurons. The properties of dendrodendritic synapses between "local circuit" interneurons, characteristic of the retina and the olfactory bulb, suggest fascinating new concepts of reciprocal linkage and information processing; the possible existence and function of such connections in other brain regions, such as the cerebral cortex, is now being investigated in various laboratories.

Recent studies have begun to elucidate the mechanisms that couple metabolic processes with the synthesis of transmitters and neurohormones and their regulation according to functional requirements. Coupling has been demonstrated between the postsynaptic membrane and the genetic expression of the messenger RNAs that code for the enzymes needed for transmitter synthesis. Linkage also exists between the cell soma and the cellular membrane to regulate the synthesis of membrane material and its incorporation via the Golgi apparatus into the cell membrane.

Neuroplasm is constantly synthesized and transferred down the axon. Its synthesis is regulated by linkage with the cell membrane, in which are located receptors and other transductive mechanisms. The role of microtubules in the fast transport of materials from the cell soma through its axonal and dendritic extensions is thought by many to be a cooperative process involving the microtubular subunits and calcium ions.

Mechanisms by which organisms sense visual, olfactory, gustatory, hormonal, neurotransmitter, mechanical, and electrical stimuli operate at or near the limits of sensitivity. The typical system utilized for transmodal transduction includes an input-specific receptor and a molecular amplifier system that alters the polarization of the postsynaptic membrane (for stimulation or inhibition) or gives rise to action potential waves in sensory axons.

Many processes that occur at the cellular, tissue, and whole-brain level may, in a formal sense, be considered cooperative in nature: a small input may generate a large output. All-or-nothing, phase-like transitions that are sensitive to environmental parameters are characteristic of brain function, and changes at one locus may be rapidly transmitted to a distant locus or to an entire surround (volume or holistic effect). Dynamic patterns may arise when chemical reactions in a distributed system are coupled by diffusion; for example, under nonequilibrium thermodynamic conditions, functional linkage processes are involved in cooperative pacemaker assemblies, oscillating fields, pulse distribution, and other coupled phenomena (see Katchalsky, Rowland, and Blumenthal, 1974). The dense interactions of neurons in some brain centers has led to the consideration of domains of cooperative neural activity (Freeman, 1975).

The detection of weak electrical fields by the brain is another field or volume effect that displays highly cooperative characteristics, according to Adey (Chapter 15).

At the perceptual level, the phenomenon of visual depth perception (stereopsis) illustrates cooperativity in an experiential mode that is grasped more vividly than can be conveyed to most by mathematical analysis (Julesz, 1974; see also Szentágothai and Arbib, 1974).

Reserved for a possible future conference is a consideration of other aspects of neuroscience, particularly at the level of brain regions or of the brain as a whole. It is hoped that this book will stimulate interest in functional linkage, especially among neuroscientists who may see in the phenomenology and the physicochemical principles new and productive ways of approaching neuroscience problems, including those of higher brain functions.

REFERENCES

Adair, G. S. (1925): The hemoglobin system. *J. Biol. Chem.*, 63:493–545.
Bohr, C. (1903a): Die Sauerstoffaufnahme des genuinen Blutfarbstoffes und des aus dem Blute dargestellten Hamoglobins. *Zentr. Physiol.*, 17:688–711.
Bohr, C. (1903b): Theoretische Behandlung der quantitativen Verhaltnisse bei der Sauerstoffaufnahme des Hamoglobins. *Zentr. Physiol.*, 17:682–688.
Bohr, C., Hasselbalch, K., and Krogh, A. (1904): Ueber einen in biologischer Beziehung wichtigen Einfluss, den die Kohlensäurespannung des Blutes auf dessen Sauerstoffbindung übt. *Skand. Arch. Physiol.*, 16:402–412.
Caldin, E. F. (1964): *Fast Reactions in Solution.* New York: John Wiley & Sons.
Chance, B. (1960): Catalysis in biochemical reactions. *Z. Elektrochem.*, 64:7–13.
Christiansen, J., Douglas, C. G., and Haldane, J. S. (1914): The absorption and dissociation of carbon dioxide by human blood. *J. Physiol.*, 48:245–271.
Drabkin, D. L. (1958): *Thudichum, Chemist of the Brain.* Philadelphia: University of Pennsylvania Press.
DuBois-Reymond, E. (1848): *Untersuchungen über thierische Elektrizität.* Berlin: Reimer.
Edsall, J. T. (1972): Blood and hemoglobin. *J. Hist. Biol.*, 5:205–257.
Eigen, M., ed. (1960): Bericht über das Internationale Kolloquium über schnelle Reaktionen in Lösungen. Hahnenklee/Harz, 14–17 September 1959. *Z. Elektrochem.*, 64:1–204.
Eigen, M., and De Maeyer, L. (1963): Relaxation methods. In: *Investigations of Rates and Mechanisms of Reaction,* edited by S. L. Friess, E. S. Lewis, and A. Weissberger, pp. 895–1054. *Technique of Organic Chemistry. Vol. 8, Part II.*
Einstein, A. (1920): Schallausbreitung in teilweise dissoziierten Gasen. *Sitz. ber. Preus. Akad. Wiss., Physik. Math. Kl.,* Berlin, pp. 380–385.
Erlanger, J., and Gasser, H. S. (1937): *Electrical Signs of Nervous Activity.* Philadelphia: University of Pennsylvania Press.

Freeman, W. J. (1975): *Mass Action in the Nervous System.* New York: Academic Press (*in press*).

Hartridge, H., and Roughton, F. J. W. (1923): A method of measuring the velocity of very rapid chemical reactions. *Proc. Roy. Soc. A,* 104:376–394.

Hill, A. V. (1910): The possible effects of the aggregation of the molecules of haemoglobin on its dissociation curves. *J. Physiol.,* 40:iv–vii.

Hodgkin, A. L., and Huxley, A. F. (1952): A quantitative description of membrane current and its application to conduction and excitation in nerve. *J. Physiol.,* 117:500–544.

Ising, E. (1925): Beitrag zur Theorie des Ferromagnetismus. *Z. Physik.,* 31:253–258.

Julesz, B. (1974): Cooperative phenomena in binocular depth perception. *Amer. Sci.,* 62:32–53.

Katchalsky, A. K., Rowland, V., and Blumenthal, R. (1974): *Dynamic Patterns of Brain Cell Assemblies.* MIT Press, Cambridge.

Koshland, D. E., Jr. (1958): Application of a theory of enzyme specificity to protein synthesis. *Proc. Nat. Acad. Sci.,* 48:98–104.

Koshland, D. E., Jr., Nemethy, A., and Filmer, D. (1966): Comparison of experimental binding data and theoretical models in proteins containing subunits. *Biochemistry,* 5:365–385.

Kramers, H. A., and Wannier, G. H. (1941*a*): Statistics of the two-dimensional ferromagnet. Part I. *Phys. Rev.,* 60:252–262.

Kramers, H. A., and Wannier, G. H. (1941*b*): Statistics of the two-dimensional ferromagnet. Part II. *Phys. Rev.,* 60:263–276.

Lillie, R. S. (1923): *Protoplasmic Action and Nervous Action.* Chicago: University of Chicago Press.

Meixner, J. (1943*a*): Zur Thermodynamik der irreversible Prozesse in Gase mit reagierenden dissoziierenden und anregbaren Komponenten. *Ann. Physik.,* 43:244–270.

Meixner, J. (1943*b*): Absorption und Dispersion des Schalles in Gasen mit chemisch reargierenden un anregbaren Komponenten. *Ann. Phys.,* 43:470–487.

Monod, J., Changeux, J.-P., and Jacob, F. (1963): Allosteric proteins and cellular control systems. *J. Mol. Biol.,* 6:306–329.

Monod, J., Wyman, J., and Changeux, J.-P. (1965): On the nature of allosteric transitions: A plausible model. *J. Mol. Biol.,* 12:88–118.

Newell, G. F., and Montroll, E. W. (1953): On the theory of the Ising model of ferromagnetism. *Rev. Mod. Phys.,* 25:353–389.

Novick, A., and Szilard, L., (1954): Experiments with the chemostat on the rates of amino acid synthesis in bacteria. In: *Dynamics of Growth Processes,* edited by E. J. Boell, pp. 21–32. Princeton, N.J.: Princeton University Press.

Perutz, M. F., Rossmann, M. G., Cullis, A. F., Muirhead, H., Will, G., and North, A. C. T. (1960): Structure of haemoglobin. A three-dimensional Fourier synthesis at 5.5 Å resolution, obtained by x-ray analysis. *Nature,* 185:416–422.

Porter, G. (1963): Flash photolysis. In: *Investigation of Rates and Mechanisms of Reactions,* edited by S. L. Friess, E. S. Lewis, and A. Weissberger, pp. 1055–1106. *Technique of Organic Chemistry, Vol. 8, Part II.*

Quarton, G. C., Melnechuk, T., and Schmitt, F. O., eds. (1967): *The Neurosciences—A Study Program.* New York: Rockefeller University Press.

Roughton, F. J. W. (1960): The origin of the Hartridge-Roughton rapid reaction method and its applications to the reactions of haemoglobin in intact red blood corpuscle. *Z. Elektrochem.,* 64:3–4.

Schellman, J. A. (1955): The stability of the hydrogen-bonded peptide structures in aqueous solution. *Compt. Rend. Trav. Lab Carlsberg, Ser. Chim.,* 29:230–259.

Schmitt, F. O., editor-in-chief (1970): *The Neurosciences—Second Study Program.* New York: Rockefeller University Press.

Schmitt, F. O., and Worden, F. G., eds. (1974): *The Neurosciences—Third Study Program.* Cambridge, Mass.: M.I.T. Press.

Swazey, J. P. (1969): *Reflexes and Motor Integration: Sherrington's Concept of Integrative Action.* Cambridge, Mass.: Harvard University Press.

Szentágothai, J., and Arbib, M. A. (1974): *Neurosciences Res. Prog. Bull.* (*in press*).

Umbarger, H. E. (1956): Evidence for a negative-feedback mechanism in the biosynthesis of isoleucine. *Science,* 123:848.

Wyman, J. (1948): Heme proteins. *Adv. Prot. Chem.,* 4:407–531.

Wyman, J. (1963): Allosteric effects in hemoglobin. *Cold Spring Harbor Symp. Quant. Biol.,* 28:483–489.

Wyman, J., and Allen, D. W. (1951): The problem of the heme interactions in hemoglobin and the basis of the Bohr effect. *J. Polymer Sci.,* 7:499–518.

Yates, R. A., and Pardee, A. B. (1956): Control of pyrimidine biosynthesis in *Escherichia coli* by a feedback mechanism. *J. Biol. Chem.,* 221:757–770.

Zimm, B. H., and Bragg, J. K. (1959): Theory of the phase transition between helix and random coil in polypeptide chains. *J. Chem. Phys.,* 31:526–535.

Functional Linkage in Biomolecular Systems, edited by
F. O. Schmitt, D. M. Schneider, and D. M. Crothers.
Raven Press, New York © 1975.

FUNDAMENTAL PRINCIPLES OF FUNCTIONAL LINKAGE

An entire conference might well have been devoted to the basis in bio-physical chemistry of the major phenomena of functional linkage: co-operativity, allosteric interaction and control, transductive coupling and amplification. However, although no thorough review of this subject matter exists, it was the purpose of the conference, and of this book, to indicate the importance of functional linkage in biology and to point to the particular significance of functional linkage in neuroscience. Therefore, the exposition of basic principles has been limited to two chapters.

In Chapter 1, cooperative transitions and the principles that govern their occurrence are illustrated by the familiar examples of helix-coil transitions in the nucleic acids and tertiary and quaternary conformational changes in proteins; consideration is also given to the less familiar example of structural transitions in polysaccharides. Although lipids also show cooperative behavior, they are dealt with separately in the following section because of their tendency to aggregate into the layered structures that are the basis of membrane organization.

The discussion in Chapter 2 focuses on allosterism and other mecha-nisms, such as enzyme polymerization-depolymerization, that are used for the regulation of enzymic activity. Such allosteric interactions, between the subunits of single proteins and between linked proteins, underlie many of the membrane level control processes that are discussed in later chapters.

Amplification can be achieved in biochemical systems by controlling the activity of enzymatic catalysts. Several examples are presented in Chapter 2 to demonstrate the way in which small changes in ligand concentration can produce large alterations in enzymic activity; a resultant increase of am-plifier gain results when such systems are coupled within membranes. Amplification is present in many cooperative processes, such that a signal of small magnitude elicits one of much larger magnitude. Particularly im-pressive cases of such amplification will be discussed in the section on transductive coupling in sensory receptor-effector systems.

Functional Linkage in Biomolecular Systems, edited by
F. O. Schmitt, D. M. Schneider, and D. M. Crothers.
Raven Press, New York © 1975.

Chapter 1

Fundamental Principles of Cooperative and Transductive Coupling

FUNDAMENTAL PRINCIPLES OF COOPERATIVE PROCESSES:

Bruno Zimm

Many cooperative processes can be examined theoretically if one assumes that each object in an ensemble can exist in *only* two states. These processes include such basic biological phenomena as the alternation of enzyme subunits between two different conformations having different enzymic activities and the transformation of DNA base pairs from Watson-Crick helix to random coil.

The Four-Subunit Enzyme as an Illustrative Example

The differences between cooperative and noncooperative transitions can be illustrated with the simple example of a four-subunit enzyme in which each subunit may exist in either of two conformational states, referred to as (+) and (−), where the (+) form is enzymatically active. The mathematical analysis of this example is familiar in connection with the binding of small molecules to proteins, which has been widely discussed (see van Holde, 1971).

If there is no cooperativity among the four enzyme subunits, the probability of any subunit assuming the (+) or (−) state is independent of the conformation of the other subunits. It is therefore possible to define for each subunit a single equilibrium, or "stability," constant, s, for the ratio of subunits in the two states:

$$s = \frac{n_+}{n_-} \tag{1}$$

where n_+ and n_- are the average number of subunits in the (+) and (−) states, respectively, averaged over the ensemble of molecules. This stability constant can be related to the standard free-energy change for the reaction by the relationship

$$\Delta G^0 = G_+{}^0 - G_-{}^0 = -RT \ln s \tag{2}$$

In general, s will be a function of such parameters as temperature, pressure, pH, and allosteric effector concentration.

17

The quantity of interest is usually the fraction of subunits in the (+) state, θ:

$$\theta = \frac{n_+}{n_+ + n_-} \tag{3}$$

All possible states of the ensemble of four subunits must be considered in order to calculate θ, as shown in Table 1. The relative free energy of the $(-)(-)(-)(-)$ state is arbitrarily taken as zero. There is one $(-)(-)(-)(-)$ state, four states (of equal probability, since they have equal energy) having one subunit in the (+) state, and so on. θ can be calculated with this information and equation (1). A statistical calculation for all subunits in the (+) state shows that θ is given by (see van Holde, 1971)

$$\theta = \frac{0 + 4s + 12s^2 + 12s^3 + 4s^4}{Q} \tag{4}$$

and

$$\theta = \frac{1}{4} \frac{s}{Q} \frac{dQ}{ds} \tag{5}$$

where Q is the partition function and is given by

$$Q = 1 + 4s + 6s^2 + 4s^3 + s^4 \tag{6}$$

Q is a sum of the products of the number of ways a given energy state may be formed, multiplied by the stability constant raised to a power equal to

TABLE 1

		Free energy
(1)	$(-)(-)(-)(-)$	0
(2)	$(+)(-)(-)(-)$ $(-)(+)(-)(-)$ $(-)(-)(+)(-)$ $(-)(-)(-)(+)$	ΔG^0
(3)	$(+)(+)(-)(-)$ $(+)(-)(+)(-)$ $(+)(-)(-)(+)$ $(-)(+)(+)(-)$ $(-)(+)(-)(+)$ $(-)(-)(+)(+)$	$2 \Delta G^0$
(4)	$(+)(+)(+)(-)$ $(+)(+)(-)(+)$ $(+)(-)(+)(+)$ $(-)(+)(+)(+)$	$3 \Delta G^0$
(5)	$(+)(+)(+)(+)$	$4 \Delta G^0$

the number of (+) conformations for that state (see Table 1). Equation (6) for Q is equivalent to

$$Q = (1 + s)^4 \qquad (7)$$

Q is thus the partition function of a system of four independent units, each having a (−) and a (+) state, with relative weights of 1 and s, respectively. Substitution of equation (7) into equation (5) yields

$$\theta = \frac{s}{1 + s} \qquad (8)$$

as would be expected for independent subunits.

The transition between (−) and (+) states can be induced by varying the concentration of a ligand that binds only to the (+) state. The variation of the stability constant with the concentration of ligand, C_L, can be found by an elementary, though tedious, calculation, and is given by

$$s = s_0(1 + K_B C_L) \qquad (9)$$

where K_B is the binding constant and s_0 is the value of s in the absence of ligand. s increases as C_L increases, encouraging the shift from (−) to (+) conformation. A calculation of θ versus C_L for a noncooperative transition will yield a hyperbolic curve of the form shown in Fig. 1.

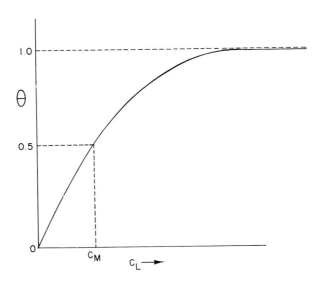

FIG. 1. The fraction of subunits in a four-subunit enzyme θ in the active (+) state as a function of ligand concentration (C_L) when no cooperativity exists between the subunits. C_M is the concentration at which $s = 1$ and θ is 0.5. When C is less than C_M, s is less than 1, and when C is greater than C_M, s is larger than 1 and θ is greater than 0.5.

A Cooperative Transition with No Intermediate States

In a transition with no intermediate states, in which only the $(-)(-)(-)(-)$ and $(+)(+)(+)(+)$ are possible, a shift in one subunit from the $(-)$ to the $(+)$ conformation forces the other three subunits to shift simultaneously to the $(+)$ conformation. In this case

$$Q = 1 + s^4 \tag{10}$$

and

$$\theta = \frac{s^4}{1 + s^4} \tag{11}$$

and a plot of θ versus C_L is sigmoidal (Fig. 2).

Given the most general case of an enzyme having N subunits (Fig. 3) (van Holde, 1971)

$$\theta = \frac{s^N}{1 + s^N} \tag{12}$$

Cooperative Transition with Nucleation Parameters

Most real physical systems show cooperative behavior that is intermediate between the noncooperative case and a transition with no intermediate states. In terms of our simple four-subunit model, a conformational change in one subunit from $(-)$ to $(+)$ makes it easier (energetically more

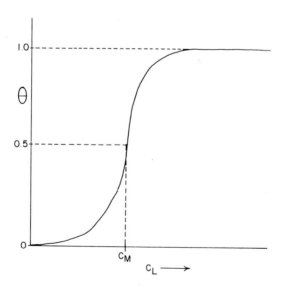

FIG. 2. The fraction of subunits in a four-subunit enzyme (θ) in $(+)$ $(+)$ $(+)$ $(+)$ state as a function of ligand concentration when no intermediate states are possible. As in the noncooperative case (Fig. 1), C_M is the value of C_L at which $\bar{s} = 1$; θ is still 0.5 at C_M.

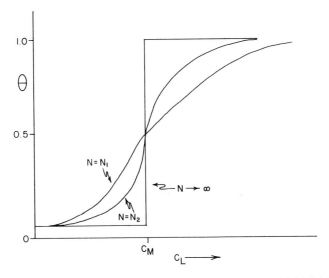

FIG. 3. The fraction of subunits in an N-subunit enzyme (θ) in the (+) (+) (+) (+) state as a function of C_L for a completely cooperative transition in which no intermediate states are possible. The steepness of the sigmoidal curve increases as N increases ($N_2 > N_1 > 1$); a true phase transition, indicated by a discontinuity in the θ versus C_L curve, is approached as $N \rightarrow \infty$.

favorable) for the other subunits to change conformation from (−) to (+). It is thus more difficult to shift the conformation of the first subunit than to shift the others. This can be expressed in mathematical terms in a manner analogous to the previous cases described, making the simplifying assumption that all other subunits are affected in the same way by the first conformational change, that is, that they have the same stability constant. The stability constant for a (−) to (+) conformational change for the first subunit is defined as σs, where s is the stability constant for the (−) to (+) conformational change for the succeeding subunits, and σ is less than unity, since the first conformational change is more difficult.

For this cooperative case, the partition function for the four-subunit example is

$$Q = 1 + 4\sigma s + 6\sigma s^2 + 4\sigma s^3 + \sigma s^4 \qquad (13)$$

Substitution into equation (4) will give an expression for θ in terms of σ and s. Again, plots of θ versus C_L will yield a sigmoidal curve.

A comparison of θ versus C_L for three values of σ are shown in Fig. 4; smaller values of σ yield more cooperative, sharper transitions. In physical terms, the transition becomes more cooperative as the difficulty of making the first conformational change, sometimes called the nucleation step, increases relative to subsequent steps. Once the difficult first conformational

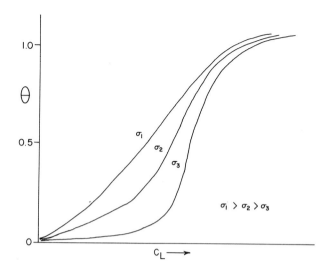

FIG. 4. The fraction of subunits in a four-subunit enzyme in the (+) state (θ) as a function of ligand concentration (C_L) for three values of σ, where σ is the relative degree of difficulty for the conformational change of the first subunit versus that of the other three. $\sigma_1 > \sigma_2 > \sigma_3$.

change is made, subsequent changes can occur with less difficulty given only a small change in experimental conditions, such as ligand concentration, thus giving rise to sharper, more sigmoidal curves.

Helix-coil transitions in nucleic acids and polypeptides can be examined theoretically in a similar manner. The simplest model for formation of a DNA helix by the association of two complementary random coils assumes only one type of base pair (Fig. 5). The most difficult step in forming a helix is "nucleation," through the formation of the first base pair. This step is difficult partly because of the translational entropy loss involved in bringing

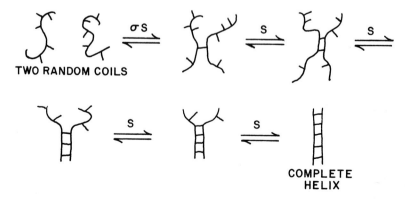

FIG. 5. The formation of a DNA helix having five base pairs.

the two strands together and partly because of the lack of vertical stacking energy with only one base pair. After the first base pair is formed, however, subsequent pairs have different stabilities, and a DNA molecule containing all four nucleotides has a broader, less sharp transition than one in which a single type of base pair predominates. Helix-coil transitions in nucleic acids are usually studied as a function of temperature, and can therefore be related to the stability constant, s, by the Van't Hoff relationship:

$$\frac{d \ln s}{dT} = \frac{\Delta H}{RT^2}$$

The relationship between θ and T is sigmoidal, and variations in the shape of the curves with variation in σ and helix length are similar to the simplified example of a helix with only one type of base pair.

It must be emphasized that sigmoidal curves in themselves do not *necessarily* imply cooperative transitions. The variation of θ with some thermodynamic variables to which s may be functionally related, especially when there is a logarithmic relationship, as with pH, may produce sigmoidal curves even if the transition is totally noncooperative. The sigmoidal shape is in this case an artifact of the method of plotting the data. This means that cooperativity must generally be defined with reference to some model noncooperative process, such as the titration of a monobasic acid in the case of a pH-driven transition.

Cooperation between subunits of macromolecular systems results in sharper transitions; in extreme cases the transitions approach all-or-none characteristics. Such transitions are likely to have evolved in living organisms, where it is advantageous that a large effect result from a small stimulus. The theoretical analysis of such transitions relies heavily on the use of model systems, among which systems with subunits having only two (+ or −) states, such as we have used in this discussion, are among the most useful. Such model systems are frequently called Ising models, after a model of ferromagnetism proposed by that investigator in 1925 (Ising, 1925).

L. Klotz noted that an Ising model assumes that each component of a collection of objects can exist in only two states; for example, a nucleic acid base pair can exist either in a helix or a random coil, not in any intermediate states. It also assumes that the state of an object is influenced only by its nearest neighbors.

Consider a one-dimensional Ising model in which each unit can exist in states 1 or 2:

$$
\begin{array}{ccccc}
\textcircled{1} & \textcircled{1} & \textcircled{2} & \textcircled{2} & \textcircled{1} \\
n-2 & n-1 & n & n+1 & n+2
\end{array}
$$

In such a system, the state of the nth object is dependent only on the states of the $n - 1$ and $n + 1$ objects. Cooperativity means that the existence of an object in state 2 increases the probability that its two nearest neighbors will exist in state 2, through an effect on the free energy of the system.

In a two-dimensional Ising model, which might be used to describe a lipid monolayer, each object has more nearest neighbors than it does in a one-dimensional system:

② ② ①
① ② ①
① ① ②

This increased complexity of interaction makes description and analysis of the two-dimensional system much more difficult, and the three-dimensional model is so complex that the equations have never been solved.

SOME BASIC PRINCIPLES OF TRANSDUCTIVE COUPLING:

Donald M. Crothers

In a transductive process, there is a transformation or conversion of energy between one mode and another, as in the transduction of a light impulse to an electrical current by a multiplier tube. In biological systems, the general modality of energy is chemical, and the problem is to understand how the energy of a chemical reaction is transduced to do various kinds of work. One must also deal with the reverse process in which other forms of energy are converted into chemical form, as in the transduction of light energy to a nerve impulse, possibly via intermediate processes that utilize chemical energy. For simplification, this section will deal primarily with the utilization of chemical energy to generate mechanical or osmotic work; however, these principles apply in a more general sense.

One important problem is the generation of forces from the molecular motions present in a living system. A force can be generated from molecular motion when there is a greater probability for motion in one direction than another; the simplest example is the pressure exerted by a gas. As shown in Fig. 6a, there is a greater probability for motion in the $P_1 \rightarrow P_2$ direction when $P_1 > P_2$. Hence there is greater transfer of momentum in this direction and a net force at the boundary. This force can be calculated as the derivative of the potential energy with respect to distance.

Diffusion is a second way in which force can be generated by molecular motion when there is a greater probability of molecular movement in one direction than another. Given a concentration gradient of a solute as a function of linear distance x (Fig. 6b), the number of molecules moving toward the region of lower concentration will exceed that in the reverse direction, since they all have equal probability of undergoing Brownian motion. As in the case of two gases at different pressures, the average force can be calculated from the gradient of the chemical potential with respect to

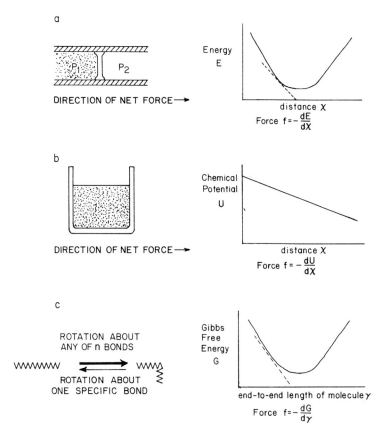

FIG. 6. Force generation as the result of molecular motion. A force will be generated: (a) when there is a greater probability for motion in one direction than another, as for two gases at different pressures, separated by an impermeable but moveable barrier; (b) as the result of diffusion; and (c) due to intramolecular elasticity (see text for discussion).

distance. Balancing this force against the viscous drag in the steady state yields the first law of diffusion. It is important to recognize the conceptual connection between molecular motion and the average force on the molecules, which arises from the greater probability of motion in one direction than another.

Similar forces can be produced by changing the internal structure of a macromolecule, as, for example, when rotation occurs about a carbon-carbon bond (Fig. 6c). Extension of the chain will be opposed by a restoring force against extension, since there is again a difference in probability between the two directions of movement. The fully extended chain can achieve a more folded state by rotation about any one of n bonds, while the production of a fully extended molecule requires rotation about a particular bond. There is therefore greater probability of motion to form the more folded structure, and consequently a restoring force to assume this state results. As in the previous cases, the free energy can be plotted as a function of the end-to-end distance γ, and the force will be the gradient of free energy with respect to γ. The Gibbs free energy is enthalpy minus the temperature times entropy term $(G = H - TS)$ and need not have any energy component; it can be comprised solely of entropy or probability. This means that a restoring force is present even if the two states of the molecular have identical energies, in which case the force derives solely from the greater probability of motion of one kind.

Molecular elasticity can also be coupled to a well-defined conformational change. This is illustrated in Fig. 7a by a helix-coil transformation. The free energy is a function of the end-to-end length of the molecule, and the force is therefore the gradient of free energy with respect to length. If the reaction conditions are adjusted so that the molecule is 50% helix in the absence of any applied force, the equilibrium can be displaced in either direction by applying a compressive or extensive force; the length of the macromolecule can thus be coupled to an applied force.

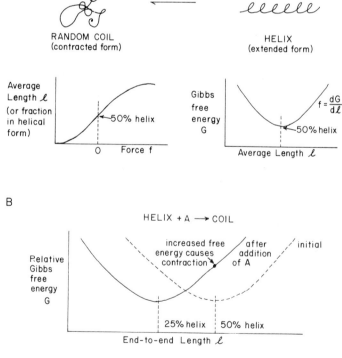

FIG. 7. (a) Elasticity coupled to a helix-coil transformation. (b) A chemical reaction can alter this helix-coil equilibrium. Addition of a small molecule generates a force (makes the probability of $h \rightarrow c$ greater than $c \rightarrow h$.)

The equilibrium between two forms can be altered by chemical reactions that produce a greater probability for movement in one direction. This is illustrated in Fig. 7*b* for a small molecule (A) that binds more readily to the coil than to the helix, and will therefore shift the equilibrium toward the coiled form under any specific reaction condition. The instantaneous effect of adding A is to increase the free energy relative to the value at equilibrium, thus producing a force (dG/dl) that will cause the molecule to contract. This force results from the greater probability for the helix to coil conversion than that for coil to helix.

An excellent illustrative example of force generation by a chemical reaction is found in the mechanochemistry of collagen fibers. The addition of LiBr to the fibers shifts the helix-coil equilibrium toward the coiled, contracted form, decreasing the fiber length and increasing tension; the binding of LiBr to the fiber thus does mechanical work (Rubin, Piez, and Katchalsky, 1969; Fig. 8*a*). In this example, the binding of LiBr to the collagen fibers transduces the chemical energy of the reaction to a contractile process. A

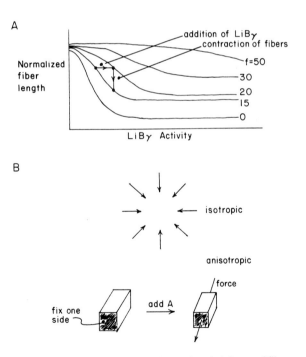

FIG. 8. (*a*). The cooperative effect of LiBr activity on the shrinkage of fibers under constant tensile force. The force, *f*, is expressed as grams on a pulley (Rubin et al., 1969). (*b*) A chemical reaction cannot be transduced to a vector force in an isotropic phase. For example, within a gel of collagen fibers, the addition of A (LiBr) will produce contraction. But the spherical symmetry within the isotropic gel will result in a net directional force of 0. Only when the medium is nonisotropic can a directional force be produced as in (*a*).

cyclic process could be produced by the addition of a mechanism for LiBr removal.

However, it is not possible to generate a force vector from a chemical reaction unless the system is made anisotropic in some manner, since in an isotropic medium the resultant of vector forces is zero (Fig. 8b). The collagen gel can be made anisotropic by fixing one side and measuring the force exerted on the other; the system is anisotropic because one particular dimension is selected.

As shown in Fig. 9, a chemical reaction can also be used to drive an active transport system. The production of X' from X in some unspecified manner produces a greater probability for the movement of K⁺ in one direction than the other; this is the equivalent of an average force on the K⁺ molecules and yields osmotic work. Such a system can function only when the membrane is asymmetric; that is, the conversion of X to X' must occur on only one side.

Cooperative interactions in this type of system amplify the effect of any change in conditions (Fig. 10). A cooperative transition yields a steep sigmoid curve, compared to a broader transition for a noncooperative system. When molecular length is again plotted as a function of the concentration of a small molecule that binds to one of two conformations of a macromolecule and shifts the equilibrium between them, a cooperative interaction amplifies the net change in length for any given change in the log (concentration) (Fig. 10a).

There is a less obvious relationship between cooperativity and the amount of force that can be generated by the transition (Fig. 10b). If the free energy is plotted as a function of the length of the molecule, which varies between the lengths of the coiled and helical forms, the free energy in a discontinuous phase transition will be the same for the two phases when they are at equilibrium. Similarly, at any given value of length displacement, the slope of free energy versus length will be greater for a noncooperative than a cooperative transition; that is, the cooperativity

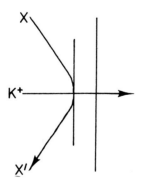

FIG. 9. The use of a chemical reaction, the conversion of X to X', to drive the transport of K⁺.

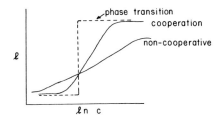

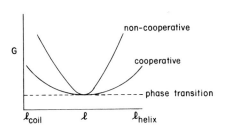

FIG. 10. The role of cooperativity in force-generating systems. (a) Cooperativity amplifies the net change in length resulting from any given Δ ln c. (b) Cooperativity reduces the force produced by any given Δl displacement.

reduces the force generated for a given Δl displacement. The noncooperative system is thus a superior force generator.

Another way of stating the same conclusion is that the elasticity of a cooperative system is greater than that of a noncooperative one. Elasticity arising from the order-disorder lipid phase transition could be important for the mechanical stability of cell membranes, since it would allow the membrane to respond to sudden osmotic changes by expanding or contracting.

A cooperative reaction also results in an increased available free energy for any given concentration perturbation $\Delta \ln c$ (Fig. 11). When the fraction of molecules in one state (θ) is determined as a function of concentration, the available free energy produced by a change in concentration from C_1 to C_2 is calculated by

$$\Delta G = \frac{RT(\Delta \ln c)(\Delta \theta)}{2}$$

which is greater at a given $\Delta \ln c$ for a cooperative than a noncooperative transition. Thus, the available free energy for any given concentration displacement is larger for a cooperative transition than for a noncooperative one.

Cooperativity also has a significant effect on the kinetics of a molecular transition, generally producing a net decrease in relaxation rates. In a noncooperative system, each unit is uncoupled from its neighbors and independently relaxes at its elementary rate. However, in a cooperative

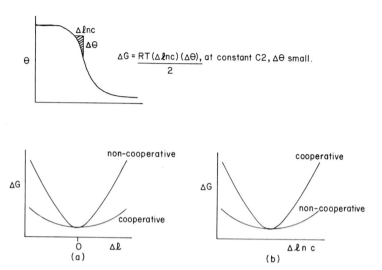

FIG. 11. A comparison of the amount of free energy available for a cooperative and noncooperative transition. Cooperativity reduces the force produced for a given Δl (a) and increases the available free energy produced by any given $\Delta \ln c$ (b).

system, reactions are more probable at boundary regions, and a sequence of steps must occur before a system has sampled all available configurations.

These principles may be illustrated by a simple model of messenger RNA (mRNA) translocation based on the mechanics of unfolding of transfer RNA (tRNA), whose structure has been determined crystallographically (Kim, Quigley, Suddath, McPherson, Sneden, Kim, Weinzierl, and Rich, 1973). A combination of relaxation kinetics and magnetic resonance methods has been used to document the sequence of steps involved in the unfolding of the macromolecule in response to increased temperature (Crothers, Cole, Hilbers, and Shulman, 1974). The initial step is transient unfolding of the dihydrouridine (DHU) helix at the junction between the two parts of the "L" structure (Fig. 12). This is followed by a full melting of the DHU helix and a tertiary interaction between the loop regions of the molecule, which are not involved in double-helix formation.

This highly specific series of molecular transformations may possibly be related to the generation of the force required to drive the movement of mRNA relative to the ribosome during the translation process, as illustrated in Fig. 13. One hypothesis is the following: First the peptide chain is transferred to the second (2) tRNA and the spent tRNA (1) is removed. The amino acid acceptor region of the L structure then moves simultaneously to the P site of the ribosome, with disruption of the DHU helix and tertiary structure. This could be thermodynamically coupled to removal of a bound Mg^{2+}, thus destablizing the helix. The ordered structure could then re-form and contract, producing movement of the mRNA and the

tRNA^{fMet} (E.coli)

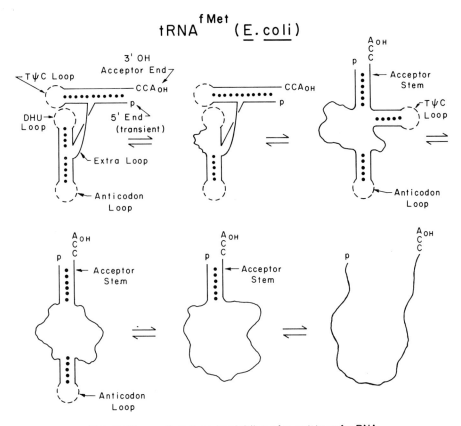

FIG. 12. Thermally induced unfolding of *E. coli* transfer RNA.

anticodon. The result is a simple transduction mechanism for driving the motion of an mRNA chain by the cyclic opening and closing of part of a macromolecule, with the necessary anisotropy provided by the difference between the A and P sites on the ribosome. No direct evidence presently

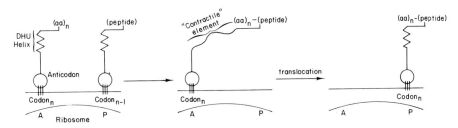

FIG. 13. A postulated mechanism for utilizing the opening and closing of the tRNA mole-cule in translation.

supports such an hypothesis; it is presented only to illustrate how cyclic conformational changes can be used to generate a force.

SHARPNESS AND KINETICS OF COOPERATIVE TRANSITIONS:

Gerhard Schwarz

When dealing with cooperativity in biological systems, one is generally most interested in the effect of a change in an external parameter such as ligand concentration on the equilibrium constant for a given reaction. Although the sharp transition from one state of high stability to another such state that is characteristic of a cooperative process can also be achieved by noncooperative means, much larger interaction energies would be required and the transition would therefore occur much more slowly. Thus, the sharp and fast transitions that are required in biological systems require the use of cooperative interactions, such as the individually weak forces involved in a series of hydrogen bonds or hydrophobic interactions. The essential features of cooperative transitions in biological systems are thus high stability below a certain threshold, but a sharp and rapid transition above it.

These cooperative transitions can be used for control and regulation in biological systems in the same way that electronic devices are used for these same purposes. The close similarity between the characteristics of electronic tubes and those of cooperative transitions is illustrated in Fig. 14.

Quantitative calculations involving cooperative transitions are usually

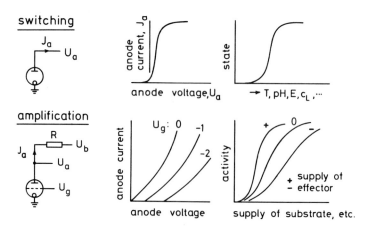

FIG. 14. The sharp transition of anode current as a function of anode voltage in a simple electronic switching device is analogous to the cooperative transition of the state of a biologically significant macromolecular structure as a function of external parameters. A close similarity to a simple electronic amplification device can also be demonstrated when grid voltage is compared to effector concentration (shift of threshold!).

based on the theoretical Ising model, in which cooperative interactions occur only between elementary reaction sites that are nearest neighbors, as discussed in the preceding section. Each of these sites is assumed to be able to exist in one of two states, for example, A or B. A plot of θ (the overall degree of transition) versus the stability constant s (the equilibrium constant for A $\rightleftharpoons$ B when half of the nearest neighbors are in state A, half in state B) always has the sigmoid shape characteristic of a cooperative reaction if the cooperative transition occurs in a system in which each site is associated with only two neighbors, as in a linear chain (Engel and Schwarz, 1970; Schwarz, 1970). The stimulus required to change this simplified system from one state to the other may be described by the necessary change of ln s. This critical stimulus is proportional to the square root of the general cooperativity parameter σ (see Fig. 18); the smaller σ, the smaller the change necessary to shift the state of the system (after the threshold has been reached). However, a true phase transition, having an infinite slope of θ versus s, can be achieved only when more than two neighbors are involved, as in the at-least-two-dimensional system indicated in Fig. 15, or when the interactions are of infinite magnitude or infinite range.

In view of the electrical excitability of nerve membranes, it is of particular interest that the application of an electric field strength E to a cooperative system alters the equilibrium constant according to the van't Hoff relationship:

$$\frac{\partial \ln s}{\partial E} = \frac{\Delta M}{RT}$$

where ΔM is the difference in the partial molar electrical moments (parallel to E) of reaction products and reactants (Bergmann, Eigen, and DeMaeyer, 1963; Schwarz, 1967). A change of ln s is therefore produced when an electric field is applied to a biological macromolecule. A much higher electric field than can be reached in biological systems would be required to induce a transition in a noncooperative system, whereas a much lower

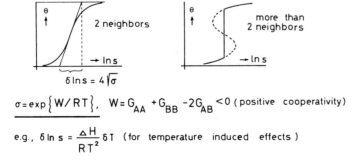

$$\sigma = \exp\{W/RT\}, \quad W = G_{AA} + G_{BB} - 2G_{AB} < 0 \text{ (positive cooperativity)}$$

e.g., $\delta \ln s = \dfrac{\Delta H}{RT^2} \delta T$ (for temperature induced effects)

FIG. 15. Cooperative transitions based on the interaction of nearest neighbors (Ising model) with negligible end effects.

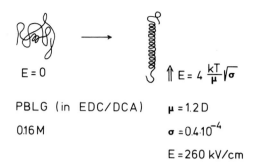

$$E = 0 \qquad \uparrow E = 4\,\frac{kT}{\mu}\sqrt{\sigma}$$

PBLG (in EDC/DCA) $\mu = 1.2\,D$

0.16 M $\sigma = 0.4 \cdot 10^{-4}$

                     $E = 260\ kV/cm$

FIG. 16. A conformational helix-coil transition induced by an electric field in poly (γ-benzyl L-glutamate) (PBLG) in a mixture of ethylene dicholaride (EDC) (EDC)/dichloroacetic acid (DCA) (μ is the dipole moment per helical subunit, i.e., per hydrogen bond; it is parallel to the helix axis).

electric field density is sufficient to induce a transition in a system having a high degree of cooperativity. The well-known case of the helix-coil transition of polypeptides is shown in Fig. 16 (Schwarz and Seelig, 1968).

Although the existence of cooperativity permits rather fast transitions, they must nevertheless always be slower than the elementary processes for the individual sites. For example, the elementary process in an α-helix-coil transition is hydrogen bond formation, which has a reaction time of about 10^{-10} sec (Bergmann et al., 1963). The total reaction time is increased by the cooperative interactions, but to a much lower extent than if large interaction and activation energies were involved.

The kinetics of such conformational transitions of linear polymers can be examined in chemical relaxation experiments (Schwarz and Engel, 1972), which examine the system as it returns to a stable state following the application of a slight perturbation. The relaxation process is described by a number of relaxation times, τ, and respective amplitudes, the so-called relaxation spectrum (Eigen and DeMaeyer, 1963; Schwarz, 1968). Using the linear Ising model, without end effects, a spectrum of four relaxation

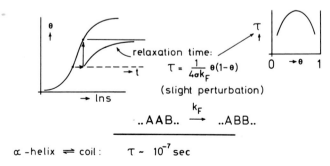

FIG. 17. Chemical relaxation of a conformational change in a one-dimensional system with strong cooperative interactions.

times is found; however, only one of them has a finite amplitude for a conformational transition having a strong degree of cooperativity (Schwarz, 1972). This is illustrated in Fig. 17. Values for τ of approximately 10^{-7} sec predicted by an approach to a mean relaxation time (Schwarz, 1965) have been experimentally confirmed (Schwarz and Seelig, 1968; Zana, 1972).

COOPERATIVE INTERACTIONS IN POLYSACCHARIDES:

David A. Rees

Long-chain polysaccharides of plant origin have been used as model systems to determine the types of interactions that might occur in the carbohydrate-containing molecules of vertebrates, such as those in the intercellular space. These plant polysaccharides form gels that contain as much as 99% water, whose structure results from the formation of noncovalent cross-links (Fig. 18a; Rees, 1969, 1972). The formation of these cross-links is a cooperative phenomenon similar to that shown by the nucleic acids, and a stable structural entity results from the accumulation of many hydrogen bonds and other weak forces (Fig. 18b). Sol-gel transitions show sigmoidal kinetics, and involve the same type of nucleation and propagation steps as those described by Zimm for nucleic acid transitions. Discontinuities in the repeating sequence of sugar moieties produce helix terminations, which make possible cross-linking between strands and the formation of a stable gel network (Rees, Steele, and Williamson, 1969; Fig. 18a).

The formation of ordered polysaccharide structures is strongly dependent on the nature and sequence of the sugar residues, with the conformation determined by the bond torsion angles between the sugar rings. The two most important classes of polysaccharide conformation are the ribbon and helix (Rees and Scott, 1971; Rees, 1973), and these may interact to form ribbon sheets or multiple helices (Fig. 18a).

For example, the carrageenans, a class of polysaccharides that has a repetitive -A-B-A-B- structure, form stable double helices in solution (Rees et al., 1969; McKinnon, Rees, and Williamson, 1969; Bryce, McKinnon, Morris, Rees, and Thom, 1974). As in the nucleic acids, the helix-coil transition is a cooperative process. A sigmoidal relationship has been demonstrated for optical rotation as a function of temperature, indicating that melting is a cooperative process (Fig. 19; McKinnon et al., 1969), and the available evidence strongly suggests that the transition from coil to helix occurs by a switch mechanism, rather than involving a series of intermediate states (Bryce et al., 1974; Reid, Bryce, Clark, and Rees, 1974).

The alginates, whose sequences of acidic sugar residues are of the types

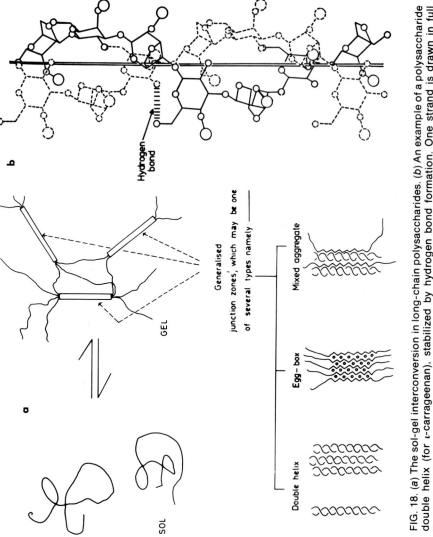

FIG. 18. (a) The sol-gel interconversion in long-chain polysaccharides. (b) An example of a polysaccharide double helix (for ι-carrageenan), stabilized by hydrogen bond formation. One strand is drawn in full lines, the other in broken lines. Large circles represent sulphate ester groups. The hydrogen bond indicated in the figure is repeated by helical symmetry, engaging all the sugar hydroxy groups to form a network of interstrand hydrogen bonding.

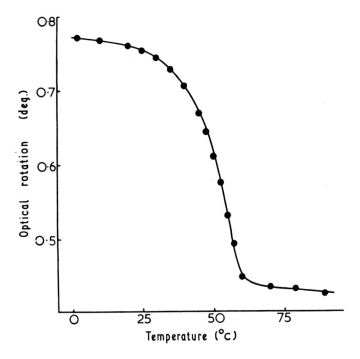

FIG. 19. Optical rotation as a function of temperature for ι-carrageenan segments.

-A-A-A, -B-B-B-, and -A-B-A-B-, undergo a Ca^{2+}-induced association into Ca^{2+}-containing "egg-box" structures (Kohn and Larsen, 1972; Figs. 18a and 20). Extensive evidence indicates that the formation of these structures is a cooperative process. A sharp transition to the egg-box structure is obtained only when the appropriate sequence within the polysaccharide chain is at least 16 to 20 units in length (J. Boyd, E. R. Morris, D. A. Rees, and D. Thom, *personal communication*). This minimal length requirement is comparable to that found for the nucleic acids, in which a minimum of 30 nucleotide units must be present for a cooperative transition to a stable

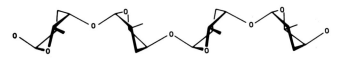

FIG. 20. Conformation of the poly (L-guluronate) sequences in alginates as they are presumed to exist in the proposed egg-box structure (Grant, Morris, Rees, Smith, and Thom, 1973). These buckled chains pack with Ca^{2+} ions in the manner shown schematically in Fig. 18a. Substituents on the sugar rings are not shown, except for the bond to the equatorial carboxylate (note that this projects toward the cavity that is occupied by Ca^{2+}). Ten sugar oxygen atoms are closely packed around Ca^{2+} to form a favorable co-ordination shell.

helix to occur. A sigmoid curve is observed for mixtures of Ca^{2+} and Na^+ when the binding of Ca^{2+} is determined as a function of the Ca^{2+}/Na^+ ratio (Kohn and Furda, 1968). A distinct transition point is also observed when bound Ca^{2+} is determined as a function of ester groups removed from pectin (Kohn and Furda, 1968).

Cooperative interactions are a general characteristic of any macromolecule that contains many similar repeating units. The principles of cooperativity apply to proteins, nucleic acids, and polysacccharides. This characteristic is thus a general biological principle.

CONSTRUCTION OF CONTROL AND SELF-ORGANIZING SYSTEMS:

Manfred Eigen

An extremely sensitive response system is produced when its components interact cooperatively and the system is maintained in the region of greatest sensitivity. An excellent example of such a biological system is the hemoglobin molecule.

Given that:

$$\frac{\partial \ln K}{\partial T} = \frac{\Delta H}{RT^2}$$

a steep response to a small change in temperature can be obtained if the enthalpy, ΔH, is large. Although this can occur in the absence of any cooperativity, as also noted by Schwarz, the appropriate entropy change, ΔS – defining a transition temperature T_t by $T_t \Delta S = \Delta H$ – cannot be achieved at room temperature unless the number of degrees of freedom in the system is severely restricted. This restriction can be achieved most readily in a cooperatively interacting system of repeating components, such as a nucleic acid. This type of repetitive system can undergo hysteresis, as can any structure containing large interacting domains. The advantages of hysteresis depend on evolutionary selection. For example, a nucleic acid chain 100 nucleotides in length may have a cooperativity factor σ of 10^4 and a reaction enthalpy per nucleotide of 10 kcal/mole. A helix-coil transition can be triggered in such a system by a 1% δT.

A conformational change in a protein subunit involves the cooperative interaction of many amino acids. A change in one subunit will force a change in others if there are many structural links between them. Such a system, involving steep transformations, can be used as control "switches" analogous to those in electronics.

The anode-cathode voltage across a vacuum tube (triode) or a corresponding transistor is analogous to a substrate-product reaction whose rate is controlled by the equilibrium between the inactive and active forms of an enzyme (Fig. 21). In the same way that a small change in grid current

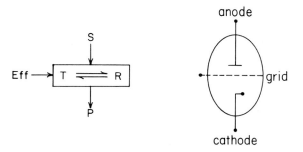

FIG. 21. Analogy between a vacuum tube and a substrate-product reaction whose rate is controlled by an effector (Eff) that alters the equilibrium between inactive (T) and active (R) forms of an enzyme.

produces a large change in the voltage across the tube, a small change in enzymic effector and the T $\rightleftharpoons$ R equilibrium produces a major alteration in the S $\rightarrow$ P conversion.

Such a system can be used either as an all-or-none switch or for amplification and control. This general design can be used as the basis for several types of systems:

1. If the product favors the higher-affinity R state, the system will show positive feedback.

2. If the product favors the lesser-affinity T state, the system will show negative feedback.

3. If the substrate favors the R state, the system can exhibit threshold behavior.

4. If the substrate favors the T state, the system can show negative resistance and may exhibit control behavior in a similar way as a positive feedback system.

A combination of these four types of responses can be used to generate all possible forms of electronic control systems, particularly if linked to irreversible devices, and a similar possibility exists for biological systems.

Given the system X_i, which can be a single molecule, a macromolecule with many subunits, a membrane, and so on, having some given rate of formation and degradation, that is:

$$\Rightarrow X_i \Rightarrow$$

it is possible to determine what the response of the system X_i will be to a small change in a variable such as the concentration of X_i. A matrix of nine possible responses can be constructed for the system (Fig. 22): (+) is a positive response, that is, a change equal in sign with the original (e.g., positive fluctuation, increased rate in response to a small increase in concentration); (−) is a negative response, which means a sign opposite to that of the original fluctuation; and (0) represents an indifference with respect to any change. Only two of these are potential control systems that could

RATE OF FORMATION

FIG. 22. Possible response of a fluctuation of the concentration of X_i in the rate of formation or degradation. (+) is a response having the same sign as the fluctuation (e.g., increased rate in response to a small increase of concentration), (−) is a response with opposite sign (e.g., a decreased rate for an increase in concentration), and (0) represents a lack of change. S = stable, because after any change the system ultimately returns to the (reference) steady state; D = exhibits drift behavior if any noise is present; U = unstable; C = potential control system.

convert a cooperative structural behavior into a cooperative temporal one, as in an allosteric enzyme (Eigen, 1973). Either positive or negative feedback could be incorporated into such a system. Systems that utilize this type of control may have been selected for during the process of evolution. In biological systems, conversions of structural to temporal events are frequently mediated by conformational changes within allosteric proteins.

In many membrane-bound enzymes, conformational changes release Ca^{2+}, which in turn triggers or controls the subsequent reaction process. Every biological example of a functionally linked system discussed in subsequent chapters utilizes Ca^{2+} in some way. This almost universal use of Ca^{2+} leads to a consideration of what properties are responsible for its unique position.

The preference for Ca^{2+} over other divalent cations such as Mg^{2+} may be simply explained by its coordination chemistry. Although the stability constants for these ions do not differ significantly, their substitution rates are markedly different; the rates of Mg^{2+} and Ca^{2+} substitutions in water are 10^5/sec and 10^8/sec, respectively. A stability constant of 10^5 to 10^7 has been calculated as ideal for a trigger system operating within the physiological concentration range. If the "on" rate of Mg^{2+} is 10^5, its "off rate" is 1/sec, yielding a stability constant of 10^5 and a fast exchange. Mg^{2+} would be suitable only for a competitive system, where it is frequently found (Eigen and Hammes, 1963).

REFERENCES

Bergmann, K., Eigen, M., and DeMaeyer, L. (1963): Dielektrische Relaxation als Folge chemischer Relaxation. *Ber. Bunsenges. physik. Chem.*, 67:819–826.
Bryce, R. A., McKinnon, A. A., Morris, E. R., Rees, D. A., and Thom, D. (1974): Chain conformations in the sol-gel transitions for polysaccharide systems, and their characterization by spectroscopic methods. *Disc. Faraday Soc. (in press)*.
Crothers, D. M., Cole, P. E., Hilbers, C. W., and Shulman, R. G. (1974): The molecular mechanism of thermal unfolding of *E. coli* tRNA^fhet. *J. Mol. Biol.*, 87:63–89.

Eigen, M. (1973): In: *The Physicist's Conception of Nature,* edited by J. Mehra, p. 594. Boston: Reidel Publishing Co.

Eigen, M., and DeMaeyer, L. (1963): Relaxation methods. In: *Technique of Organic Chemistry. Volume VIII. Investigation of Rates and Mechanisms of Reactions,* edited by S. L. Friess, E. S. Lewis, and A. Weissberger, pp. 895–1054. New York: Interscience Publishers.

Eigen, M., and Hammes, G. (1963): Elementary steps in enzyme reactions (as studied by relaxation spectrometry). *Adv. Enzymol.,* 25:1–38.

Engel, J., and Schwarz, G. (1970): Cooperative conformational transitions of linear biopolymers. *Angew. Chem. Int. Ed.,* 9:389–400.

Grant, G. T., Morris, E. R., Rees, D. A., Smith, P. J. C., and Thom, D. (1973): Biological interactions between polysaccharides and divalent cations: The egg-box model. *FEBS Letters,* 32:195–198.

Ising, E. (1925): Beitrag zur Theorie des Ferromagnetismus. *Z. Physik,* 31:253–258.

Kim, S. H., Quigley, G. J., Suddath, F. L., McPherson, A., Sneden, D., Kim, J. J., Weinzierl, J., and Rich, A. (1973): Three dimensional structure of yeast phenylalanine transfer RNA: Folding of the polynucleotide chain. *Science,* 179:285–288.

Kohn, R., and Furda, I. (1968): Binding of calcium ions to acetyl derivative of pectin. *Collect. Czech. Chem. Commun.,* 33:2217–2225.

Kohn, R., and Larsen, B. (1972): Preparation of water-soluble polyuronic acids and their calcium salts, and the determination of calcium ion activity in relation to the degree of polymerization. *Acta Chem. Scand.,* 26:2455–2468.

McKinnon, A. A., Rees, D. A., and Williamson, F. B. (1969): Coil to double helix transition for a polysaccharide. *Chem. Commun.,* 12:701–702.

Rees, D. A. (1969): Structure, conformation, and mechanism in the formation of polysaccharide gels and networks. *Adv. Carbohydrate Chem. Biochem.,* 24:267–332.

Rees, D. A. (1972): Polysaccharide gels. A molecular view. *Chem. and Ind.,* pp. 630–636.

Rees, D. A. (1973): *M. T. P. Internat. Rev. Sci., Org. Chem.,* 7:251.

Rees, D. A., and Scott, W. E. (1971): Polysaccharide conformation. Part VI. Computer model-building for linear and branched pyranoglycans. Correlations with biological function. Preliminary assessment of inter-residue forces in aqueous solution. Further interpretation of optical rotation in terms of chain conformation. *J. Chem. Soc. B,* pp. 469–479.

Rees, D. A., Steele, I. W., and Williamson, F. B. (1969): Conformational analysis of polysaccharides. III. The relation between stereochemistry and properties of some natural polysaccharide sulfates. *J. Polymer Sci. C,* 28:261–276.

Reid, D. S., Bryce, T. A., Clark, A. H., and Rees, D. A. (1974): The helix-coil transition in gelling polysaccharides. *Disc. Faraday Soc. (in preparation).*

Rubin, M. M., Piez, K. A., and Katchalsky, A. (1969): Equilibrium mechanochemistry of collagen fibers. *Biochemistry,* 8:3628–3637.

Schwarz, G. (1965): On the kinetics of the helix-coil transition of polypeptides in solution. *J. Mol. Biol.,* 11:64–77.

Schwarz, G. (1967): On dielectric relaxation due to chemical rate processes. *J. Phys. Chem.,* 71:4021–4030.

Schwarz, G. (1968): Kinetic analysis by chemical relaxation methods. *Rev. Mod. Phys.,* 40:206–218.

Schwarz, G. (1970): Cooperative binding to linear biopolymers. I. Fundamental static and dynamic Properties. *Eur. J. Biochem.,* 12:442–453.

Schwarz, G. (1972): Chemical relaxation of co-operative conformational transitions of linear biopolymers. *J. Theor. Biol.,* 36:569–580.

Schwarz, G., and Engel, J. (1972): Kinetics of cooperative conformational transitions of linear biopolymers. *Angew. Chem. Int. Ed.,* 11:568–575.

Schwarz, G., and Seelig, J. (1968): Kinetic properties and electric field effect of the helix-coil transition of poly (γ-benzyl L-glutamate) determined from dielectric relaxation measurements. *Biopolymers,* 6:1263–1277.

Van Holde, K. E. (1971): *Physical Biochemistry,* pp. 51–78. Englewood Cliffs, N.J.: Prentice-Hall.

Zana, R. (1972): On the detection of the helix-coil transition of polypeptides by ultrasonic absorption measurements in the megahertz range. Case of poly-L-glutamic acid. *J. Amer. Chem. Soc.,* 94:3646–3647.

Functional Linkage in Biomolecular Systems, edited by
F. O. Schmitt, D. M. Schneider, and D. M. Crothers.
Raven Press, New York © 1975.

Chapter 2

Allosteric Interactions in Enzyme Systems

FUNCTIONAL LINKAGE AS A BASIC PRINCIPLE OF BIOLOGY:

Daniel E. Atkinson

Correlation and regulation, two of the primary characteristics of living systems, both imply and underlie function. All living processes occur as the result of, and are correlated with, functional linkage; this principle is thus at the very heart of biology.

Any discussion of biological processes must always involve oversimplification, because biomolecular reactions are always part of a larger whole. Biomolecular processes may be of some interest in their own right, but their biological significance relates to their effects on a larger system. The properties of an enzyme are meaningful only in terms of the reaction that it catalyzes; the properties of the reaction are meaningful only in terms of the metabolic sequence in which it occurs; the properties of the sequence are meaningful only in terms of overall metabolism; and overall metabolism is meaningful only in terms of the growth and reproduction of the organism.

The black-box approach, in which the intermediate mechanisms between a stimulus and its induced response are not considered, can lead, and has led, to much useful information in physiology and biophysics. It poses questions that a mechanistically oriented approach can then be used to solve. However, this approach is limited and in a sense outmoded.

In contrast, biochemists deal with small portions of large systems, and frequently become so intrigued with the properties of these parts that they forget that they are, *in situ,* functioning elements within a complex interacting system. If we study proteins only as macromolecules, or enzymes as catalysts, again our approach is limited and we obtain information that is of limited use in itself.

These two basic approaches must be combined in order to obtain information that is biologically meaningful. Every aspect of an organism is designed by mutation and selection, but we must remember that while it is molecular detail that mutates, it is overall organismic function that is selected. Both the molecular and the black-box approaches must be used, but the area of real interest is in the linkage between them, the ways in which molecular detail is responsible for the overall response or for the living functioning organism.

REGULATION OF ENZYMIC ACTIVITY:

Gordon G. Hammes

Characterization of Enzyme Systems

The most common method of characterizing an enzyme reaction is to plot the initial steady-state velocity as a function of substrate concentration (Fig. 1). Some degree of regulation can be achieved when this function is a simple hyperbolic isotherm, as the reaction velocity reaches a limiting value at high concentrations of substrate. Systems characterized by nonhyperbolic isotherms permit more versatile control (Fig. 1a). A sigmoidal isotherm (positive cooperativity) has a narrow region of concentration in which a small concentration change produces a much larger alteration in reaction rate than can occur with a hyperbolic isotherm. When the system shows negative cooperativity, the concentration range over which regulation occurs is broadened, and relative changes in rate are large at low concentrations and small at high concentrations.

Allosteric activators and inhibitors can alter enzymic activity either by changing the binding characteristics of the enzyme or by changing its

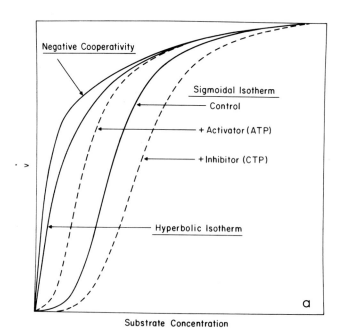

Substrate Concentration

FIG. 1a. Reaction velocity, v, as a function of substrate concentration, for noncooperative systems (hyperbolic isotherm) and for K systems showing positive (sigmoidal isotherm) and negative cooperativity.

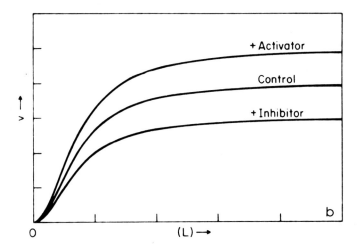

FIG. 1*b*. A V-type regulatory system, in which the intrinsic catalytic activity of the enzyme is altered by the binding of an activator or inhibitor, but the binding characteristics of the enzyme are unaltered.

intrinsic catalytic activity (maximal velocity). In the former case, termed a K system, binding is broadly interpreted in terms of both kinetic and equilibrium measurements. In these systems, an allosteric inhibitor makes a sigmoidal binding curve more sigmoidal, while an allosteric activator makes it less sigmoidal (Fig. 1*a*); the maximum velocity of the reaction is unaltered. The latter systems, in which the level of catalysis is altered, are referred to as V systems (Fig. 1*b*). The addition of an activator or inhibitor to this type of system increases or decreases the maximum velocity of the reaction. A single enzyme system may show a combination of K and V responses, resulting in highly complex and responsive control.

Equilibrium Binding Phenomena

A general formulation for the binding of a ligand, L, by a protein, P, that contains n binding sites, can be developed as follows:

$$P + L \rightleftharpoons PL_1 \qquad K_1 = \frac{(PL)}{(P)(L)}$$

$$PL_1 + L \rightleftharpoons PL_2 \qquad K_2 = \frac{(PL_2)}{(PL_1)(L)}$$

$$\vdots \qquad\qquad \vdots$$

$$PL_{n-1} + L \rightleftharpoons PL_n \qquad K_n = \frac{(PL_n)}{(PL_{n-1})(L)}$$

where the K_i are binding constants.

The binding isotherm is usually expressed as the moles of ligand bound per mole of enzyme, r, which can be written as a function of the equilibrium constants for n reactions. For the above case,

$$r = \frac{K_1(L) + 2K_1K_2(L)^2 + \cdots + nK_1K_2 \cdots K_n(L)^n}{1 + K_1(L) + \cdots + K_n(L)^n}$$

Either positive or negative cooperativity or a combination of both can be present in this type of system, depending on the values of the individual binding constants. The limiting case in which all n sites are independent and equivalent has a hyperbolic binding isotherm, and the equation for r simplifies to

$$r = \frac{nK(L)}{1 + K(L)}$$

Another possible model is to assume m classes of independent sites with n_i equivalent sites in each class. In this case,

$$r = \sum^{m} \frac{n_iK_i(L)}{1 + K_i(L)}$$

Expansion of this equation indicates that this model can generate only negative cooperativity. Thus, an apparent negative cooperativity in the experimental binding isotherm may be due to the existence of different classes of sites rather than to interactions between sites. In practice, it is extremely difficult to distinguish between these two possibilities. These basic binding equations can be utilized to help interpret the detailed binding mechanism for allosteric enzymes.

Several basic molecular models have been proposed to explain equilibrium binding phenomena. All of these models propose that the molecular basis of regulation involves the alteration of protein subunit interactions by conformational changes of the subunits. The concerted model of Monod, Wyman, and Changeux (1965; Fig. 2) postulates that the enzyme contains interacting subunits, that their interactions are altered by ligand binding, and that these alterations result from conformational changes in the subunits. Furthermore, all subunits must be in either one conformation or the other, with no intermediate states; that is, the conformational transition is concerted. A sigmoidal binding isotherm results if it is assumed that the substrate binds much more tightly to one of the two enzyme conformations (e.g., the circles), and that in the absence of substrate the enzyme exists almost entirely in the conformation having the lower affinity (e.g., the squares). Very little binding of substrate will occur at low substrate concentrations, since only a small amount of the enzyme will be in the tight, higher-affinity binding state, but the addition of more substrate will shift the equilibrium to this state. Finally, the enzyme will be almost entirely

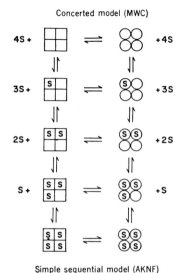

Concerted model (MWC)

Simple sequential model (AKNF)

FIG. 2. The concerted allosteric model for equilibrium binding to a four-subunit enzyme (Monod, et al., 1965), and the sequential allosteric model for equilibrium binding to a four-subunit enzyme (Adair, 1925; Koshland, et al., 1966). The squares and circles represent different subunit conformations, and S is the substrate.

in the high-affinity binding state, and the extent of binding will increase rapidly with increasing substrate concentration, thus producing a sigmoidal binding isotherm.

This mechanism can be described formally as

$$nL + R_0 \overset{L_0}{\rightleftharpoons} T_0 + nL$$
$$\updownarrow \qquad \updownarrow$$
$$(n - 1)L + R_1 \rightleftharpoons T_1 + (n - 1)L$$
$$\vdots \qquad \vdots$$
$$R_n \rightleftharpoons T_n$$

$$\frac{r}{n} = \frac{L_0 c\alpha(1 + c\alpha)^{n-1} + \alpha(1 + \alpha)^{n-1}}{L_0(1 + c\alpha)^n + (1 + \alpha)^n}$$

$$c = \frac{K_R}{K_T}; \qquad \alpha = \frac{(L)}{K_R}; \qquad L_0 = \frac{T_0}{R_0}$$

where R_i and T_i represent the two states of the enzyme and K_R and K_T are the intrinsic binding constants for the two different states of the enzyme. Although this equation can be used to generate sigmoidal binding isotherms, it cannot yield negative cooperativity. Regulation by inhibitors and activators can be introduced by assuming that an activator binds preferentially to the tight-binding (active) form, thereby decreasing the sigmoidicity of the binding isotherm, while an inhibitor binds preferentially to the weak-binding (inactive) state and therefore increases the sigmoidicity of the binding isotherm.

A second molecular model is that of Adair, Koshland, Nemethy, and Filmer (Adair, 1925; Koshland, Nemethy, and Filmer, 1966; Fig. 2). This model resembles that of Monod et al. (1965) in many respects, but it postulates a sequential change in subunit conformation as each ligand binds to the enzyme, rather than a concerted transition. This model postulates that the binding of substrate induces a conformational change in the subunit, thereby altering the subunit interactions and the effective binding constant for addition of the next ligand molecule. Either positive or negative cooperativity in the binding isotherm can be generated with this model. The effects of inhibitors and activators can be explained by postulating that the subunit conformation and subunit interactions are altered by their binding, thereby in turn altering the effective binding constants for substrate.

As shown in Fig. 3, and as recently pointed out by Wyman (1972), these two models are actually special cases of a more general allosteric model. This figure has been somewhat simplified by neglecting the permutations that can occur when more than one substrate molecule is bound. Although the differences between the two models have often been emphasized, their molecular bases are actually quite similar. Both are based on the premises that there are conformational changes in protein subunits, that subunit interactions are altered by ligand binding, and that these alterations are the

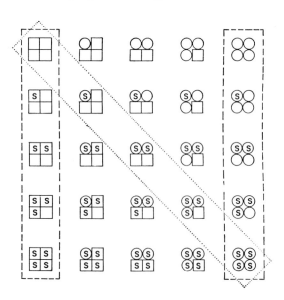

FIG. 3. A general allosteric model for a four-subunit protein. The two end columns represent the Monod, Wyman, and Changeux model, while the diagonal represents the Adair, Koshland, Nemethy, and Filmer model. The squares and circles represent different subunit conformations, and S is the substrate.

basis of enzyme regulation. The primary difference between them is the premise of concerted versus sequential conformational changes, but these are only limiting cases of the more general model.

Steady-State Kinetics

Relatively few direct binding measurements have been made for regulatory enzymes; instead, they are usually characterized by measuring steady-state initial velocities. The interpretation of such steady-state kinetic measurements is frequently complex, in contrast to the relatively straightforward meaning of thermodynamic binding measurements.

Table 1 indicates various situations that may occur in steady-state kinetics. The simplest case is that all substrate binding equilibria adjust rapidly relative to the catalytic process. If the turnover number is identical for all sites, the initial velocity, v, is directly proportional to the extent of equilibrium binding, and the proportionality constant is the maximum velocity, V_M. An assumption frequently made in interpreting steady-state measurements is that the kinetic parameter is directly proportional to the thermodynamic quantity. When this is actually the case, the system can be characterized in a true thermodynamic sense using only kinetic measurements.

TABLE 1. *Steady-state kinetics of regulatory enzymes*

---

1. Binding equilibria adjusted rapidly
   a. Turnover number at all sites identical

$$v = V_M r$$

   b. Turnover number different at each site

   MWC–2 turnover numbers
   AKNF–n turnover numbers

2. Nonequilibrium
   a. K_M not an equilibrium constant
   b. Independent equivalent sites, but alternative pathways for multisubstrate enzymes
   c. Classes of sites, cooperativity in binding

Unfortunately, many other situations may also occur. For example, a system in which substrate binding equilibrates rapidly compared to the catalytic process may have a different turnover number at each site. Such a system will have an intrinsic catalytic activity that varies with the degree of saturation of the enzyme sites. In the Monod, Wyman, and Changeux model, the R and T forms each can have a different turnover number, while n different turnover numbers may exist in the Adair, Koshland, Nemethy, and Filmer model. Interpretation of the velocity isotherm would be quite complex in the latter case.

Still more complex are those cases in which the binding steps are not adjusted rapidly relative to the other steps in the enzyme mechanism, and a steady state must therefore be assumed. For example, systems in which the Michaelis constant is not an equilibrium constant may be important in biological systems. Thermodynamic and kinetic measurements on such systems may lead to markedly different values for the apparent binding constant.

A multisubstrate enzyme might also contain independent and equivalent sites with multiple kinetic pathways. In this case the initial velocity isotherm might be nonhyperbolic (Sweeny and Fisher, 1968). Although this type of system is not actually cooperative, it does provide a possible method of biological regulation and linkage through a kinetic rather than an equilibrium mechanism.

Still a third possibility is the existence of cooperativity in the binding, but with the binding process not being adjusted rapidly relative to other steps in the catalytic mechanism. Because of their complexity, such systems have not yet been seriously considered.

Polymerization-Depolymerization as a Regulatory Process

Enzyme polymerization appears to be utilized as a regulatory mechanism in a number of enzyme systems. The basic premise is that the ligand can bind to both the monomer and polymer, but that the tightness of binding differs in the two states and/or the intrinsic catalytic activity of each aggregation state differs (cf. Frieden and Colman, 1967; Nichol, Jackson, and Winzor, 1967).

A simple polymerization-depolymerization regulatory mechanism can be formulated as follows:

$$xE \underset{}{\overset{K}{\rightleftharpoons}} E_x \qquad K = \frac{(E_x)}{(E)^x}$$

$$K_E \quad \begin{array}{c} E + L + L \rightleftharpoons EL \\ \vdots \\ EL_{n-1} + L \rightleftharpoons EL_n \end{array} \qquad\qquad \begin{array}{c} E_x + L \rightleftharpoons E_xL \\ \vdots \\ E_xL_{m-1} + L \rightleftharpoons E_xL_m \end{array} \quad K_{EX}$$

$$r = \frac{n\alpha(1 + \alpha)^{n-1} + K(E)^{x-1}mc\alpha(1 + c\alpha)^{m-1}}{(1 + \alpha)^{n-1} + xK(E)^{x-1}(1 + c\alpha)^m}$$

$$\alpha = K_E(L) \qquad c = \frac{K_{EX}}{K_E}$$

Two aggregation states are postulated, E and E_x, having n and m binding sites with intrinsic binding constants K_E and K_{EX}. In the equation for r, the enzyme concentrations are calculated in terms of the monomer molecular weight. The binding isotherm for such a system is identical to that for the Monod, Wyman, and Changeux model when $x = 1$. The binding isotherm again can resemble that of a cooperative system, but this apparent cooperativity is due to the presence of more than one enzyme aggregate rather than to an interaction between sites. Such a system may also show kinetic differences, in which the reaction rate differs for the monomer and polymer, rather than the extent of binding.

Slow Kinetic Responses

Until now, it has been implicitly assumed that the regulatory processes occur rapidly relative to the catalytic rate of the enzyme reaction. However, this need not be the case; several instances are known in which the regulatory process appears to be relatively slow. These enzyme systems have been termed "hysteretic" (Frieden, 1970). Slow kinetic responses may result from slow conformational changes, slow ligand displacement, or slow polymerization-depolymerization, and may be quite important in biological systems.

As an example, consider a system in which there is a slow conformational change from E to E' and from ES to ES':

$$E + S \rightleftharpoons ES \rightleftharpoons E'S \rightleftharpoons E' + S$$
$$\downarrow \qquad \downarrow$$
$$P + E \rightleftharpoons E' + P$$

The initial steady-state velocity for such a system can be written as

$$\frac{d(P)}{dt} = v_\infty + (v_0 - v_\infty)e^{-k't}$$

where $k' = f(S, k_i, K_i)$, $v_0 = $ initial steady-state velocity at 0 time, and $v_\infty = $ initial steady-state velocity at infinite time.

The lag period before the ultimate steady-state velocity is reached is characterized by the rate constant k', which is a function of substrate concentration, the rate constants, and the equilibrium constants. This lag period is several hours or longer in some enzyme systems, and provides a "time" buffer for the regulatory process. The metabolic significance of such time buffering has not yet been elucidated.

Transient Measurements

Transient kinetic measurements can provide new information about regulatory systems, since enzyme concentrations can be made comparable to ligand concentrations. Under these conditions, it is possible to detect reaction intermediates and to study elementary steps in the reaction mechanism, rather than to determine overall kinetic parameters that are complex functions of individual rate constants, as is the case for steady-state kinetic measurements. Several regulatory enzymes have been studied with rapid mixing and relaxation techniques, two of the most prevalent methods for studying very fast reactions (Hammes, 1974; Hammes and Wu, 1974).

For the MWC mechanism, involving a concerted conformational change, it can usually be assumed that ligand binding will be rapid relative to the conformational change. Given this assumption, only three time constants (relaxation times) are sufficient to characterize the system when it is near equilibrium. Two of these relaxation times characterize the binding steps and decrease as the substrate concentration increases, while the third characterizes the conformational transition and may either increase or decrease as the substrate concentration increases.

In contrast, if ligand binding is rapid relative to the conformational transitions, the AKNF model would have $2n$ relaxation times, where n is the number of ligand binding sites on the enzyme. Given this assumption, n relaxation times would be associated essentially with ligand binding and would decrease as the substrate concentration increases, while the other n relaxation times would be associated primarily with the conformational transitions and could either increase or decrease with increasing substrate concentration. Although it is possible to differentiate between these two mechanisms by transient kinetic measurements, in practice this is quite difficult. The guiding principle generally adopted has been to assume the simplest possible mechanism that is consistent with all of the data.

Examples

Glyceraldehyde 3-phosphate dehydrogenase catalyzes the reaction:

3-phosphoglyceraldehyde $+ P_i + NAD^+$
$$\rightleftharpoons 1,3 \text{ diphosphoglycerate} + NADH + H^+$$

The enzymes isolated from a number of different sources are quite similar; they all contain four identical or nearly identical polypeptide chains and have similar molecular weights. However, the enzyme from different sources can be catagorized as belonging to at least two classes with regard to the mechanism of NAD^+ binding.

The binding of NAD^+ by the rabbit muscle enzyme involves extreme negative cooperativity, and its behavior appears to be consistent with the AKNF model (Conway and Koshland, 1968; DeVijlder and Slater, 1968). The binding of each NAD^+ induces a conformational change in the subunit to which it is bound, and a spectrum of relaxation times is observed (Hammes, Lillford, and Simplicio, 1971). In contrast, the yeast enzyme has a sigmoidal NAD^+ binding isotherm, and the observed transient kinetics can be quantitatively explained by the MWC model (Kirschner, 1971).

Two enzymes having the same metabolic function, similar polypeptide chains, and a similar subunit structure can thus utilize two different limiting allosteric models. This again emphasizes the essential similarity of these models; they both involve conformational changes of the subunits and modulation of the binding process by altering the interactions between subunits.

A more complex case, and one that is in a sense more interesting, because it has a clear-cut and important metabolic function, is the catalysis by asparate transcarbamylase of the carbamylation of aspartic acid:

carbamyl phosphate + aspartic acid → carbamylaspartic acid
+ phosphate → → → → → → cytidine triphosphate

This enzyme catalyzes the metabolic branch-point reaction in the synthesis of pyrimidine nucleotides, and the reaction is inhibited by the end product of the sequence, cytidine triphosphate (CTP) (Gerhart and Pardee, 1962). The multiple arrows indicate symbolically the enzyme reactions occurring between the carbamylation reaction and the production of CTP. The binding of aspartic acid has a sigmoidal binding isotherm, and CTP behaves as a classical feedback inhibitor (Fig. 1a). Aspartate transcarbamylase contains two types of subunits, catalytic and regulatory, that can be separated and reconstituted. The enzyme is also activated by ATP (Fig. 1a), and the balance of the two nucleotides may regulate the relative amount of purine and pyrimidine nucleotide synthesis.

The binding of effector molecules (ATP and CTP) by aspartate transcarbamylase shows negative cooperativity, whereas substrate binding shows positive cooperativity; thus both types of cooperativity can be utilized by a single enzyme. The extent of inhibition or activation is directly proportional to the amount of effector ligand bound. The binding of ATP and CTP produce the same conformational change. Their opposite effects on catalysis can be explained by assuming the existence of an equilibrium between two conformations, X_1 and X_2, one of which is much more catalytically active than the other:

$$E + ATP \rightleftharpoons X_1 \rightleftharpoons X_2$$
$$E + CTP \rightleftharpoons X_2 \rightleftharpoons X_1$$

Both ATP and substrates favor the formation of the active X_2 state, while CTP favors the catalytically inactive X_1 state. This simple two-state model is somewhat analogous to the AKNF model, with the actual conformational change being independent of the fraction of ligand sites occupied; the negative cooperativity occurs in the initial binding steps.

Additional regulatory processes are observed when the binding of carbamyl phosphate and succinate (an aspartate analogue) to the enzyme is considered. At high concentration of carbamyl phosphate, a relaxation process is observed at various succinate concentrations with the native

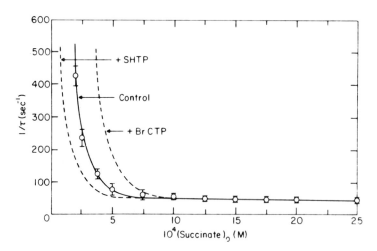

FIG. 4. The reciprocal relaxation time associated with succinate binding to native aspartate transcarbamylase as a function of succinate concentration (Hammes and Wu, 1971). BrCTP is the inhibitor, 5-bromo CTP, and SHTP is the activator, 6 mercapto-9-β-D-ribofuranosyl purine.

enzyme, but not with the isolated catalytic subunit. As shown in Fig. 4, the reciprocal relaxation time for this process decreases as the succinate concentration increases, until a limiting value is reached. The simplest interpretation of this behavior is that a concerted transition of the MWC type is involved in the regulatory process. As predicted, inhibitors and activators shift the curve in opposite directions along the concentration axis. The enzyme can be envisaged as rapidly alternating between two conformations, with the binding of succinate decreasing the rate of this transition until the enzyme is saturated with succinate. This conformational transition has been shown to differ from that discussed above as being involved in the binding of activators and inhibitors.

Still a third conformational transition is associated with the binding of carbamyl phosphate. These three sets of conformational transitions are coupled in a manner somewhat analogous to a minicomputer system, except that the control element is the conformational state. Each control element responds primarily to one type of metabolite, but all of the elements are coupled in such a way that no one metabolite can predominate (cf. Jacobson and Stark, 1973, and Hammes and Wu, 1974, for a more comprehensive review of this enzyme). Similar complex regulation mechanisms will probably be found in many other regulatory enzymes whenever a high degree of fine tuning is required of the regulatory process.

A still more complex regulatory mechanism is apparently utilized by the enzyme phosphofructokinase, a key control enzyme in glycolysis that catalyzes the phosphorylation of fructose-6-phosphate:

$$ATP + \text{fructose 6-phosphate} \rightleftharpoons ADP + \text{fructose 1,6-phosphate}$$

The rabbit muscle enzyme has a sigmoidal initial velocity versus fructose 6-phosphate concentration isotherm below about pH 7.5, but a hyperbolic isotherm above this pH. It is activated by Mg^{2+}, P_i, AMP, ADP, fructose 6-phosphate, and a number of other metabolites, and is inhibited by MgATP and citrate. This enzyme, which contains only a single type of subunit, is also involved in complex aggregation equilibria. Different molecular aggregates are simultaneously present within the cell, and the specific activity of the enzyme is a function of aggregate size (Fig. 5). Moreover, the aggregation equilibria are altered by allosteric effectors and substrates. The enzyme exists predominantly in the almost inactive dimer form in the presence of citrate, and activators induce its aggregation. The most effective activators induce the formation of tetramers or larger aggregates, having the same specific activity, and a combination of activators and inhibitors results in the formation of intermediate aggregates. Although polymerization may be an important regulatory mechanism utilized by this enzyme, additional regulatory mechanisms are also utilized.

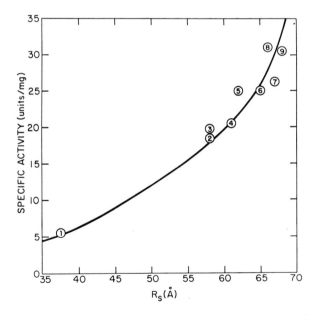

FIG. 5. Specific activity of rabbit muscle phosphofructokinase as a function of Stoke's radius at pH 7.0. The numbers indicate the following ligands: (1) 5 mM citrate; (2) 0.1 M phosphate, pH 7.0; (3) 10 mM Mg^{2+}; (4) 5 mM MgAMP; (5) 5 mM ATP-0.5 mM Mg^{2+}; (6) 5 mM MgATP; (7) 0.1 M phosphate, pH. 8.0; (8) 10 mM fructose 6-phosphate; and (9) 5 mM fructose 1,6-diphosphate (Lad, Hill, and Hammes, 1973).

Conclusion

A variety of possible modes of regulation are possible in enzyme systems. Some involve true cooperative interactions for which it is possible to characterize the equilibrium binding constants, while in other cases kinetic phenomena may provide a linkage that produces the same effect as would true cooperativity. Regulatory mechanisms may also utilize processes such as polymerization, which can alter both reaction velocities and substrate binding (cf. Hammes and Wu, 1974, for a more detailed review).

REFERENCES

Adair, G. S. (1925): The hemoglobin system. VI. The oxygen dissociation wave of hemoglobin. *J. Biol. Chem.,* 63:529–545.

Conway, A., and Koshland, D. E., Jr. (1968): Negative cooperativity in enzyme action. The binding of diphosphopyridine nucleotide to glyceraldehyde 3-phosphate dehydrogenase. *Biochemistry,* 7:4011–4022.

De Vijlder, J. J. M., and Slater, E. C. (1968): The reaction between NAD$^+$ and rabbit-muscle glyceraldehydephosphate dehydrogenase. *Biochim. Biophys. Acta,* 167:23–34.

Frieden, C. (1970): Kinetic aspects of regulation of metabolic processes. *J. Biol. Chem.,* 245:5788–5799.

Frieden, C., and Colman, R. (1967): Glutamate dehydrogenase concentration as a determinant in the effect of purine nucleotides on enzymatic activity. *J. Biol. Chem.,* 242:1705–1715.

Gerhart, J. C., and Pardee, A. B. (1962): The enzymology of control by feedback inhibition. *J. Biol. Chem.,* 237:891–896.

Hammes, G. G., ed. (1974): *Investigation of Rates and Mechanisms. Part II. Investigation of Elementary Reaction Steps in Solution and Very Fast Reactions,* 3rd ed. New York: John Wiley & Sons.

Hammes, G. G., Lillford, P. J., and Simplicio, J. (1971): Mechanism of nicotinamide-adenine binding to rabbit muscle glyceraldehyde 3-phosphate dehydrogenase. *Biochemistry,* 10:3686–3693.

Hammes, G. G., and Wu, C.-W. (1971): Relaxation spectra of aspartate transcarbamylase. Interaction of the native enzyme with aspartate analogs. *Biochemistry,* 10:1051–1057.

Hammes, G. G., and Wu, C.-W. (1974): *Adv. Biophys. Bioeng.,* 3:1–33.

Jacobson, G. R., and Stark, G. R. (1973): *The Enzymes,* 9:225.

Kirschner, K. (1971): Kinetic analysis of allosteric enzymes. *Curr. Top. Cellular Regulation,* 4:167–210.

Koshland, D. E., Jr., Nemethy, G., and Filmer, D. (1966): Comparison of experimental binding data and theoretical models in proteins containing subunits. *Biochemistry,* 5:365–385.

Lad, P. M., Hill, D. E., and Hammes, G. G. (1973): Influence of allosteric ligands on the activity and aggregation of rabbit muscle phosphofructokinase. *Biochemistry,* 12:4303–4309.

Monod, J., Wyman, J., and Changeux, J.-P. (1965): On the nature of allosteric transitions: A plausible model. *J. Mol. Biol.,* 12:88–118.

Nichol, L. W., Jackson, W. J. H., and Winzor, D. J. (1967): A theoretical study of the binding of small molecules to a polymerizing protein system. A model for allosteric effects. *Biochemistry,* 6:2449–2456.

Sweeny, J. R., and Fisher, J. R. (1968): An alternative to allosterism and cooperativity in the interpretation of enzyme kinetic data. *Biochemistry,* 7:561–565.

Wyman, J. (1972): On allosteric models. *Curr. Topics Cell. Reg.,* 6:209–226.

Functional Linkage in Biomolecular Systems, edited by
F. O. Schmitt, D. M. Schneider, and D. M. Crothers.
Raven Press, New York © 1975.

MOLECULAR INTERACTIONS IN MEMBRANE AND MODEL SYSTEMS

Biological membranes occupy a unique position in molecular biology in that they serve to regulate the flow of substances between the extracellular and intracellular environments. They also act as a "floor space" on which to mount molecular machinery to accomplish various purposes, for instance, to sense external signals, to transduce signals transmodally, to permit, through their fluid properties, the aggregation of various component systems into assemblies, and to induce and transmit excitability changes, and other vital functions. Functional linkage underlies these processes, through cooperative, allosteric, or transductive mechanisms.

The systems considered in this section vary in complexity from pure lipid films to cell membranes. Although the combination of protein and lipid within biological membranes produces vastly more complex systems than the simpler model membrane systems, the behavior of such systems can more readily be understood by applying the principles elucidated by studies of their component parts than by studies of the cell membrane as an organelle.

Chapter 3 deals with lipid phase changes and emphasizes the critical effect of perturbations in ionic (particularly mono/divalent cation) environment; reference is also made to the simultaneous existence of domains of ordered and of fluid nature and the possibility of pulsatile discharge of cations with intrafilm alterations. Chapter 4 considers both model and biological membranes, and ranges from deductions about the lipid-protein organization of cellular membranes to a consideration of lipid-protein interaction, particularly the effects of lipid on enzyme activity. Also considered is the reconstitution of a biological activity by recombination of four components of a particular system (two transferease enzymes, a lipid and a lipopolysaccharide). Chapter 5 features a model membrane system, and discusses an ingenious method for altering the transpenetrability of bacterial membranes by alterations in membrane lipids; these studies demonstrate that the proper lipid environment is crucial to vital membrane functions such as transport. Finally, Chapter 6 considers a type of functional linkage whose importance is only now becoming generally recognized. It involves an analysis by nonequilibrium thermodynamics of chemidiffusional linkage through linear and nonlinear flows. Also considered are the role of cooperativity in membrane excitability and certain model systems. The material in this and in the previous section provides a basis for subsequent discussion of the ways in which the principles of membrane function elucidated in relatively simple systems are used to control cellular functions.

Functional Linkage in Biomolecular Systems, edited by
F. O. Schmitt, D. M. Schneider, and D. M. Crothers.
Raven Press, New York © 1975.

Chapter 3

Molecular Interactions in Lipid Bilayers

COOPERATIVE STRUCTURAL CHANGES IN LIPID BILAYERS*:

Hermann Träuble and Hansjörg Eibl

Lipid phase transitions involve the cooperative interaction of many
hydrocarbon chains; this situation is present in lipid bilayers. Phase transitions in lipid bilayers approximate the two-dimensional phase transitions
for which theoretical models have been developed (Adam, 1970, 1973;
Schwarz, 1971; Marčelja, 1973; Nagle, 1973, 1974).

Although most biological membranes exist in a fluid state, studies of
lipid phase transitions are of importance because they permit the analysis
of structural-functional relationships in both relatively simple model systems (cf. Papahadjopoulos and Kimelberg, 1973), and occasionally in intact
plasma membranes (Schairer and Overath, 1969; Overath, Hill, and
Lamnek-Hirsch, 1971a; Overath, Schairer, Hill, and Lamnek-Hirsch,
1971b; Wilson, Rose, and Fox, 1970; Blazyk and Steim, 1972). Studies
with bacterial membranes that exhibit lipid phase transitions in response to
small changes in temperature have provided direct evidence of coupling
between certain membrane transport systems and the degree of order or
fluidity within the membrane lipids (Overath and Träuble, 1973). This
demonstration of lipid phase transitions in natural membranes indicates
that part of the lipids form a continuous phase, with direct hydrocarbon-
chain interactions. Phase-transition studies will help to elucidate the basic
interactions, possible conformations, and structural changes that occur
within the lipid part of biological membranes, and perhaps also some of
the principles involved in lipid-protein interaction.

Lipid phase transitions have now been shown to be far more versatile
than has generally been assumed, in that they can be triggered by alteration
of parameters such as pH, ionic strength, and the concentration of divalent
cations, in addition to temperature. The reverse situation also occurs—
that is, structural changes in lipid membranes can alter the environmental
ionic composition; the binding of protons and divalent cations to charged

---

* Part of the studies on the release of ions during phase transitions were performed in response to discussions at the conference, and have therefore been added to this section.

lipid surfaces differs in the ordered and fluid states. Lipid surfaces thus provide a reservoir of cations, and structural changes in the lipid matrix can release ion pulses into the environment. This provides a direct mechanism for the coupling between membrane structural changes and cellular processes that are dependent on divalent cations or on a defined pH.

Characterization of Lipid Phase Transitions

Aqueous dispersions of synthetic lipids containing lipid lamellae (liposomes) show a highly endothermic phase transition that is characterized by an increase in entropy when they are heated above a characteristic temperature, T_t.

At the transition temperature, the free enthalpies ($G = H - TS$, H = enthalpy, S = entropy, T = absolute temperature) of the ordered and fluid states are equal, and the transition temperature T_t is

$$T_t = \frac{\Delta H}{\Delta S} \tag{1}$$

For dipalmitoyl lecithin ($T_t \sim 41°C$), the enthalpy change, ΔH, at the transition is 8.66 kcal mole^{-1} and the entropy change, ΔS, is 27.6 cal deg^{-1} mole^{-1} (Phillips, Williams, and Chapman, 1969; cf. Phillips, 1972). In addition to these thermodynamic parameters, the transition is characterized by its width (steepness), kinetics, cooperativity and, in some cases, hysteresis.

More quantitative information can be obtained by comparing the calorimetric heats with van't Hoff heats calculated from the temperature coefficient of the "equilibrium constant" of the transition (Träuble, 1971). A cooperativity factor, σ, equal to the square of the ratio of calorimetric and van't Hoff heats, has a value of unity when the transition is noncooperative, and decreases with increasing cooperativity. σ has values of $\sim 10^{-3}$ for the order $\rightarrow$ fluid transition of distearoyl, dipalmitoyl, and dimyristoyl lecithins, indicating a high degree of cooperativity. As the chain length of the lecithin increases, σ decreases, indicating that the cooperativity of the transition increases with increasing chain length. Since the number of lipid molecules acting cooperatively, N, is $N \approx 1/\sigma^2$, it is estimated that $N \approx 30$.

The T_t also increases with hydrocarbon chain length. For saturated lecithins, increasing the hydrocarbon chain length by two CH_2 groups increases T_t by about 17°C. For a given chain length, T_t decreases with the degree of unsaturation. For example, distearoyl phosphatidylethanolamine (C18 cephalin) has a $T_t \sim 82°C$, but $T_t \sim 41°C$ with one *trans* double bond per chain (*trans* 18:1 cephalin); and $T_t \sim 15°C$ with one *cis* double bond per chain (*cis* 18:1 cephalin) (Overath and Träuble, 1973).

The transition also depends on the chemical structure of the lipid polar groups. The values of T_t for saturated cephalins are about 26°C higher than those of lecithins having the same chain length, because the less bulky polar groups of cephalin allow electrostatic attraction between the lipid molecules and a tighter packing in bilayers. In addition, the transition depends on the extent of hydration for water contents below about 20%, and is sensitive to impurities or foreign molecules incorporated into the lipid structure, as discussed by Metcalfe in the next section.

Structural changes occurring during lipid phase transitions have been examined by X-ray analysis, nuclear magnetic resonance (NMR), electron spin resonance (ESR), Raman spectroscopy, volumetric measurements, and fluorescence techniques (for reviews see Chapman and Wallach, 1968; Oldfield and Chapman, 1972; Phillips, 1972; Träuble, 1972). An increased rotational freedom of the hydrocarbon chains of the lipids occurs as the temperature is increased in the region of the T_t; with respect to the entire bilayer, an order → fluid transition occurs. The changes that occur during the transition are illustrated in Fig. 1. Below T_t the lipid hydrocarbon chains have a relatively rigid all-*trans* configuration, as indicated by sharp 4.19 Å reflexes in low-angle X-ray studies (Ladbrooke, Williams, and Chapman,

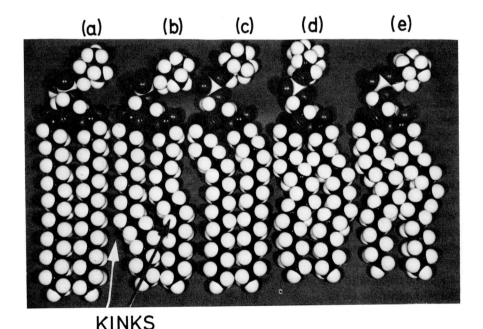

(a)   (b)   (c)   (d)   (e)

KINKS

FIG. 1. Proposed conformations assumed by the hydrocarbon chains in a layer of disaturated lecithin molecules below, during, and above the thermal phase transition. (a) All-*trans* conformation ($T < T_t$); (b), (c) molecules with one kink per hydrocarbon chain; (d), (e) molecules with two kinks per hydrocarbon chain ($T > T_t$). (From Träuble and Haynes, 1971.)

1968). During the transition, highly mobile rotational isomers (kinks) are formed by the *trans-gauche* isomerization of C—C bonds (Träuble, 1972), which can be directly demonstrated by laser Raman spectroscopy (Lippert and Peticolas, 1971). This results in chain shortening, and increases the distance between the molecules, thus producing a lateral expansion of the entire bilayer. For dipalmitoyl lecithin, the order → fluid transition increases the area per molecule from 48 $\mathring{A}^2$ to 65–70 $\mathring{A}^2$ (Phillips and Chapman, 1968), and reduces the bilayer thickness ~6 to 7 $\mathring{A}$. The magnitude of these changes indicates that about two kinks must occur within each hydrocarbon chain during the transition (Träuble and Haynes, 1971). The bilayer volume increases by 1 to 2%, as expected from the presence of pockets of free volume at the kinks (Träuble and Haynes, 1971; Melchior and Morowitz, 1972; Overath and Träuble, 1973).

In addition to lateral expansion, rapid lateral diffusion of the lipid molecules also occurs above the thermal transition temperature (Devaux and McConnell, 1972; Träuble and Sackmann, 1972), as a result of decreased van der Waals interactions and a decreased activation energy for molecular displacements. A diffusion coefficient of about 10^{-8} cm²/sec is observed in the fluid state, whereas lateral diffusion cannot usually be detected below the transition temperature.

The current view of bilayer structure in the fluid state has been strongly influenced by spin-label experiments in which the so-called order parameter, *S*, has been measured along the hydrocarbon chains using fatty acid labels with nitroxide radicals at different positions (*S* is a measure of the average orientation of the chain segment at the position of the NO group). Such studies revealed a continuous, exponential decrease of the order parameter from the polar region to the chain ends (Seelig, 1970, 1971; Hubbell and McConnell, 1971), suggesting that the bilayer structure is ordered near the polar region and disordered in the interior.

However, recent deuterium magnetic resonance studies (Charvolin, Manneville, and Deloche, 1973; Seelig and Niederberger, 1974), which reflect the unperturbed bilayer structure, show that the order parameter is *constant* over most of the chain length, with a rapid decrease near the last three carbon atoms. This result is in good agreement with the expectations from the kink model (Träuble, 1971). A prominent feature of this model is a shift of part of the hydrocarbon chain perpendicular to its long axis (Fig. 1b)—for example, the trans sequences remain parallel to each other but are displaced on their lattice position by approximately 1.5 $\mathring{A}$; they thus have the same order parameter. Since the correlation time of the *trans-gauche* interconversion is less than 10^{-9} sec (Horwitz, Michaelson, and Klein, 1973), kinks must be pictured as fluctuating rapidly up and down the chain, with lifetimes of the individual conformations shorter than 10^{-6} sec. In deuterium experiments, this leads to a constant order parameter. The fluid state of a bilayer should therefore be visualized not as a dis-

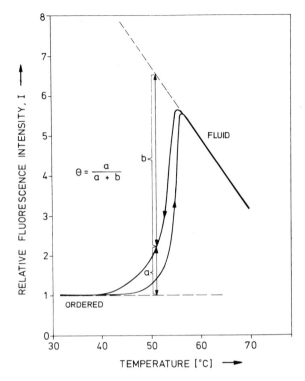

FIG. 2. Fluorescence indication of thermal phase transitions in dimyristoyl phosphatidic acid dispersions using N-phenylnaphtylamine (NPN) as the fluorescent indicator. 2.5×10^{-4} M lipid, pH 6, 1.7×10^{-6} M NPN; excitation: 350 nm, emission 420 nm. The increased fluorescence intensity in the fluid state is due to an increased free volume within the bilayer at $T > T_t$. The transition temperature T_t is determined as the temperature where the degree of conversion $\theta = 0.5$. (From Träuble and Eibl, 1974.)

ordered but rather as a defective *ordered* state (see also Horwitz et al., 1973; Seiter and Chan, 1974).

Lipid phase transitions can be detected easily by optical methods such as 90°-light scattering, absorption, or fluorescent probing (Träuble, 1972). For example, the fluorescent probe N-phenylnaphtylamine (NPN) has a much higher quantum yield in a medium of low polarity than in water. This probe molecule is poorly soluble in water and preferentially partitions into a lipid bilayer in the fluid state, when the free volume is increased and the lipid molecules are loosely packed. As shown in Fig. 2, the fluorescence intensity may increase up to fivefold during the order → fluid transition due to penetration by the probe of the nonpolar lipid phase. Transition temperatures determined by fluorescence measurements agree with those determined by several independent methods, provided the label concentration is sufficiently small not to perturb the lipid structure.

Biological Relevance, Effect on Membrane Proteins, and Membrane Function

There is no known example in which *thermally* induced lipid phase transitions are involved in a biological process. However, recent evidence (Träuble, Eibl, and Sawada, 1974) suggests that the elastic properties of lipid films that are related to their ability to show phase transitions are utilized in the lung alveolar surface. Lipids extracted from the film lining the lung alveolae show a broad thermal transition between 20 and 40°C. It appears that phase transitions in this film are induced *in vivo* by changes in surface pressure, and that this process is essential for the easy opening and closing of lung alveolae during respiration.

As mentioned previously, the lipids of most biological membranes are in the fluid state, suggesting that fluidity is required for the normal activity of membrane proteins. However, biological membranes that will undergo thermal phase transitions can be obtained from *Mycoplasma laidlawii*, *Micrococcus lysodeicticus,* and certain mutants of *E. coli* that are auxotrophic for unsaturated fatty acids (Silbert and Vagelos, 1967). Defined alterations of the hydrocarbon chain composition of the membrane phospholipids can be made by supplementing the growth medium with specific fatty acids (Silbert, Ruch, and Vagelos, 1968; Schairer and Overath, 1969).

The cell membranes of such bacteria and the lipids extracted from their membranes undergo phase transitions similar to those observed in model systems (Fig. 3). Studies with such mutants showed a variety of carrier-mediated transport processes to be a function of membrane fluidity (galactoside transport/Schairer and Overath, 1969; sugar and amino acid transport/Esfahani, Limbrick, Knutton, Oka, and Wakil, 1971). Overath and Träuble (1973) have shown a clear correlation of transport rate for β-galactoside, similar to the results described for glucoside transport by McConnell and Fox in Chapter 5.

How might such structural-functional correlations be explained in molecular terms, that is, as a result of the order → fluid phase transition in the membrane lipids? One of the simplest possibilities is that the lipid matrix serves primarily as a "solvent" for (integral) membrane proteins, and that the fluidity of this solvent determines both the rotational and diffusional freedom of these proteins and their ability to undergo functional conformational changes.

A simple model illustrating how lipid mobility might influence the rotational freedom of a membrane protein is shown in Fig. 4. The rotational motion of the protein molecule embedded in the lipid lattice will be a function of the frequency with which lipid molecules enter and leave the vicinity of any protrusion from an otherwise cylindrical surface, that is, on the lateral diffusion rate of the lipid. The coefficient of rotational diffusion of the protein, D_r, may be written (Träuble and Sackmann, 1973) as

$$D_r \ (\mathrm{rad^2 \ sec^{-1}}) = \frac{1}{2} \frac{v\lambda^2}{R^2} \qquad (2)$$

and the corresponding rotational correlation time as

$$\tau = \frac{(2\pi)^2}{D_r} \qquad (3)$$

where v is the frequency of lateral displacement of the lipid molecules, R is the radius of the protein molecule, and λ is the average distance between lipid molecules. Assuming $R = 15$ Å, $\lambda = 10$ Å, and $v = 10^7 \ \mathrm{sec^{-1}}$ yields $\tau = 18 \ \mu\mathrm{sec}$. A rotational correlation time of the same magnitude (20 $\mu\mathrm{sec}$) has been determined by Cone (1972) for the rotation of rhodopsin in the photoreceptor membrane (see Chapter 11).

Applying a similar "free-volume" consideration to the lateral mobility of a protein within a lipid lattice, the lateral diffusion coefficient D_P of the protein (Sackmann, Träuble, Galla, and Overath, 1973) is calculated by

$$D_P = \frac{1}{\pi} \frac{F_L}{F_P} D_L$$

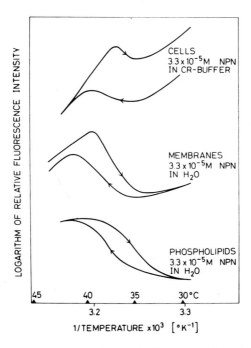

FIG. 3. Fluorescence demonstration of thermal phase transitions in whole cells, membranes, and phospholipids of *E. coli* fatty acid auxotrophs grown in the presence of *trans* 18:1 fatty acids. Probe: NPN. Lipid concentration: 2 × 10⁻⁴ M, cells: protein concentration 1.9 mg/ml. The transition temperature is similar for the intact membranes and isolated lipids, indicating that the *in vivo* system can undergo thermally induced lipid phase transitions. (From Overath and Träuble, 1973.)

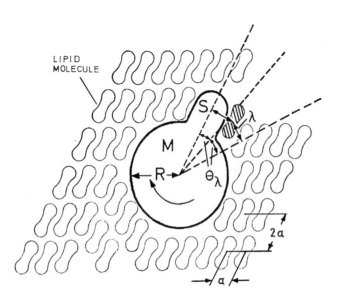

LIPID MOLECULE

FIG. 4. Factors controlling the rotational motion of a membrane protein, M, embedded in a lipid layer (view from above), *a* = lattice constant of lipid hydrocarbon chains, λ = average distance between lipid molecules. Rotation of M by an elementary angle θ_λ requires that temporarily a vacancy is created near the protrusion S on M by lateral displacement of a lipid molecule. The rate of lateral diffusion of the lipid molecules determines the rotational correlation time of M. (From Träuble and Sackmann, 1973.)

where F_P is the cross-sectional area of the protein molecule and F_L is the molecular area of one lipid molecule ($F_L = 70$ Å^2). For $D_L = 3 \times 10^{-8}$ cm^2/sec and a cylindrical protein of radius 15 Å, $D_P = 10^{-9}$ cm^2/sec. Again, this value is in good agreement with results obtained by Poo and Cone (1974) for the lateral diffusion of rhodopsin in the photoreceptor membrane $[D_P = (3.5 \pm 1.5) \times 10^{-9}$ cm^2/sec for frogs].

Thus, the rotational and lateral diffusion of a membrane protein do appear to be simple consequences of the lateral motion of the membrane lipids. If one assumes that the function of a membrane protein is dependent on its rotational or lateral motion, that function will be inhibited when lipid motion is reduced, as in the ordered lipid state ($T < T_t$).

It is, of course, also possible that the lipid state directly affects the protein conformation. This possibility was indicated by a recent study (Träuble et al., 1974) of the influence of lipid phase transitions on the conformation of a serum apoprotein that interacts strongly with lipids. Circular dichroism and intrinsic fluorescence measurements demonstrated a reversible conformational change of the protein induced by the lipid phase transition.

The Induction of Lipid Phase Transitions at Constant Temperature

Träuble and Eibl (1974) recently demonstrated that phase transitions can be induced in charged lipid bilayers at constant temperature by altering parameters that are biologically significant, including pH, ionic strength, and divalent cation concentration, variations that alter the charge on the polar head groups of the lipids. Qualitatively, any environmental alteration that increases the charge on the polar groups should favor the fluid state as the result of lateral electrostatic repulsion.

Given the simplest case, in which the charges on the lipid polar groups within the bilayer can be considered to be uniformly distributed, the effect of a charge alteration on the thermal transition can be estimated using the Gouy-Chapman theory of the electrical double layer (cf. Overbeek, 1952). In a charged lipid bilayer, part of the free enthalpy of the system is due to electrostatic interactions at the membrane surface. The electrical charge density is reduced at the order → fluid transition due to lateral expansion of the lipid lamellae. The total change in enthalpy at the transition, ΔH, therefore contains an electrostatic component, $\Delta\Gamma$, in addition to a nonelectrostatic term, ΔH^0.

Thus, from equation (1), the transition temperature T_t may be written as

$$T_t = \frac{\Delta H}{\Delta S} = \frac{\Delta H^0}{\Delta S} + \frac{\Delta\Gamma}{\Delta S} \tag{4}$$

indicating that the change in T_t due to electrostatic interactions is

$$\Delta T_t = \frac{\Delta\Gamma}{\Delta S} \tag{5}$$

When the bilayer charge is uniformly distributed, Γ is a simple function of the area of the bilayer, F, and the electrical double layer energy per square centimeter of the system (Φ):

$$\Gamma = F \cdot \Phi \tag{6}$$

Both F and Φ change at the transition temperature, and

$$\Delta\Gamma = F \cdot \Delta\Phi + \Phi \cdot \Delta F$$
$$(-) \qquad (+) \tag{7}$$

Since lateral expansion occurs during the transition, $\Phi\,\Delta F$ is positive, while $F\,\Delta\Phi$ is negative due to the charge dilution that accompanies the expansion. The negative $F\,\Delta\Phi$ is the dominating term. According to the classical Gouy-Chapman theory for 1:1 electrolytes at high potentials, the free energy of the interface per square centimeter is

$$\Phi = \frac{2kT}{e} \cdot \frac{\sigma}{f} \tag{8}$$

where kT is the Boltzmann temperature, e is the elementary charge, σ is the number of the elementary charges on the lipid molecule, and f is the area per molecule.

Substitution into equation (5) for ΔT_t yields the final expression

$$\Delta T_t \approx \frac{-2RT}{\Delta S} \cdot \frac{\Delta f}{f} \cdot \sigma \approx -\gamma \cdot \sigma \qquad (9)$$

that is, the transition temperature is a direct function of the charge on the lipid molecules.

In equation (9), Δf is the increase in molecular area at the order → fluid transition and R is the gas constant (1.9865 cal deg^{-1} mol^{-1}). Since this equation has negative sign, any increase in charge will reduce the transition temperature, and any decrease in charge will increase it. Inserting $\Delta S = $ 22.4 cal deg^{-1} mol^{-1} (calorimetric value of ΔS for ^{14}C-lecithin), $f = 70$ Å^2, and $\Delta f = 22$ Å^2, $\Delta T_t \approx -18°C$ for a one-elementary-unit increase in charge. This value is only an estimate, because ΔS might also be a function of charge density; no experimental evidence is yet available on this point. An increase in charge at constant temperature should therefore induce an order → fluid phase transition, and a decrease in charge should induce a fluid → order reversal. The charge per polar group can be varied experimentally by changing the pH or by the adsorption of divalent cations to negatively charged lipids. These effects were examined in dispersions of dimyristoyl phosphatidic acid (PA) and dimyristoyl methyl phosphatidic acid (MPA) (Fig. 5).

The pK's for the dissociation of the two protons of dimyristoyl phosphatidic acid are pH 3 and pH 8.5, indicating that the lipid molecules can exist in three states, having zero, one, or two elementary charges. If α is the degree of dissociation ($0 \leq \alpha \leq 2$), the charge per polar group is $\sigma = \alpha \cdot e$, where e is the elementary charge. Equation (9) predicts that an increase in pH, which would increase the charge on the phospholipid by removing protons, should decrease the transition temperature. A series of transition curves from pH 3.4 to pH 11.3 (Fig. 6) does show such a decrease in T_t, from 53°C at pH 3.4 to 25°C at pH 11.3. The dependence of T_t on pH (Fig. 7) can be quantified using equation (9). T_t is linearly related to the degree of dissociation, α, which can be calculated from the titration curve. A plot of T_t versus α yields a straight line whose slope is $-23°C$ (Fig. 7), a value that agrees reasonably well with the $-18°C$ estimated from equation (9) using the value of ΔS for dimyristoyl phosphatidylcholine.

One consequence of this dependence is that, within the temperature range where T_t is dependent strongly on pH, it should be possible to induce lipid phase transitions at constant temperature by small changes in pH. This effect is shown in Fig. 8. At a constant temperature, a transition from the fluid to the ordered state could be triggered by decreasing the pH and a subsequent increase in pH returned the system to the fluid state. It is therefore possible to trigger lipid transitions at a constant temperature by extremely small changes in pH that can occur physiologically. Indeed, Lehninger (Chapter 7) noted that a change of 0.2 pH units is sufficient to induce the mitochondrion to shift between the active and inactive states. A second way in which surface charge might be altered physiologically is by the surface adsorption of divalent cations, which should increase T_t

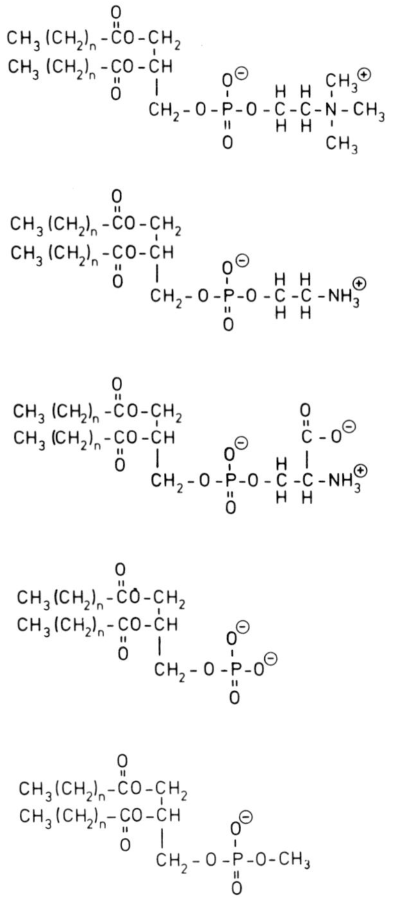

CH$_3$(CH$_2$)$_n$-CO-CH$_2$
CH$_3$(CH$_2$)$_n$-CO-CH
CH$_2$-O-P-O-C-C-N-CH$_3$

PHOSPHATIDYL-
CHOLINE
(LECITHIN)

CH$_3$(CH$_2$)$_n$-CO-CH$_2$
CH$_3$(CH$_2$)$_n$-CO-CH
CH$_2$-O-P-O-C-C-NH$_3$

PHOSPHATIDYL-
ETHANOLAMINE
(CEPHALIN)

CH$_3$(CH$_2$)$_n$-CO-CH$_2$
CH$_3$(CH$_2$)$_n$-CO-CH
CH$_2$-O-P-O-C-C-NH$_3$
C-O

PHOSPHATIDYL-
SERINE

CH$_3$(CH$_2$)$_n$-CO-CH$_2$
CH$_3$(CH$_2$)$_n$-CO-CH
CH$_2$-O-P-O

PHOSPHATIDIC-
ACID
(PA)

CH$_3$(CH$_2$)$_n$-CO-CH$_2$
CH$_3$(CH$_2$)$_n$-CO-CH
CH$_2$-O-P-O-CH$_3$

PHOSPHATIDIC-
ACID METHYLESTER
(MPA)

FIG. 5. The chemical structures of several phospholipids. Lecithin and cephalin are electrically neutral at neutral pH but have large electrical dipole moments. PA and MPA have (two, one) ionizable protons, and are negatively charged at neutral pH.

as the result of lowered surface charge density. A series of transition curves for phosphatidic acid in the presence of Mg^{2+} (Fig. 9a) showed that the transition is shifted to higher temperatures and the curves become flatter as the cation concentration increases; that is, Mg^{2+} tends to stabilize the ordered structure. A plot of T_t versus the molar ratio $m = [\text{Mg}^{2+}]/[\text{PA}]$ shows a sharp increase of T_t for $m \lesssim 0.5$ and saturation at higher Mg^{2+} concentrations (Fig. 9b). The interaction of divalent cations with phosphatidic acid bilayers is thus governed by stoichiometric relations. These data imply that for properly chosen, constant values of pH and temperature, divalent cations can induce a fluid → order transition.

The decrease in fluorescence signal I in the fluid state ($T > T_t$) with in-

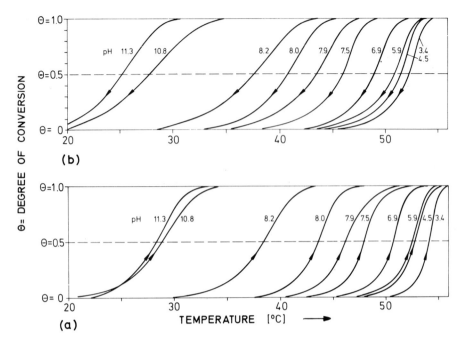

FIG. 6. Transition curves of phosphatidic acid bilayers (10^{-4} M PA, 0.5 M NaCl) as a function of pH; derived from fluorescence measurements using NPN (1.5×10^{-6} M) as probe. (a) increasing, (b) decreasing temperature.

creasing Mg^{2+} (Fig. 9a) indicates a decreased penetration of the fluorescence probe NPN into fluid lipid lamellae. This suggests that, in addition to the increase in T_t, Mg^{2+} increases the order in fluid bilayers. Qualitatively, Ca^{2+} influences the lipid structure in the same way as Mg^{2+}. The effects of divalent cations on the lipid structure may be completely reversed by the addition of EDTA. These results confirm the proposed role of divalent cations as stabilizers of biological membranes (Triggle, 1972).

In contrast to divalent cations, monovalent cations do not adsorb to lipid phosphate groups (Abramson, Katzman, and Curci, 1965; Hauser and Dawson, 1967; McLaughlin and Szabo, 1971) and would not be expected to affect T_t. However, in a series of phosphatidic acid transition curves measured at pH 8 to 10, increasing the NaCl or KCl concentration decreased the transition temperature (Fig. 10a). A plot of T_t versus increasing salt concentration (Fig. 10b) shows a sharp initial decrease at lower concentrations, with a plateau reached at 1.0 to 1.5 M. The net change in T_t can be as great as $-15°C$ over this concentration range. Again, this means that a small increase in ionic strength in the proper temperature range will induce a transition from the ordered to the fluid state (Fig. 11).

The effects of monovalent cations can be explained by Gouy-Chapman theory. For a charged surface consisting of polar groups with ionizable

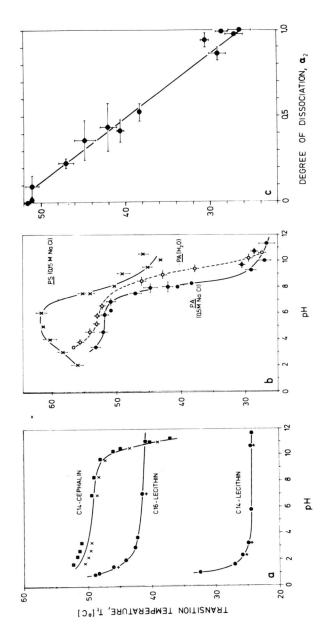

FIG. 7. Transition temperature T_t of different saturated phospholipids as a function of pH. (a) For lecithins, T_t decreases when the phosphate groups (pK $\sim$ 1.5) are ionized. (b) T_t of dipalmitoyl phosphatidylserine (PS) and dimyristoyl phosphatidic acid (PA); the curves for PA reflect the ionization behavior of the molecules. Ionization of the second proton leads to a sharp decrease in T_t between pH 7 and 9 (compare Fig. 6). (c) A plot of T_t versus the degree of dissociation gives a straight line with slope −23°C for PA. (From Träuble and Eibl, 1974.)

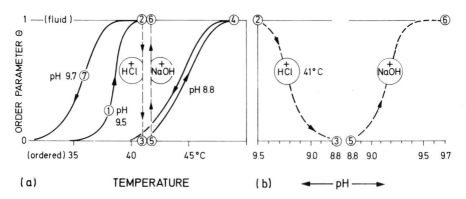

FIG. 8. Phase transitions of dimyristoyl phosphatidic acid bilayers triggered by temperature and pH. The degree of conversion, θ, was derived from fluorescence measurements
using NPN as an indicator. Circled numbers show the sequence of measurements. The
addition of HCl to fluid bilayers at 41°C, pH 9.5 induces a transition to the ordered state
(2) → (3) as indicated by the temperature scan (3) → (4) recorded after the titration at pH
8.8. Addition of NaOH to the ordered bilayers at 41°C, pH 8.8 induces reversal to the fluid
state (5) → (6) as shown by the subsequent temperature scan at pH 9.7 (7).

protons, the degree of dissociation α is a function of surface potential
ψ_0:

$$\alpha = \frac{1}{1 + K^0 \exp\left(\dfrac{e\psi_0}{kT}\right) [H^+]} \tag{10}$$

where K^0 is the "intrinsic" association constant, and the exponential factor
accounts for the electrostatic forces attracting the protons to the negatively
charged surface; $[H^+]$ is the proton concentration. The surface potential,
ψ_0, is a function of the ionic strength, μ. For phosphatidic acid above pH 7,
the surface potential will decrease from 160 mV at 0.1 μ to 100 mV at 1.0
μ. This indicates that the degree of dissociation, α, will increase with increasing ionic strength, thus increasing the surface charge density and
decreasing T_t. That this is the correct explanation of the monovalent cation
effect is indicated by the close agreement between the observed and calculated dependence of T_t on salt concentration (Fig. 10).

In the presence of divalent cations, an increase in monovalent cation
concentration should influence the state of the lipid bilayer by inducing the

FIG. 9. Effect of Mg^{2+} on the transition of phosphatidic acid bilayers (2.5×10^{-4} M lipid,
0.14 M NaCl). (a) Fluorescence transition curves for different Mg^{2+} concentrations, pH
9.2, 4×10^{-6} M NPN. The presence of Mg^{2+} shifts the transition to a higher temperature,
flattens the transition curves, and decreases the fluorescence intensity in the fluid state
($T > T_t$); (b) Transition temperature T_t as a function of the molar ratio $[Mg^{2+}]/[PA]$ at
different pH's (6 to 10.5). Arrows indicate measurements at increasing and decreasing
temperature. (From Träuble and Eibl, 1974.)

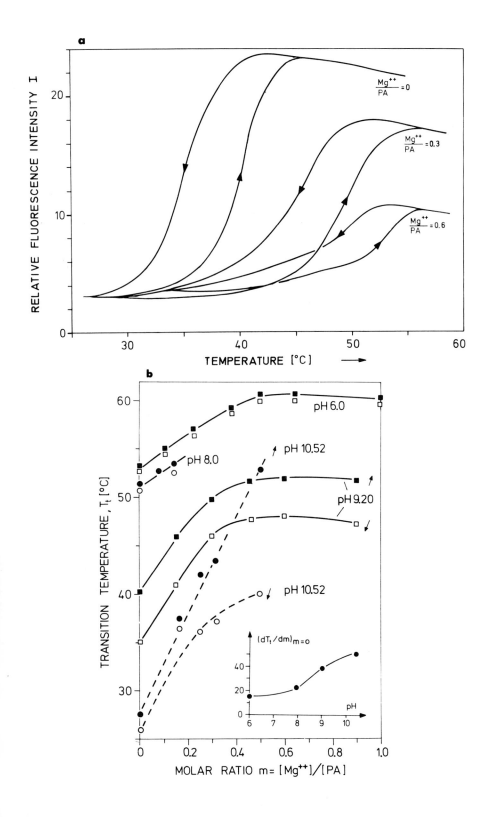

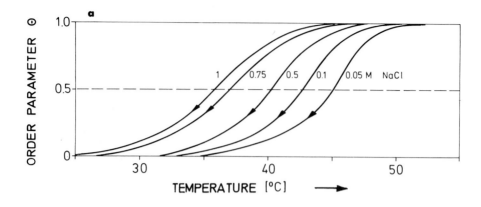

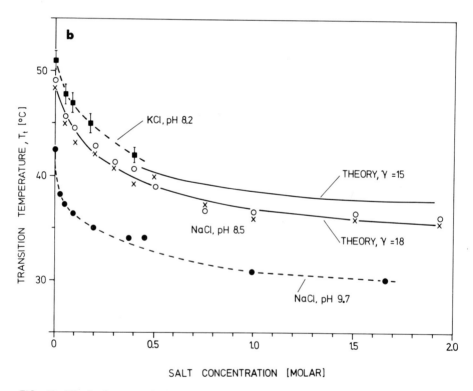

FIG. 10. Effect of monovalent cations on the transition of phosphatidic acid bilayers. (a) A series of normalized transition curves at increasing concentrations of NaCl; 10^{-4} M PA, pH 8.5, 10^{-6} M NPN. The transition of the salt-free dispersion is at about 50°C (not shown). (b) T_t as a function of salt concentration. The net decrease in T_t reached for high ionic strength shows a maximum at about pH 9. The parameter γ is defined in Eq. 9. (From Träuble and Eibl, 1974.)

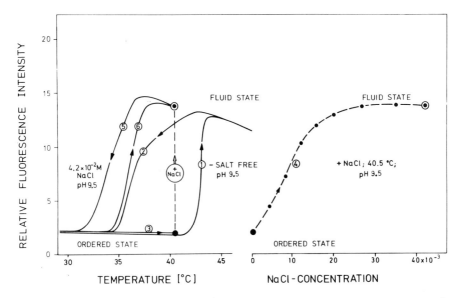

FIG. 11. NaCl-induced order → fluid transition of phosphatidic acid bilayers at 40.5°C, pH 9.5. Whether a PA bilayer system will exist in the fluid or ordered state is a complex function of temperature, ionic composition, and pH: (1) a temperature scan at pH 9.5 in salt-free medium, (2) hysteretic return, (3) temperature increased to 40.5°C; (4) NaCl titration at 40.5°C, pH 9.5, induces a order → fluid transition, (5) and (6) temperature scan in the presence of 4.2×10^{-2} M NaCl shows a decreased T_t from that in salt-free medium (1), confirming that the monovalent cations favor the fluid state. (From Träuble and Eibl, 1974.)

release of bound divalent cations, since the binding constant for divalent cations is decreased by a lowered surface potential. These effects are described in more detail for methyl phosphatidic acid.

Divalent and monovalent cations thus have opposing effects on membrane fluidity, with divalent cations favoring the ordered and monovalent favoring the fluid state. Within a certain temperature range a transition in either direction can be induced at constant temperature by slight alterations in the ionic balance in the region of the membrane. The system becomes even more delicately balanced when we consider these ionic effects in combination with variations in pH.

Although phosphatidic acid is a useful compound for the investigation of ionic interactions at charged lipid surfaces, quantitative analysis of the data is complicated by the fact that protolytic reactions may occur over the whole pH range. To avoid this, dimyristoyl methylphosphatidic acid (MPA) has been synthesized by methylation of one of the hydroxyl groups in PA (Fig. 5). The polar group of MPA thus has only one ionizable proton that is fully dissociated for pH values above pH 5. Studies with this model system allowed more rigorous testing of the concepts developed using phosphatidic acid. Thermal transition curves for MPA were measured, and a

T_t-pH diagram was constructed as described for phosphatidic acid (Fig. 12). In the region of proton dissociation, between pH 2 and pH 5 (pK ~ 3.5), the transition temperature decreases with increasing pH from T_t ~ 46°C (T_t for pH < 2) to T_t ~ 28°C (pH > 5). The net decrease in T_t due to the appearance of one elementary charge per polar group is −18°C, which is in close agreement with the theoretical prediction and the results for the second dissociation step of phosphatidic acid. For pH values above pH 5, each polar group of methyl phosphatidic acid has one elementary charge, and interactions with divalent cations can be studied without complications due to the presence or displacement of protons. As with phosphatidic acid, the addition of Ca^{2+} to MPA dispersions increases the transition temperature (Fig. 13a). However, over a relatively wide range of Ca^{2+} concentration, when the molar ratio [Ca^{2+}]/[MPA] was ≲ 3, the transition curve of MPA exhibits a biphasic shape. The first step of the transition occurs at a temperature characteristic of the Ca^{2+}-free system (~30°C), the second is char-

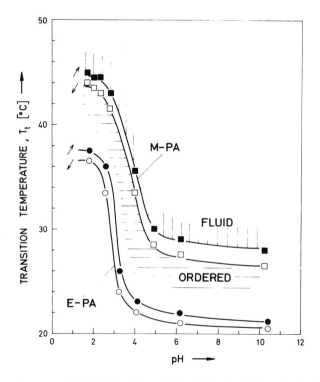

FIG. 12. Dependence on pH of the transition of dimyristoyl methyl- and ethylphosphatidic acid bilayers (2.5 × 10⁻⁴ M lipid, 0.1 M NaCl). T_t decreases by about −18°C as a result of proton dissociation between pH 2 → 5.0. The T_t values are derived from NPN fluorescence measurements, 4.10⁻⁶ M NPN, excitation at 350 nm, emission at 420 nm. Arrows indicate measurements at decreasing and increasing temperature.

acteristic of the Ca^{2+}-saturated system ($\sim 50°C$). Since prolonged sonication did not alter these curves, the biphasic behavior cannot be due to limited accessibility of the lipid polar groups to Ca^{2+}; in addition, thin-layer chromatography of the lipids showed only a single spot. Since the second transition temperature is that characteristic of a 1:2 complexation between Ca^{2+} and the lipid polar groups, it appears that, for low Ca^{2+} concentrations, a certain fraction of the lipids does not bind Ca^{2+}, whereas another part binds the ion. The interaction with Ca^{2+} thus appears to be a cooperative "all-or-none" process (Changeux, Thiery, Tung, and Kittel, 1967). Ca^{2+} appears to induce cluster formation and phase separation (see McConnell, Chapter 5) in these single-component model membranes. The amplitude of the upper transition increases with increasing Ca^{2+} concentration, while that of the lower transition decreases and finally disappears (Fig. 13a).

Above pH 5, the addition of monovalent cations to MPA does not alter the transition temperature. In contrast, the transition temperature decreases continuously with increasing NaCl concentration when samples are saturated with Ca^{2+} prior to the addition of NaCl. For example, at 0.6 M NaCl, the transition temperature is decreased from $T_t \sim 48$ to $50°C$ to ~ 35 to $38°C$ (Fig. 13c).

This decrease of T_t is similar to the decrease in the T_t of PA with increasing ionic strength. In the latter case, the ionic strength released protons from the polar heads, whereas in this case Ca^{2+} ions are released from the polar groups of MPA. This increases the charge density at the lipid surface, which decreases the transition temperature according to Eq. (9).

Ion Pulses Associated with Lipid Phase Transitions

The studies discussed thus far have dealt with the induction of lipid phase transitions at constant temperature by ionic interactions at the lipid polar groups. Of equal interest is the complementary question, that is, whether lipid phase transitions can trigger the release or adsorption of cations at the membrane surface. Such effects would be predicted, because cation binding to a charged lipid membrane is strongly dependent on the surface potential, ψ_0. However, the value of ψ_0 differs for the ordered and fluid states due to the difference in molecular packing (or the surface charge density) in the two states. These predicted effects of lipid phase transitions on the ionization of lipid phosphate groups can be studied easily by measuring the bulk pH of unbuffered phospholipid dispersions as a function of temperature. As is shown in Fig. 14a, the order $\rightarrow$ fluid transition leads to an abrupt decrease in bulk pH, and this effect is reversed when the sample is cooled back through the fluid $\rightarrow$ order transition. Similar changes in bulk pH have been reported for dispersions of the neutral lipids dimyristoyl

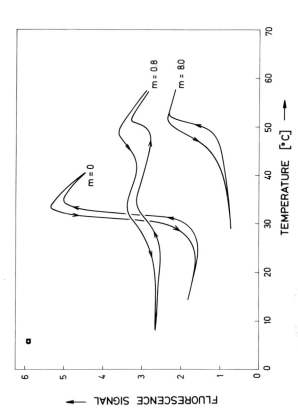

FIG. 13. (a) Effect of Ca^{2+} on the transition of methylphosphatidic acid bilayers (2.5×10^{-4} M lipid) in distilled water of pH 7.8; m = molar ratio $[Ca^{2+}]/[MPA]$. For Ca^{2+} concentrations $0 < m \lessgtr 3$, the transition is biphasic with part of the lipid exhibiting a "Ca^{2+}-free" transition (30°C), and part a "Ca^{2+}-saturated" transition (50°C). With increasing Ca^{2+} concentration, the fluorescence amplitude of the first transition decreases while that of the higher transition increases. (b) T_t as a function of the molar ratio $[Ca^{2+}]/[MPA]$. The transition is biphasic for lower Ca^{2+} con-

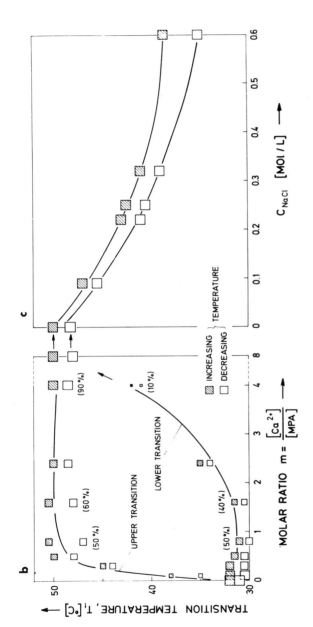

centrations ($m < 3$), with a lower "Ca²⁺-free" transition at $T_t \sim 30°C$ and an upper "Ca²⁺-saturated" transition at $T_t \sim 50°C$. Sonication of the dispersions in the presence of Ca²⁺ does not alter this behavior. The area of the square symbols is proportional to the relative amplitudes of the two transitions. (c) Addition of NaCl to samples with $m = 8$ lowers the transition temperature again, suggesting that Ca²⁺ is released from the lipids.

LIPID BILAYERS

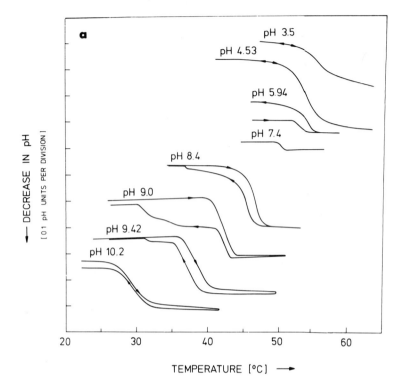

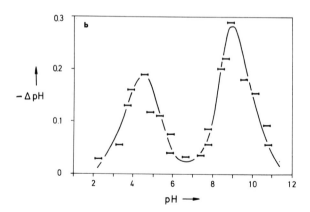

FIG. 14. Proton pulses at the transition of phosphatidic acid bilayers. (a) Abrupt changes in bulk pH are observed at the transition of unbuffered PA dispersions (2.3×10^{-3} M, 2×10^{-3} M NaCl), indicating that protons are released from the phosphate groups at the order → fluid transition. (b) Dependence of pH change at the transition on the bulk pH; maxima occur at the two pK's.

lecithin and dipalmitoyl lecithin (Abramson, 1970), but we have been unable to reproduce these results with highly purified lecithins.

The decrease in pH at the order → fluid transition ($-\Delta$pH) depends both on the bulk pH and on the lipid concentration. For 2.3×10^{-3} M phosphatidic acid, the values of $-\Delta$pH ranged between 0.02 and 0.3 pH units, with maxima near pH 4 and pH 9 (pK regions; Fig. 14b), and a pronounced hysteresis near the second pK. Qualitatively, the decrease in pH is due to the decrease in surface charge density and surface potential produced by bilayer expansion at the order → fluid transition. The electrostatic attraction of protons to the lipid surface is therefore smaller above T_t, and protons are released from the phosphate groups.

Because of their potential importance for several physiological processes (Triggle, 1972), it is even more interesting to examine whether lipid structural changes might produce pulses of divalent cations at a membrane surface. The binding of calcium to charged lipid lamellae in the ordered and fluid states were examined using the absorption indicator murexide, which shows pronounced spectral changes with increasing Ca^{2+} concentration (Fig. 15; Schwarzenbach and Gysling, 1949; Eigen and Winkler, 1970). When methyl phosphatidic acid is added to such a solution at pH 8, the optical density at 480 nm decreases again and reaches the value of the pure murexide, directly demonstrating that the lipid adsorbs increasing amounts of Ca^{2+}, thereby reducing the Ca^{2+} available for complex formation with murexide. Since Ca^{2+} has a much higher affinity for charged MPA bilayers than for murexide, the lipid-Ca^{2+} interaction is virtually unaffected by the presence of murexide.

The fraction of calcium bound to the lipid surface in the ordered and fluid states can be estimated from the calibration curve shown in Fig. 15b (20°C) and another measured at 55°C. As is shown in Fig. 16, Ca^{2+} was adsorbed more readily to lipid lamellae in the ordered state. For example, when $[MPA]/[Ca^{2+}] = 1.5$, about 65% of the calcium was bound at 20°C, whereas only 40% was bound at 55°C. This suggests that Ca^{2+} ions are released from the lipid surface during the order → fluid transition, which resembles the release of protons discussed above. The expected release of Ca^{2+} from the lipid surface can be observed directly as an abrupt change in the temperature dependence of murexide absorption at the transition temperature.

The interplay between divalent cations and negatively charged lipids therefore has two main aspects: (1) Divalent cations can induce a fluid → order transition in the lipid structure at constant temperature; (2) pulses of divalent cations appear at the membrane surface during the lipid phase transition, which corresponds to a release of Ca^{2+} from the lipid surface at the order → fluid transition or to an adsorption of Ca^{2+} at the fluid → order reversal. The lipid surface can therefore be considered as a reservoir of divalent cations that can be activated by structural changes within the lipid lamellae.

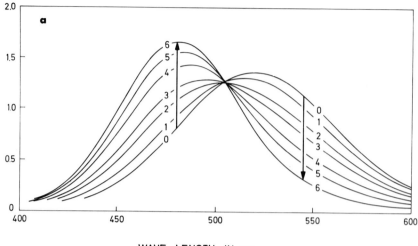

WAVE LENGTH IN nm ⟶

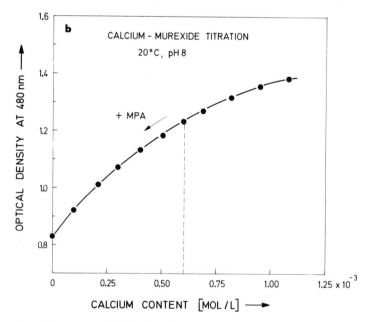

FIG. 15. (a) Spectrophotometric titration of murexide (10^{-4} M murexide, 0.05 M NaCl) with Ca^{2+} at 20°C, pH 5. Curve 0: in the absence of Ca^{2+}; (1): 0.59×10^{-3} M Ca^{2+}; (2): 1.74×10^{-3} M Ca^{2+}; (3): 3.06×10^{-3} M Ca^{2+}; (4): 6.85×10^{-3} M Ca^{2+}; (5): 12.42×10^{-3} M Ca^{2+}; (6): 33.52×10^{-3} M Ca^{2+} (an excess of Ca^{2+}). (b) Spectrophotometric titration of murexide with Ca^{2+} at 480 nm, at 20°C; 10^{-4} M murexide, 10^{-2} M Tris, pH 8. OD values are corrected for dilution. A stability constant for the Ca^{2+}-murexide reaction was estimated as $K = 1250$. Note that only a small fraction of the total Ca^{2+} is associated with murexide (10% for 1.2×10^{-4} M Ca^{2+}, 5% for 8×10^{-4} M Ca^{2+}). When methyl phosphatidic acid is added to a sample containing for example 0.6×10^{-3} M Ca^{2+} the optical density decreases again and approaches the initial (Ca^{2+}-free) value at high MPA contents.

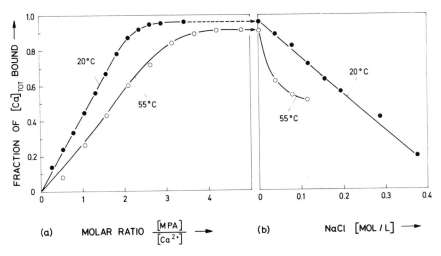

FIG. 16. Binding of Ca^{2+} to methylphosphatidic acid bilayers in the ordered (20°C) and in the fluid state (55°C) at pH 8, at which the lipid phosphate groups are fully ionized and each polar group has one negative charge. The diagram is constructed from spectrophotometric titrations of murexide at 480 nm. (*a*) MPA was added to a solution of 10^{-4} M murexide containing 6.10^{-4} M Ca^{2+}, 10^{-2} M Tris, pH 8. The initial OD was 1.24 (cf. Fig. 15*b*). From the resulting decrease in OD 480, the fraction of Ca^{2+} bound to the lipid was calculated. At 20°C the total Ca^{2+} is bound when [MPA]/ $Ca^{2+}] \gtrsim 2$. For a given ratio $m = $ [MPA]/ $[Ca^{2+}]$, more Ca^{2+} is bound below the transition (20°C) than above, suggesting that Ca^{2+} is released from the lipid surface at the order → fluid transition. (*b*) Addition of NaCl to MPA-saturated samples (all Ca^{2+} bound to the lipid) causes an increase in OD 480, indicating that Ca^{2+} is released from the lipid with increasing ionic strength (compare Fig. 13).

Ion Exchange at Charged Lipid Bilayers

The simplest explanation for the reversal of the effect of Ca^{2+} (increase in T_t) by an increase in ionic strength would be that increasing ionic strength releases Ca^{2+} from the lipid surface. This was found to occur in experiments using murexide as a Ca^{2+} probe: the addition of NaCl to a mixture of MPA and Ca^{2+} released Ca^{2+}. These observations explain the decrease in transition temperature with increasing ionic strength of Ca^{2+}-containing dispersions of MPA (cf. Fig. 13*c*).

On the basis of the studies discussed thus far, it would be predicted that the ionization of lipid phosphate groups will increase with increasing ionic strength, and that divalent cations displace protons from the phosphate groups. Such effects have been observed by Abramson, Katzman, Gregor, and Curci (1966) for phosphatidic acid prepared from egg lecithin. Analogous experiments were performed in the present study with dimyristoyl phosphatidic acid at temperatures above and below the phase transition.

Both monovalent and divalent cations decrease the pH of unbuffered dispersions of phosphatidic acid (Fig. 17). The effectiveness of the mono-

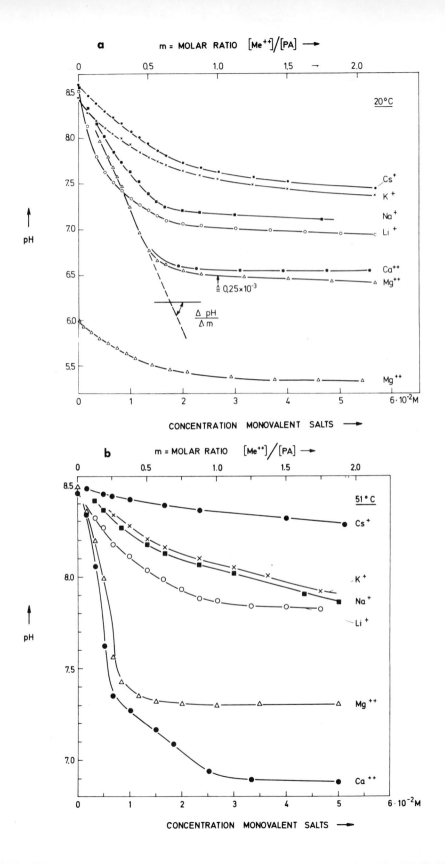

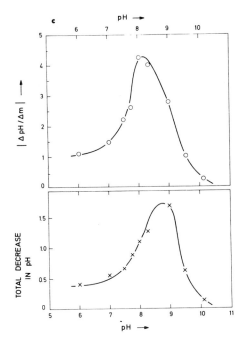

FIG. 17. Ion exchange at phosphatidic acid bilayers below and above the phase transition. The addition of monovalent cations (Li$^+$, Na$^+$, K$^+$, Cs$^+$) and divalent cations (Mg^{2+}, Ca^{2+}) to unbuffered PA dispersions (2.5×10^{-4} M lipid) decreases the bulk pH, indicating that protons are released from the lipid phosphate groups. (a) 20°C ($T < T_t$), (b) 51°C ($T > T_t$). Note: for the divalent cations, the (upper) abscissa is calibrated in units of $m = $ molar ratio [Mg^{2+}]/[PA]. (c) With Mg^{2+}, the net decrease in pH and the initial slope of the pH $- m$ curves were studied over a wider range of the initial pH (2.5×10^{-4} M lipid). Maxima occur at the second pK.

valent cations decreases with increasing ionic radius in the sequence Li$^+ >$ Na$^+ >$ K$^+ >$ Cs$^+$. The proton release is smaller at 51°C, well above the lipid transition, than at 20°C, below the transition. Much greater effects are observed with the divalent cations, which interact with the lipid polar groups in a stoichiometric way. However, the decrease in pH is smaller at 51°C than at 20°C, and marked differences were observed between Mg^{2+} and Ca^{2+} at the higher temperature (Fig. 17*b*).

These experiments show that rather complex ion-exchange phenomena may take place at the surface of charged lipid lamellae in the presence of divalent and monovalent cations, and that abrupt changes occur at the lipid phase transition. The plasticity of the system is even greater in the pH regions where the phosphate groups of the lipids are not fully ionized (pH < 5 for MPA, pH < 9 for PA), when protolytic reactions are also occurring (cf. Fig. 14).

Hysteresis and Oscillations

Cooperative phenomena are often characterized by hysteresis, which manifests itself by different paths for the transition from state I to II and the reverse transition II $\rightarrow$ I — even when the external parameter is changed exceedingly slowly. Within a hysteresis loop, the system can assume different states for a given value of the external variable, depending on its past history. To quote Katchalsky and Spangler (1968): "Hysteresis is the manifestation of the existence of energy barriers preventing the direct transition from one state to another." An important characterization of many hysteresis systems are so-called scanning curves that can be traced within the hysteresis loop; the shape of these curves provides valuable information as to the character of the hysteresis (Everett and Whitton, 1952).

Hysteresis phenomena in lipid systems have not been studied systematically to date. In many cases hysteresis is not well reproducible, but depends on the method used for sample preparation, on the thermal pretreatment or aging of the samples, and so on. Recent experiments indicate that thermal transitions in dispersions of electrically neutral, synthetic pure lipids, such as synthetic lecithins, are completely reversible, provided that the temperature is changed sufficiently slowly so that thermal equilibrium can be established at any temperature.

However, pronounced and reproducible hysteresis can be observed in dispersions of charged lipids under certain conditions, as in dispersions of phosphatidic acid at pH 8.5, that is, in the middle of the second dissociation step (Fig. 18). Under the experimental conditions used in Fig. 18, the midpoint of the order → fluid transition at increasing temperature is ~40°C, whereas the reverse transition takes place at ~ 35°C. The shift between the two branches is greater for lower ionic strength.

When a series of scanning curves was recorded in which the temperature change was halted and reversed in the steep part of either the *a*scending or the *de*scending main branch, the scanning curves trace almost parallel to the upper or lower (dotted) portion of the corresponding main branches (Fig. 18). The states 1 and 1' in Fig. 18*b* are practically identical, since the scanning curves trace almost horizontally to the higher temperature.

This behavior can be interpreted in terms of a model (Preisach, 1935; Everett and Whitton, 1952) in which the system is presumed to consist of a large assembly of independent "domains" that show metastability and sharp upper and lower transitions at the characteristic temperatures T_u and T_l; these values might differ for different domains, but the difference $\Delta T = T_u - T_l$ is assumed to be constant. One consequence of this description would be that the shape of the main branches is not a characteristic feature of the transition itself, but reflects the shape of the frequency distributions $f(T_l)$ and $f(T_u)$. The frequency distributions $f(T_u)$ and $f(T_l)$ are assumed to be identical and their variance small compared to ΔT. Whether or not the assumed "domains" are identical with individual liposomes (which may be different in size) cannot be specified at present.

This model describes the main features of the scanning behavior. It is also conceivable that, for reversible transitions, the shape of the transition curve mainly reflects the distribution of T_l values for different domains. This means that the "true" transition may be much sharper than the optically measured transitions, and implies that the cooperativity parameter σ de-

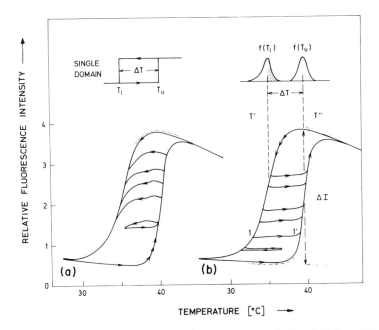

FIG. 18. Marked hysteresis is observed during the transition of phosphatidic acid bilayers at pH 8.5, 0.01 M NaCl. Fluorescence indication with NPN. The same hysteresis loop can be reproduced even when the rate of temperature change is only 1°C/20 min. (a) A series of scanning curves measured after reversal of the temperature change in the steep part of the ascending branch. (b) Scanning curves after temperature reversal in the steep part of the *descending* branch. Hysteresis decreases with increasing ionic strength. For an interpretation in terms of single domains, see text. $f(T_l)$ and $f(T_u)$ are frequency distributions of the lower and upper transition temperatures of single domains.

rived from a comparison of the apparent reaction enthalpies (which are determined by the steepness of the transition) with the true, calorimetric enthalpies represents an upper limit. The cooperative unit may therefore be much larger than the numbers calculated from the optically measured transition curves ($N \approx 30$, where N = number of lipid molecules acting cooperatively).

In phosphatidic acid dispersions, hysteresis is greatest for pH values near the second pK, which is the region with the largest difference in ionization between ordered and fluid state. Second, hysteresis is markedly reduced with increasing ionic strength, suggesting that electrostatic forces are involved in the maintenance of the barriers preventing direct transition. Electrostatic barriers have also been invoked by Neumann (1973) to explain hysteresis in polyelectrolytes. Whether the metastability of the individual domains is due to delayed nucleation or impeded growth cannot yet be determined.

Unusual hysteresis loops may be observed with PA in the presence of certain concentrations of divalent cations, as shown in Fig. 19, in which

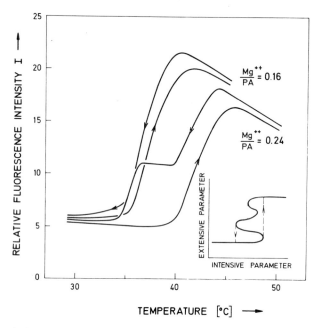

FIG. 19. Biphasic hysteresis loop of phosphatidic acid transition in the presence of Mg^{2+}, pH 10.5, 2.5×10^{-4} M lipid, 0.14 M NaCl. NPN fluorescence.

the fluid $\rightarrow$ order reversal occurs in two steps. This indicates that the extensive and intensive (external) parameters are related as depicted in the inset. These curves suggest that, in the course of the ordering process of the lipid molecules, certain intermediate lattice types are stabilized by interactions between lipids and divalent cations.

One interesting aspect of membrane hysteresis is that oscillatory phenomena may occur by coupling to catalytic processes. A theoretical analysis of such phenomena has been made by Katchalsky and Spangler (1968). The hysteresis data on these lipid systems can be used as the basis of a simple system showing oscillatory behavior, whose main components are lipid lamellae that show a sharp hysteretic transition as a function of pH (Fig. 20a); either PA or MPA could be used for this purpose. It is assumed that the order $\rightarrow$ fluid transition occurs at a proton concentration $[H^+]_l$ and the reverse transition at $[H^+]_u > [H^+]_l$. Coupled to (or embedded in) the lipid lamellae are protolytic enzymes that are fully active (excess of substrate) in the fluid state and inactive in the ordered state of the lipids. These enzymes provide a source of protons that can be switched "on" and "off" by alterations in pH (Fig. 20b). The only further requirement is that the system should be open, with an outflow of protons smaller than the production of protons by the enzymes in the "on" state.

Considering a proton concentration $[H^+] > [H^+]_u$, the enzymes are in

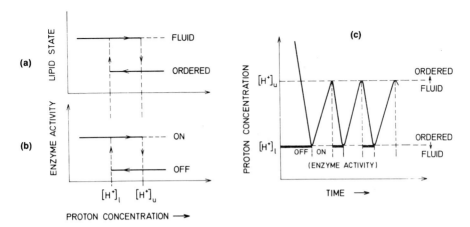

FIG. 20. Expected oscillatory behavior of the pH in a sample containing lipids with a sharp hysteretic pH transition (a), and protolytic enzymes (proton source) which can be switched "on" and "off" by the order ↔ fluid transition of the lipid bilayers (b). An outflow of protons smaller than the production is assumed (c). $[H^+]_u$: proton concentration for the fluid → ordered transition (enzymes "off"): $[H^+]_l$: proton concentration for the order → fluid reversal (enzymes "on").

the "off" state and the proton concentration in the cell decreases continuously (outflow; Fig. 20c). At $[H^+] \leq [H^+]_l$, the lipid switches into the fluid state and triggers the enzymes to produce protons at a rate higher than the outflow. Therefore, the proton concentration in the system increases until at $[H^+] \geq [H^+]_u$ the lipid switches back into the ordered state and the enzymes are turned "off." The expected oscillatory behavior of the proton concentration in the system is shown schematically in Fig. 20c.

Summary and Conclusion

The experiments described in this section indicate that a dual relationship exists between the organization of lipid molecules in charged bilayers (degree of order, packing density) and the ionic composition of the environment (pH, monovalent and divalent cations).

One result of this correlation is that small changes in ion composition are sufficient to induce cooperative changes in bilayer structure at constant temperature (order-fluid phase transition, formation of membrane mosaic patterns). Whereas divalent cations (Mg^{2+}, Ca^{2+}) tend to increase the packing density, monovalent cations tend to fluidize (or expand) the membrane structure (cf. Weiss, 1973). These effects result from charge neutralization by the association of divalent cations with negatively charged lipids, ionic strength effects expected from Gouy-Chapman theory, and ion-exchange phenomena at the lipid polar heads.

A second important result is that alterations in lipid packing (membrane structural changes) may release pulses of protons or divalent cations into the adjacent (cellular) medium. For example, the transition from an ordered to a more fluid lipid structure leads to the release of protons and/or divalent cations from the bilayer surface. The surface of charged lipid bilayers may therefore be considered as a reservoir of cations that can be activated by membrane structural changes.

In view of the known dependence of several membrane functions (transport systems, enzymatic activities) on lipid organization and the dependence of cytoplasmic processes on ion composition, these studies suggest a general way in which membrane functions might be triggered by alterations in the ionic environment and cytoplasmic processes might be regulated by changes in membrane structure.

Of particular interest is the effect of membrane structural changes on calcium binding and release. For example, in the visual system (see Chapter 11), a conformational change in rhodopsin initiated by the absorption of a photon is believed to cause the release of Ca^{2+} from the membranous discs in which the proteins are embedded. It is conceivable that the Ca^{2+} ions are released as the result of structural changes in the membrane lipids induced by the conformational change in the rhodopsin. It is also possible that the released Ca^{2+} ions directly affect the structure of synaptic or axonal membranes to enhance or reduce nerve activity.

Another example is the mitochondrion (see Chapter 7), in which the binding of Ca^{2+} to a small part of the surface, or a change of 0.2 pH units, is sufficient to alter the structure of the entire organelle. Again, these effects could be caused by alterations in the state of the membrane lipids (the inner membrane of mitochondria contains about 20% cardiolipin). Similar considerations may apply to other examples presented throughout this volume in which alterations in the state of a membrane are correlated to cytoplasmic processes: Small perturbations in the ion composition may provide the functional linkage.

THE DYNAMIC PROPERTIES OF LIPID MOLECULES:

James C. Metcalfe*

Examination of the dynamic aspects of lipid behavior within membranes requires methods which, unlike spin-label or fluorescence techniques, permit a discrimination of the different lipid species without perturbing the organization of the lipids around the membrane proteins. One such technique is nuclear magnetic resonance (NMR) of ^{13}C-labeled lipid molecules. ^{13}C spectra of phospholipids at the natural abundance level of 1%

* The studies in this section were performed in collaboration with N. J. M. Birdsall, A. G. Lee, and G. B. Warren.

show well-resolved resonances from many of the carbon nuclei within a phospholipid molecule. For example, all six of the chemically distinct polar headgroup carbons of dipalmitoyl lecithin are resolved, and six of the fatty acid chain carbons are separated from the main methylene envelope (C4–13) (Fig. 21a). When specific groups in the lipid structure are enriched with ^{13}C, the spectrum is dominated by the resonances of the enriched nuclei; this is shown in Fig. 21b for dipalmitoyl lecithin in which one of the quaternary methyl groups has been selectively enriched. Alternatively, enriched lipids can be obtained biosynthetically, as when *E. coli* are grown with 1-^{13}C- or 2-^{13}C-labeled acetate as the sole carbon source, which provides phospholipids enriched at alternate carbons along the fatty acid chains (Birdsall et al., *in preparation*).

The NMR technique has proved useful in examining factors that affect both phase transitions and phase separations in lipid bilayers. The transition temperature of a lipid bilayer dispersion is a function of vesicle size. The transition for small sonicated vesicles of dimyristoyl lecithin (~250 Å diameter) is broadened and shifted to a lower T_t as a result of the disruption of lipid packing that is imposed by the small radius of curvature (Fig. 22a). Polyvalent cations such as Eu^{3+} increase the T_t of saturated lecithin vesicles (Fig. 22b). This is consistent with the effects described by Träuble, al-

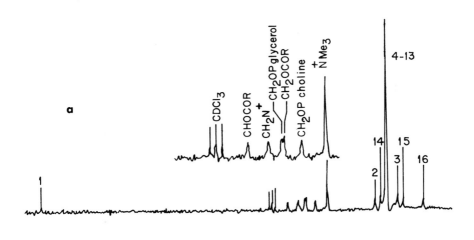

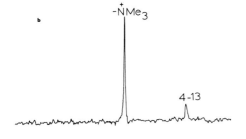

FIG. 21. (a) ^{13}C NMR spectrum at natural abundance of dipalmitoyl lecithin. Inset: expanded spectrum of glycerol choline phosphate headgroup. (b). Dipalmitoyl lecithin spectrum with $^+$NMe group enriched 20-fold with ^{13}C. This resonance now dominates the spectrum.

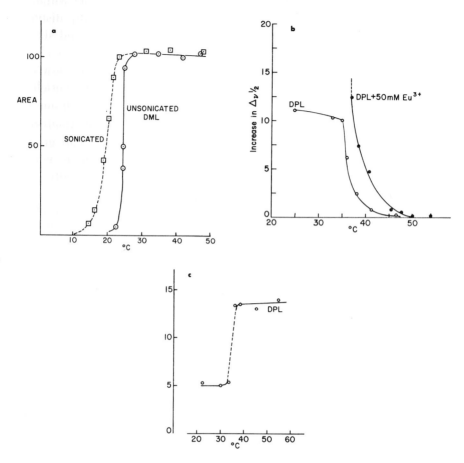

FIG. 22. (*a*) Area of the C-2 chain resonance of dimyristoyl lecithin enriched with ^{13}C at C-2, as a function of temperature. The transition is sharp and centered at 25°C in the large unsonicated vesicles, but broader and shifted to lower temperatures for the 250-Å sonicated vesicles. (*b*) The effect of 50 mM Eu^{3+} on the increase in line width of the $^{+}NMe_3$ resonance of sonicated aqueous dispersion of dipalmitoyl lecithin as a function of temperature. The line-width change defines the transition temperature, which is increased by about 5°C by 50 mM Eu^{3+}. The line width increases are measured relative to the values at 55°C. (From Levine, Lee, Birdsall, Metcalfe, and Robinson, 1973.) (*c*) The effect of temperature on the partition of 40 mM benzyl alcohol into dipalmitoyl lecithin. The T_t is centered at 37°C in the presence of 40 mM alcohol, compared with 42°C in the absence of the alcohol. (From Colley and Metcalfe, 1972.)

though the effect is smaller for the Zwitterionic lecithins than for negatively charged phospholipids, probably because the lecithins bind less Eu^{3+} ions.

Small molecules that partition into the fatty acid core of the bilayer, such as benzyl alcohol, decrease the T_t. This occurs because the alcohol must be extruded from the hydrophobic-chain region of the bilayer before the chains can crystallize. Thus, the partition coefficient of the alcohol shows

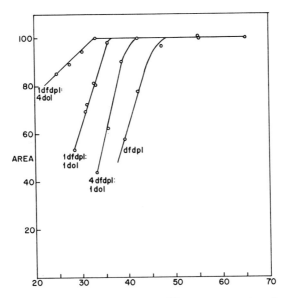

FIG. 23. Area normalized to 100 at 64°C of the ^{19}F resonance of sonicated vesicles of di-7-fluoropalmitoyl lecithin (dfDPL) as a function of temperature, in a mixture of dfDPL with dioleyl lecithin, given as molar ratios. (From Metcalfe, Birdsall, and Lee, 1972.)

an abrupt 2.5-fold increase at the phase transition. The transition temperature of dipalmitoyl lecithin is shifted from 42°C in the absence of benzyl alcohol to about 37°C at 40 mM alcohol (Fig. 22c). If phase transitions or phase separations in the axonal membrane are involved in conduction, we can speculate that the effect of local anesthetics might be to disrupt an essential feature of lipid organization.

NMR techniques can be used to detect lipid phase transitions and phase separations in mixtures of saturated and unsaturated lipids. When saturated lecithin vesicles are cooled below the transition temperature, the ^{13}C and ^{1}H chain resonances decrease abruptly in intensity. The same effect is observed in the ^{19}F NMR spectra of saturated lecithin vesicles in which a single proton of the fatty acid chains has been replaced with an ^{19}F atom. In mixtures of the unsaturated dioleyl lecithin (DOL) with the saturated ^{19}F-labeled dipalmitoyl lecithin (DPL), the loss of area occurs at lower temperatures as the proportion of DOL is increased, indicating the separation of a crystalline region of mixed lipid composition (Fig. 23). Using DOL and DPL selectively enriched with ^{13}C at different chain positions, it is now possible to observe simultaneously the phase separation of both lipids as crystalline regions are formed.

Another well-defined property of the lipid bilayer that can be examined by ^{13}C NMR is the fluidity gradient in the lipid chains. This involves the measurement of the spin lattice relaxation time, T_1, for the carbon nuclei along the chains. The T_1 relaxation time is the time constant for the first-order process of relaxation to equilibrium that occurs when a ^{13}C nucleus is excited to the nonequilibrium position of nuclear magnetization by the application of an external radiofrequency pulse. The ^{13}C T_1 relaxation times of DPL bilayer vesicles in water indicate increasing intramolecular motion for carbon atoms towards the center of the bilayer, with the terminal methyl groups of the fatty acid chains having the highest motional freedom (Fig. 24; Metcalfe, Birdsall, Feeney, Lee, Levine, and Partington, 1971; Levine, Birdsall, Lee, and Metcalfe, 1972*a;* Levine, Partington, Roberts, Birdsall, Lee, and Metcalfe, 1972*b;* Lee, Birdsall, and Metcalfe, 1973*a,b*).

The ^{13}C T_1 relaxation times are determined primarily by intramolecular motion, because ^{13}C relaxation is due mainly to directly bonded protons (Levine et al., 1972*a*). However, the proton relaxation times of phospholipid chains in bilayer vesicles are strongly influenced by intermolecular interactions (Lee et al., 1973*b*). The first indication that there was a substantial intermolecular contribution to proton relaxation in the bilayer was obtained by comparing ^{13}C and ^{1}H relaxation times for the same chemical groups in phospholipid molecules organized into different structures. Simple calculations show that the T_1 values for the protons of a methylene group in a lipid chain should be slightly longer than the corresponding ^{13}C T_1 value if the relaxation times of the different nuclei are determined by the same intramolecular motion. Thus, when the phospholipid molecules are completely dispersed in CD_3OD, the relative proton and ^{13}C relaxation times were consistent with a single intramolecular relaxation mechanism for both nuclei. This is reasonable, because the deuterium nuclei in CD_3OD in which the lipid molecules are dissolved are unable to cause a significant intermolecular relaxation of the lipid protons, and relaxation must therefore occur through the nearest protons in the same molecule. However, in the bilayer vesicles formed in water, in which the fatty acid chains are tightly packed together, the proton T_1 values for the terminal methyl groups at the center of the bilayer are smaller by a factor of 4 than the corresponding ^{13}C values, and

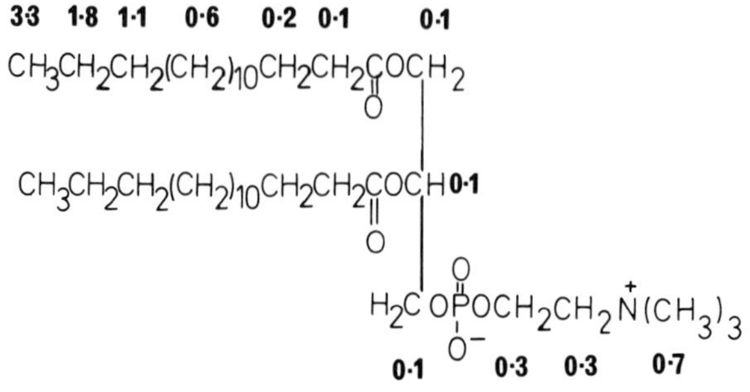

33 1·8 1·1   0·6   0·2 0·1   0·1

$$CH_3CH_2CH_2(CH_2)_{10}CH_2CH_2COCH_2$$

$$CH_3CH_2CH_2(CH_2)_{10}CH_2CH_2COCH\ 0\text{·}1$$

$$H_2C\ OPOCH_2CH_2\overset{+}{N}(CH_3)_3$$

0·1   0·3 0·3   0·7

FIG. 24. Relaxation times (in seconds) for dipalmitoyl lecithin carbons in D_2O at 52°C. (From Levine et al., 1972*a*.)

there is clearly the possibility that when the chains are tightly packed together, the protons on neighboring chains may cause mutual relaxation. To determine whether intermolecular proton relaxation was an important process in the bilayer, the proton T_1 values of the normal protonated lipid were remeasured after being highly diluted in bilayers of the same lipid with completely deuterated chains. The large increase in the proton T_1 value for the terminal methyl indicated a substantial intermolecular contribution to relaxation in the fully protonated bilayer, since the deuterium nuclei in the deuterated chains cannot cause significant intermolecular proton relaxation.

There are at least three intermolecular motions that can contribute to proton relaxation of the lipid chains in the bilayer: lateral diffusion in the plane of the bilayer, rotational diffusion about the long axis of the molecules, and a vertical oscillation of the lipid molecules. Theoretical analysis predicts that the *slowest* independent intermolecular motion will dominate the intermolecular contribution to the spin-spin relaxation time, T_2, of the protons. Therefore, the self-diffusion coefficients calculated from the proton T_2 values using the treatment of Kruger (1969) and Resing and Torrey (1963) must be less than or equal to the rate of lateral diffusion. A lower limit to the lateral diffusion coefficient can therefore be calculated from T_2, and in fact the diffusion coefficients calculated from the proton T_2 values agree closely with the *lateral diffusion* coefficients calculated from independent spin label experiments. For example, calculations from T_2 data yield a self-diffusion coefficient for egg lecithin at 20°C of 0.9×10^{-8} cm²/sec, compared with 1.8×10^{-8} cm²/sec for spin-labeled lecithin (Devaux and McConnell, 1972) and 1.0×10^{-8} cm²/sec for spin-labeled androsterone molecules in a phosphatidylcholine monolayer (Träuble and Sackmann, 1972). It was concluded that lateral diffusion is probably the slowest intermolecular motion dominating the chain proton T_2 values in the bilayer, and that proton relaxation times cannot be interpreted exclusively in terms of intramolecular motion.

The line widths of proton resonances define a relaxation time T_2^*, which must be less than or equal to the T_2 for intermolecular dipolar relaxation. It follows that a lower limit to the self-diffusion-coefficient can be calculated from T_2^* simply by measuring the proton resonance line widths of the lipid chains in bilayer vesicles. For small sonicated vesicles the linewidth T_2^* values are approximately equal to T_2, and the diffusion coefficients calculated from T_2^* are accurate. However, for larger vesicles the line widths become very broad (Chan, Seiter, and Feigenson, 1972), and Charvolin and Rigny (1972) showed that the T_2^* for unsonicated lecithin is very much smaller than the true T_2 value measured by pulse techniques. This is due to static dipolar broadening of the resonances of large, slowly tumbling vesicles, and under these conditions the T_2^* value calculated from the line width of unsonicated lecithin leads to an underestimation of the self-diffusion coefficient by about two orders of magnitude compared with the value calculated from T_2. This latter value is very similar to the diffusion coefficient calculated for sonicated lecithin vesicles, suggesting that there is no major difference in diffusion rate in the sonicated and unsonicated bilayer structures. There is therefore an inherent ambiguity in attempting to analyze proton line widths of lipid chains in biological membranes. Broad line widths *may* indicate relatively slow diffusion rates, or they may simply represent the effect of static dipolar broadening in large membrane vesicles.

This ambiguity is nicely illustrated by the proton NMR spectrum of the sarcoplasmic reticulum membrane (Fig. 25). From the line width of the sharp component of the lipid chain resonance, a lower limit to the self-diffusion coefficient of this component of 6×10^{-9} cm²/sec at 8°C and 1×10^{-8} cm²/sec at 50°C can be estimated, compared with a value of 4×10^{-9} cm²/sec for the extracted lipid. These values agree closely with that of 7.5×10^{-8} cm²/sec at 50°C calculated for spin-labeled lipid fused with sarcoplasmic reticulum (Scandella, Devaux, and McConnell, 1972). It is not known which lipids in the membrane give rise to the sharp component in the proton spectrum, to which the fast rates of lateral diffusion are attributed. The line width of the underlying broad component of the lipid chain resonances (Fig. 18) is approximately 200 Hz, which would correspond to a diffusion coefficient of $> 4 \times 10^{-10}$ cm²/sec. However, there is the obvious possibility that this value calculated from the line width is much smaller than the true diffusion rate for the reason already discussed. However, if the spectrum does indicate two pools of lipid undergoing substantially

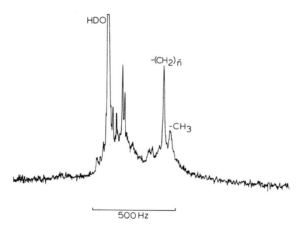

FIG. 25. ¹H NMR spectrum of sarcoplasmic reticulum at 32°C for the fluid lipid component has been calculated to be $>6 \times 10^{-9}$ cm²/sec at 8°C and $>10 \times 10^{-9}$ cm²/sec at 50°C, compared to a value of 4×10^{-9} cm²/sec for the extracted lipid. These values closely agree with that of 7.5×10^{-8} cm²/sec at 50°C calculated for spin-labeled lecithin fused with sarcoplasmic reticulum. (From Scandella et al., 1972.)

different diffusion rates, this suggests as a working hypothesis that one lipid pool may represent lipid interacting directly with membrane protein and therefore undergoing restricted lateral diffusion, and the other pool may be lipid further away from the protein undergoing the fast diffusion characteristic of a lipid bilayer unperturbed by protein. This is illustrated in Fig. 26.

Using NMR techniques on unmodified biological membranes, it is technically difficult to resolve the ambiguities in interpreting proton line widths or to test the hypothesis of an immobilized boundary layer of lipid. The multiplicity of lipid and protein components in the native membrane structure precludes detailed structural analysis. For this reason attempts have been made to reconstitute a specific membrane function using the minimum number of protein and lipid components, which would then allow specific labeling of the components of the reconstructed membrane with probe nuclei and reporter groups. The system chosen was the calcium pump of the sarcoplasmic reticulum from rabbit leg white muscle, in which a Ca^{2+}, Mg^{2+}, activated ATPase is responsible for the ATP-dependent accumulation of calcium. At least 70% of the protein in the purified sarcoplasmic reticulum consists of the ATPase.

The ATPase was purified to homogeneity by dispersing the membrane in deoxycholate (DOC), layering the dispersion above a detergent-free sucrose gradient and centrifuging. The pure ATPase (>95% pure) re-forms as particulate band within the sucrose gradient, with about 30% of the original lipid associated with the ATPase and essentially free of DOC. There is no selective retention of any particular lipid class and the ATPase remains fully activated. More than 99% of this residual lipid can be replaced by dioleoyl lecithin (DOL) when this synthetic lipid is added to the purified ATPase dispersed in DOC and the equilibrated dispersion is again centrifuged into a detergent-free sucrose gradient.

To restore calcium uptake activity to the defined complexes of DOL-ATPase, the complexes are dissolved in cholate with an excess of sarcoplasmic reticulum lipid or DOL and the cholate is then removed by dialysis.

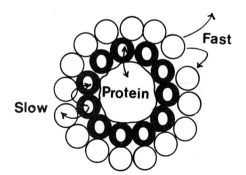

FIG. 26. Protein in the lipid bilayer of the sarcoplasmic reticulum membrane. If the two components of the proton NMR spectrum arise from slowly diffusing and more rapidly diffusing lipid, the rate of exchange between the two lipid pools would have to be $<10^{-3}$ sec to account for the spectrum.

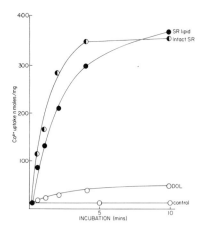

FIG. 27. Reconstitution of calcium uptake from a defined complex of ATPase-DOL (99%) and excess lipid. Filled circles, excess SR lipid; open circles, excess dioleoyl lecithin (DOL). Calcium uptake by intact SR is included for comparison (half-filled circles).

This technique is adapted from Racker (1972). The highest levels of accumulated calcium were observed in vesicles reconstituted with a 20-fold excess of sarcoplasmic reticulum lipids (Fig. 27). Much lower levels were observed when DOL was used as the excess lipid, and very little calcium uptake occurred when no lipid was added before dialysis. DOL-reconstituted vesicles tend to leak calcium, but this can be prevented by accumulating calcium in the presence of oxalate, so that the calcium inside the vesicles precipitates as calcium oxalate. Under these conditions, vesicles reconstituted with either sarcoplasmic reticulum lipids or DOL showed similar calcium uptake.

Purified ATPase complexes with dimyristoyl lecithin show a complete and reversible inhibition of ATPase activity below 23°C. This saturated lecithin has a phase transition at 25°C, and the inhibition below 23°C suggests that the enzyme may be able to function only when the lipid is in the liquid state. This observation resembles that seen for other transport systems (see Träuble, this chapter, and Chapter 5).

The calcium transport system reconstituted with defined lipids can be used to determine precisely how lipid structure affects ATPase activity and calcium uptake, and to probe structural features of the ATPase-lipid complexes, including the postulated lipid bilayer shell surrounding the ATPase exchanging relatively slowly with lipid unperturbed by protein interaction, as discussed in Chapter 4.

REFERENCES

Abramson, M. B. (1970): The effect of temperature and hydrocarbon chain structure on the titration properties of lecithin and some related phospholipids. *J. Coll. Interface Sci.*, 34:571–579.

Abramson, M. B., Katzman, R., and Curci, R. (1965): Turbidimetric studies of the interaction of aqueous micelles of phosphatidic acid with cations. *J. Coll. Sci.*, 20:777–787.

Abramson, M. B., Katzman, R., Gregor, H., and Curci, R. (1966): The reaction of cations with aqueous dispersions of phosphatidic acid. Determination of stability constants. *Biochemistry,* 5:2207–2213.

Adam, G. (1970): Theory of nerve excitation as a cooperative cation exchange in a two-dimensional lattice. In: *Physical Principles in Biological Membranes,* edited by F. Snell, J. Wolken, G. Iverson, and J. Lam, pp. 35–67. New York: Gordon & Breach.

Adam, G. (1973): Cooperative transitions in biological membranes. In: *Synergetics,* edited by H. Haken, pp. 220–231. Stuttgart: B. G. Teubner.

Blazyk, J. F., and Steim, J. M. (1972): Phase transitions in mammalian membranes. *Biochim. Biophys. Acta,* 266:737–741.

Chan, S. I., Seiter, C. H. A., and Feigenson, G. W. (1972): Anisotropic and restricted molecular motion in lecithin bilayers. *Biochem. Biophys. Res. Commun.,* 46:1488–1492.

Changeux, J. P., Thiery, J., Tung, Y., and Kittel, C. (1967): On the cooperativity of biological membranes. *Proc. Nat. Acad. Sci.,* 57:335–341.

Chapman, D., and Wallach, D. F. H. (1968): Recent physical studies of phospholipids and natural membranes. In: *Biological Membranes,* edited by D. Chapman, pp. 125–202. New York: Academic Press.

Charvolin, J., Manneville, P., and Deloche, B. (1973): Magnetic resonance of perdeutered potassium laurate in oriented soap-water multilayers. *Chem. Phys. Letters,* 23:345–348.

Charvolin, J., and Rigny, P. (1972): Transverse nuclear relaxation in lecithin bilayers. *Nature New Biol.,* 237:127–128.

Colley, C. M., and Metcalfe, J. C. (1972): The localization of small molecules in lipid bilayers. *FEBS Letters,* 24:241–246.

Cone, R. A. (1972): Rotational diffusion of rhodopsin in the visual receptor membrane. *Nature New Biol.,* 236:39–43.

Devaux, P., and McConnell, H. (1972): Lateral diffusion in spin-labeled phosphatidylcholine multilayers. *J. Amer. Chem. Soc.,* 94:4475–4481.

Eigen, M., and Winkler, R. (1970): Alkali-ion carriers: Dynamics and selectivity. In: *The Neurosciences: Second Study Program,* edited by F. O. Schmitt, pp. 685–696. New York: Rockefeller University Press.

Esfahani, M., Limbrik, A. R., Knutton, S., Oka, T., and Wakil, S. J. (1971): The molecular organization of lipids in the membrane of *E. coli:* phase transitions. *Proc. Nat. Acad. Sci.,* 68:3180–3184.

Everett, D. H., and Whitton, W. I. (1952): A general approach to hysteresis. *Trans. Faraday Soc.,* 48:749–757.

Hauser, H., and Dawson, R. M. C. (1967): The binding of calcium at lipid-water interfaces. *Eur. J. Biochem.,* 1:61–69.

Horwitz, A. F., Michaelson, D. M., and Klein, M. P. (1973): Magnetic resonance studies of membrane and model membrane systems. *Biochim. Biophys. Acta,* 298:1–7.

Hubbell, W. L., and McConnell, H. M. (1971): Molecular motion in spin-labeled phospholipids and membranes. *J. Amer. Chem. Soc.,* 93:314–326.

Katchalsky, A., and Spangler, R. (1968): Dynamics of membrane processes. *Quart. Rev. Biophys.,* 1(2):127–175.

Krüger, G. J. (1969): Magnetische Relaxation durch Translationsdiffusion in Flüssigkeiten. *Z. Naturforsch.,* 24(A):560–565.

Ladbrooke, B. D., Williams, R. M., and Chapman, D. (1968): Studies on lecithin-cholesterol-water interactions by differential scanning calorimetry and x-ray diffraction. *Biochim. Biophys. Acta,* 150:333–340.

Lee, A. G., Birdsall, N. J. M., and Metcalfe, J. C. (1973a): Measurement of fast lateral diffusion of lipids in vesicles and in biological membranes by ^{1}H nuclear magnetic resonance. *Biochemistry,* 12:1650–1659.

Lee, A. G., Birdsall, N. J. M., and Metcalfe, J. C. (1973b): NMR studies of biological membranes. *Chem. Br.,* 9:116–123.

Levine, Y. K., Birdsall, N. J. M., Lee, A. G., and Metcalfe, J. C. (1972a): ^{13}C nuclear magnetic resonance relaxation measurements of synthetic lecithins and the effect of spin-labeled lipids. *Biochemistry,* 11:1416–1421.

Levine, Y. K., Lee, A. G., Birdsall, N. J. M., Metcalfe, J. C., and Robinson, J. D. (1973): The interaction of paramagnetic ions and spin labels with lecithin bilayers. *Biochim. Biophys. Acta,* 291:592–607.

Levine, Y. K., Partington, P., Roberts, G. C. K., Birdsall, N. J. M., Lee, A. G., and Metcalfe, J. C. (1972*b*): ^{13}C nuclear magnetic relaxation times and models for chain motion in lecithin vesicles. *FEBS Letters,* 23:203–207.

Lippert, J. L., and Peticolas, W. L. (1971): Laser raman investigation of the effect of cholesterol on conformational changes in dipalmitoyl lecithin multilayers. *Proc. Nat. Acad. Sci.,* 68: 1572–1576.

Marčelja, S. (1973): Molecular model for phase transitions in biological membranes. *Nature,* 241:451–453.

McLaughlin, S. G. A., and Szabo, G. (1971): Divalent ions and the surface potential of charged phospholipid membranes. *J. Gen. Physiol.,* 58:667–687.

Melchior, D. L., and Morowitz, H. J. (1972): Dilatometry of dilute suspensions of synthetic lecithin aggregates. *Biochemistry,* 11:4558–4562.

Metcalfe, J. C., Birdsall, N. J. M., Feeney, J., Lee, A. G., Levine, Y. K., and Partington, P. (1971): ^{13}C NMR spectra of lecithin vesicles and erythrocyte membranes. *Nature,* 233:199–201.

Metcalfe, J. C., Birdsall, N. J. M., and Lee, A. G. (1972): NMR studies of dynamic features of membrane structure. *Mitochondrion/Biomembranes,* pp. 197–217. Amsterdam: North Holland Publishing Co.

Nagle, J. F. (1973): Theory of biomembrane phase transitions. *J. Chem. Phys.,* 58:252–264.

Nagle, J. F. (1974): Statistical mechanics of the melting transition in lattice models of polymers. *Proc. R. Soc. A,* 337:569–589.

Neumann, E. (1973): Molekulare Hysterese und ihre Kybernetische Bedeutung, *Angew. Chemie,* 85:430–444.

Oldfield, E., and Chapman, D. (1972): Dynamics of lipids in membranes: Heterogeneity and the role of cholesterol. *FEBS Letters,* 23:285–297.

Overath, P., Hill, F. F., and Lamnek-Hirsch, I. (1971*a*): Biogenesis of *E. coli* membranes: Evidence for randomization of lipid phase. *Nature New Biol.,* 234:264–267.

Overath, P., Schairer, H. U., Hill, F. F., and Lamnek-Hirsch, I. (1971*b*): Structure and function of hydrocarbon chains in bacterial phospholipids. In: *Dynamic Structure of Cell Membranes,* edited by D. F. Hölzl-Wallach and H. Fischer, pp. 149–164. Berlin: Springer-Verlag.

Overath, P., and Träuble, H. (1973): Phase transitions in cells, membranes and lipids of *E. coli. Biochemistry,* 12:2625–2634.

Overbeek, J. T. G. (1952): Electrochemistry of the double layer. In: *Colloid Science, I,* edited by H. R. Kruyt, pp. 115–193. Amsterdam: Elsevier.

Papahadjopoulos, D., and Kimelberg, H. K. (1973): Phospholipid vesicles (liposomes) as models for biological membranes: Their properties and interactions with cholesterol and proteins. In: *Progress in Surface Science, 4,* edited by G. Davison, pp. 139–221. New York: Plenum Press.

Phillips, M. C. (1972): The physical state of phospholipids and cholesterol in monolayers, bilayers and membranes. In: *Progress in Surface and Membrane Science, 5,* edited by J. F. Danielli, M. D. Rosenberg, and D. A. Cadenhead, pp. 139–221. New York: Academic Press.

Phillips, M. C., and Chapman, D. (1968): Monolayer characteristic of saturated 1,2-diacyl phosphatidylcholines (lecithins) and phosphatidylethanolamines at the air-water interface. *Biochim. Biophys. Acta,* 163:301–313.

Phillips, M. C., Williams, R. M., and Chapman, D. (1969): On the nature of hydrocarbon chain motions in lipid liquid crystals. *Chem. Phys. Lipids,* 3:234–244.

Poo, M., and Cone, R. A. (1974): Lateral diffusion of rhodopsin in the photoreceptor membrane. *Nature,* 247:438–441.

Preisach, F. (1935): Über die magnetische Nachwirkung. *Z. Phys.,* 94:277–302.

Racker, E. (1972): Reconstitution of a calcium pump with phospholipids and a purified Ca^{++}-adenosine triphosphatase from sarcophasmic reticulum. *J. Biol. Chem.,* 247:8198–8200.

Resing, H. A., and Torrey, H. C. (1963): Nuclear spin relaxational diffusion. III. Spin-spin relaxation. *Phys. Rev.,* 131:1102–1104.

Sackmann, E., Träuble, H., Galla, H., and Overath, P. (1973): Lateral diffusion, protein mobility and phase transitions in *E. coli* membranes. A spin-label study. *Biochemistry,* 12:5360–5369.

Scandella, C. J., Devaux, P., and McConnell, H. M. (1972): Rapid lateral diffusion of phospholipids in rabbit sarcoplasmic reticulum. *Proc. Nat. Acad. Sci.,* 69:2056–2060.

Schairer, H. K., and Overath, P. (1969): Lipid containing trans-unsaturated fatty acids change the temperature characteristic of thiomethylgalactoside accumulation in *E. coli. J. Mol. Biol.,* 44:209–214.

Schwarz, G. (1971): General cooperative kinetics of a linear Ising lattices. *Ber. Bunsenges.,* 75:40–45.

Schwarzenbach, G., and Gysling, H. (1949): Murexid als Indikator auf Calcium- und andere Metall-Ionen. *Helv. Chim. Acta,* 32:1314–1325.

Seelig, J. (1970): Spin label studies of oriented smectic liquid crystals (a model for bilayer membranes). *J. Amer. Chem. Soc.,* 92:3881–3887.

Seelig, J. (1971): On the flexibility of hydrocarbon chains in lipid bilayers. *J. Amer. Chem. Soc.,* 93:5017–5022.

Seelig, J., and Niederberger, W. (1974): Two pictures of a lipid bilayer. A comparison between deuterium label and spin-label experiments. *Biochemistry,* 13:1585–1588.

Seiter, C. H. A., and Chan, S. I. (1974): Molecular motion in lipid bilayers: An NMR line width study. *J. Amer. Chem. Soc. (in press).*

Silbert, D. F., Ruch, F., and Vagelos, P. R. (1968): Fatty acid replacements in a fatty acid auxotroph of *E. coli. J. Bacteriol.,* 95:1658–1665.

Silbert, D. F., and Vagelos, P. R. (1967): Fatty acid mutant of *E. coli* lacking a β-hydroxy-decanoyl thioester dehydrase. *Proc. Nat. Acad. Sci.,* 58:1579–1586.

Träuble, H. (1971): The movement of molecules across lipid membranes: A molecular theory. *J. Membr. Biol.,* 4:193–208.

Träuble, H. (1972): Phase transitions in lipids. In: *Biomembranes, 3,* edited by F. Kreuzer and J. F. G. Slegers, pp. 197–227. New York: Plenum Press.

Träuble, H., and Eibl, H. (1974): Electrostatic effects on lipid phase transitions: Membrane structure and ionic environment. *Proc. Nat. Acad. Sci.,* 71:214–219.

Träuble, H., Eibl, H., and Sawada, H. (1974): Respiration—a critical phenomenon. *Naturwissenschaften,* 61:344–354.

Träuble, H., and Haynes, D. H. (1971): The volume change in lipid bilayer lamellae at the crystalline-liquid crystalline phase transition. *Chem. Phys. Lipids,* 7:324–335.

Träuble, H., and Sackmann, E. (1972): Studies of the crystalline-liquid crystalline phase transition of lipid model membranes. III. Structure of a steroid-lecithin system below and above the lipid-phase transition. *J. Amer. Chem. Soc.,* 94:4499–4510.

Träuble, H., and Sackmann, E. (1973): Lipid motion and rhodopsin rotation. *Nature,* 245:210–211.

Triggle, D. J. (1972): Effects of calcium on excitable membranes and neurotransmitter action. In: *Progress in Surface and Membrane Science, 5,* edited by J. F. Danielli, M. D. Rosenberg, and D. A. Cadenhead, pp. 267–331. New York: Academic Press.

Weiss, D. E. (1973): The role of lipid in energy transmission and conservation in functional biological membranes. *Sub-Cell. Biochem.,* 2:201–235.

Wilson, G., Rose, S. P., and Fox, C. F. (1970): The effect of membrane lipid unsaturation on glucoside transport. *Biochem. Biophys. Res. Commun.,* 38:617–623.

Functional Linkage in Biomolecular Systems, edited by
F. O. Schmitt, D. M. Schneider, and D. M. Crothers.
Raven Press, New York ©1975.

Chapter 4

Lipid-Protein Interactions in Membrane and Model Systems

THE MOLECULAR ORGANIZATION OF MEMBRANES:

S. Jonathan Singer

Protein-lipid interactions are fundamental to membrane structure and function. Concepts of membrane organization have been extensively modified within the past few years. The classical Davson-Danielli (1952) model (Fig. 1a), in which membranes were postulated to consist of a poly-peptide monolayer on either side of a lipid bilayer, was proposed at a time when little was known about the structural properties of protein. A more complex model was proposed by Benson (1966), who suggested that the polypeptide chains and lipid molecules might be intertwined and organized into subunits that were repeating structural units of the membrane (Fig. 1b). This model led to considerable discussion about the nature of lipid-protein interactions, particularly in terms of the type of allosteric and cooperative effects described in Chapter 2. In addition, the model lent itself to description and analysis by the two-dimensional Ising model (see Chapter 1). However, the Benson model is inconsistent with the large body of experimental evidence showing that the bulk of the membrane lipid is organized into a bilayer.

Biological membranes are now generally thought to be mosaics (Singer,

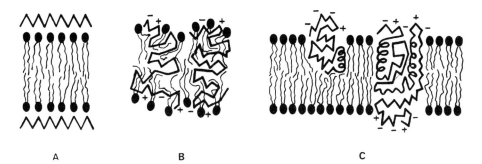

A   B   C

FIG. 1. Three versions of lipid-protein interactions within biological membranes. (a) Davson-Danielli (1952) model; (b) Benson (1966) model; (c) Mosaic model (Singer, 1971; Singer and Nicolson, 1972).

1971; Singer and Nicolson, 1972) rather than regular repeating structures, with globular proteins intercalated into an interrupted lipid bilayer (Fig. 1c; Fig. 2). This type of model suggests quite different concepts of cooperativity in membranes than those based on earlier models.

Two basic types of lipid-protein interaction may be present in mosaic membrane structures. Short-range interactions, involving lipid molecules that are in contact with the intercalated proteins (represented by the darkened areas in Fig. 2), may be specific and involve a close association of given lipid types with particular proteins. Bulk lipid effects are nonspecific, that is, the lipid is simply the solvent within which various interactions occur. Short-range interactions are probably responsible for the many observations in the literature (for a review, cf. Triggle, 1970) that specific phospholipids are required to reactivate membrane enzymes that have been previously inactivated by delipidation. Direct experimental evidence for short-range interactions is beginning to appear. For example, Jost, Griffith, Capaldi, and Vanderkooi (1973) have examined the effect of adding lipids to mitochondrial cytochrome oxidase from which nearly all lipid had been removed. When the physical state of these mixtures was examined as a function of lipid/protein ratio, using a fatty acid nitroxide label as a probe, changes in ESR spectrum with increasing amounts of a lipid indicated that the lipid was in a relatively rigid state in mixtures having a small lipid content, and that the fluidity increased as more lipid was added.

The ESR spectral data on these lipid-protein mixtures suggested that the cytochrome oxidase complex interacted strongly with a shell of lipid mole-

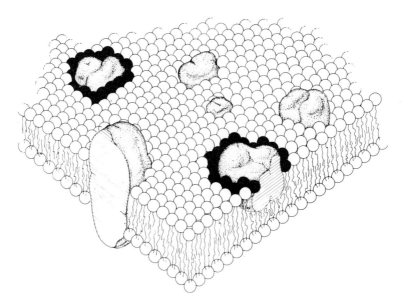

FIG. 2. Three-dimensional mosaic concept of membrane structure (From Singer and Nicolson, 1972.)

cules and that the lipid beyond this monomolecular shell had bulk solvent properties (Fig. 3). Approximately 20% of the total lipid would be bound to form such a monomolecular shell in a membrane containing this protein, while the remaining 80% would comprise the bulk phase.

Bulk lipid effects may be associated with many membrane processes that have been suggested to be cooperative phenomena. One classical example is that of fertilization, in which the interaction between the cell membrane of the ovum and a single sperm transforms the entire membrane such that it becomes completely impermeable to other sperm. The details of this process at the membrane level are completely unknown.

A similar, apparently cooperative effect occurs when a very small number of colicin E_1 molecules are bound to *E. coli* cells; this binding is followed by events that in some manner alter the entire membrane structure and kill the cell. Cramer and Phillips (1970) examined this effect with the fluorescent dye aniline naphthalene sulfonic acid (ANS), whose fluorescence intensity increases as the polarity of the medium decreases. The solubility of ANS and the quantum yield of its fluorescence are both sensitive to the physical state of the membrane. The addition of colicin E_1 to a suspension of *E. coli* (Fig. 4) produced a 100% increase in the ANS fluorescence within minutes. The rate of this increase was dependent on the amount of E_1 added, but its extent was independent of the amount. The large increase in fluorescence indicates a major structural change in the cell membrane. This alteration could be induced by the binding of as few as 70 colicin molecules per cell, indicating that it is the result of a cooperative effect that extends over most or all of the membrane surface, induced by the attachment of ligand to a relatively small number of membrane sites. The relatively slow kinetics of this process suggest that the binding of colicin to some component of the membrane surface may initiate a redistribution of some membrane components within the fluid lipid phase. It is conceivable that the attachment of colicin alters the thermodynamic balance within the membrane such that the free energy required for aggregation of certain membrane components

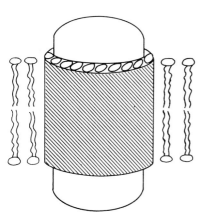

FIG. 3. Diagrammatic representation of a single protein complex and associated phospholipid in membrane cytochrome oxidase (Jost et al., 1973).

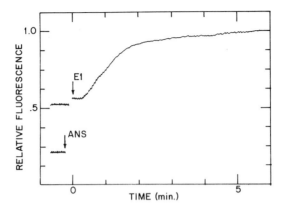

FIG. 4. Relative fluorescence of a mixture of ANS and *E. coli* cells following the addition of colicine E_1 (Cramer and Phillips, 1970).

is altered, leading to their redistribution. In addition, this redistribution could lead to permeability changes in the membrane, with resultant alterations in the metabolic state of the cell.

Although this mechanism for the killing effect of colicine E_1 on *E. coli* cells (see also Cramer, Phillips, and Keenan, 1973) may prove to be incorrect, it is presented in some detail to illustrate one way in which the bulk lipid phase of a mosaic membrane could mediate an apparent cooperative effect occurring in the membrane.

THE NONRANDOM NATURE OF MEMBRANE ORGANIZATION:

Laurens L. M. van Deenen

The erythrocyte is an excellent model system in which to examine the structural organization of biological membranes. The lipid components of the cell membrane include cholesterol, glycolipids, and phospholipids. The three major phospholipids derived from glycerol, phosphatidylcholine (PC, lecithin), phosphatidylethanolamine (PE), and phosphatidylserine (PS), all have a phosphatidic acid backbone, while the hydrocarbon chain of sphingomyelin has an amide linkage to sphingosine (Fig. 5). The degree of nonrandomness exhibited by these phospholipids was examined by selective phospholipase degradation and freeze-fracture techniques, designed to determine the phospholipid distribution in the inner and outer portions of the membrane bilayer (Verkleij, Zwaal, Roelofsen, Comfurius, Kastelijn, and van Deenen, 1973).

Incubation of intact erythrocytes with phospholipase A_2 (PLA_2), which removes one fatty acid residue from lecithin to form lysolecithin, resulted in the hydrolysis of approximately 70% of this phospholipid in the mem-

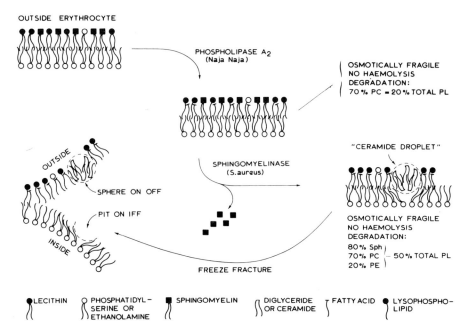

FIG. 5. Action of some phospholipases on human red cell phospholipid.

brane. Although this treatment produced increased osmotic fragility, no hemolysis occurred. The subsequent addition of sphingomyelinase, which specifically removes the polar head group of sphingomyelin, resulted in the hydrolysis of almost all of the sphingomyelin in the erythrocyte membrane, and allowed the PLA_2 to further hydrolyze $\sim 20\%$ of the membrane PE. At this point, although 50% of the total erythrocyte phospholipid had been degraded, the erythrocyte remained intact, if fragile.

In contrast, incubation of erythrocyte ghosts with these two phospholipases degraded virtually 100% of the membrane phospholipid, indicating that the selective hydrolysis of the intact cells was due to the degradation of only those phospholipids on the outer surface of the bilayer. This conclusion was further supported by freeze-fracture analyses, which demonstrated the selective alteration of the external membrane surface (Verkleij et al., 1973).

These studies indicate the membrane phospholipids to be asymmetrically distributed between the outer and inner layers. Most of the sphingomyelin and PC appears to be localized to the outer layer, while most of the PE and all of the PS is localized to the inner layer (Fig. 6). Such an assymmetry has also been proposed by Bretscher based on chemical labeling of erythrocytes and ghosts.

This apparently nonrandom distribution of lipid and protein within mem-

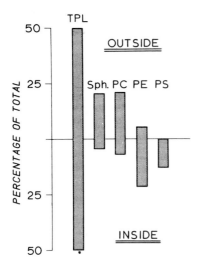

FIG. 6. Distribution of phospholipids between inner and outer layer of the human erythrocyte membrane. (From Verkleij et al., 1973.)

brane structures has also been observed for the myelin sheath. Myelin contains only three major proteins: the Al protein, the Wolfgram protein, and the Folch-Lees proteolipid.

Studies with the Al protein have attempted to answer two questions: (1) Does this particular myelin sheath protein show some degree of specificity in its interactions with lipid, and (2) are there particular regions within this fairly small molecule that have a higher affinity for lipid than others? The myelin sheath has large amounts of cholesterol, phospholipid, and cerebroside (Table 1). It contains a large amount of acidic lipid, some of which has been shown to have a high affinity for the strongly basic Al protein.

TABLE 1. *Lipid Composition of Myelin, as Weight Percent of Total Lipid*

Lipid species	Total lipid extract	Acidic lipid fraction
Cholesterol	29.3	—
Phospholipid	42.2	—
Cerebrosides	28.5	—
Cerebroside sulphate	—	36.5
Phosphatidylserine	18.0	37.0
Phosphatidylethanolamine	37.0	—
Phosphatidylinositol	1.7	3.0
Phosphatidylcholine	21.0	—
Sphingomyelin	19.2	—
Phosphatidic acid	1.2	12.4
Polyphosphoinositides	0.7	5.0
Cardiolipin	—	3.9
Unknown	1.0	2.2

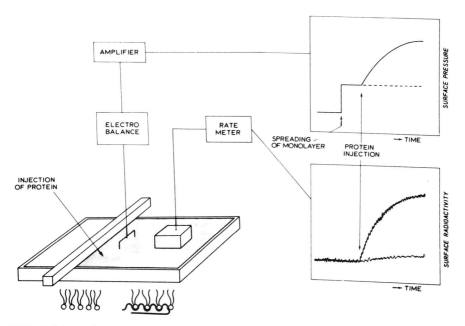

FIG. 7. Schematic representation of the technique utilized in monolayer experiments.

The interactions between lipid and the myelin proteins were examined using the monolayer technique (Fig. 7). A lipid monolayer is formed with an initial pressure of approximately 10 dynes. When a protein is injected into the subsolution, any penetration into the lipid monolayer will increase the surface pressure. It is also possible to add radioactive protein and to detect any change in surface radioactivity.

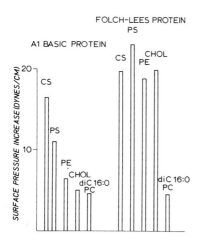

FIG. 8. The effect of basic protein and proteolipid on the interaction with different lipid monolayers (From Demel, Guerts, Van Kessel, Vossenberg, and van Deenen, 1973).

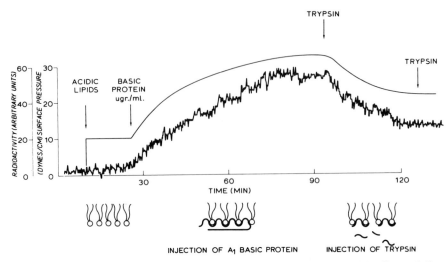

FIG. 9. The effect of the A1 protein on monolayer pressure and radioactivity. Degradation of the protein with trypsin only partially disrupts the lipid-protein interaction (From London, Demel, Guerts, Van Kessel, Vossenberg, and van Deenen, 1973.)

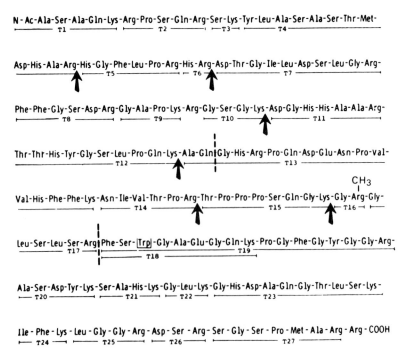

FIG. 10. The arrows indicate the peptide bonds of bovine A1 basic protein that were protected from the action of trypsin by association with acidic lipid. (From London et al., 1973.) Tryptic peptides are designated by T.

An increase in surface pressure was observed for a number of membrane lipids (Fig. 8). This effect was most pronounced with the acidic lipid fraction, particularly for sulfolipids and less for PS, while no significant penetration occurred when the monolayer contained noncharged lipids, (PE, cholesterol, and dipalmitoyl-lecithin).

Trypsin digestion of the Al protein after penetration of the monolayer decreased the surface pressure, but never to the basal pressure seen prior to penetration by the protein (Fig. 9). This suggested that digestion might be incomplete as the result of protection by the lipid of sites available to hydrolysis in solution of protein alone. This hypothesis was confirmed when the peptide map of basic protein hydrolized in aqueous solution was compared to that from trypsin-treated monolayer material. It was possible to deduce which peptide bonds had been protected by lipid (Fig. 10).

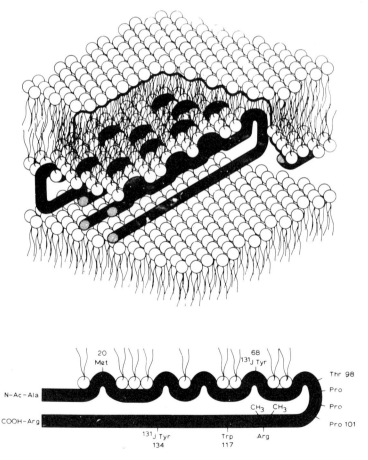

FIG. 11. Schematic representation of the binding of lipid to the A1 basic protein. (From London et al., 1973.)

These hydrolysis data, which indicated that the association of the Al protein with lipid protects a region of the molecule at the N-terminal portion, suggested a model for the localization of lipid at the Al molecule (Fig. 11).

Similar studies have been made for the Folch-Lees proteolipid. This protein has a much broader spectrum of affinity for lipids than does the Al protein and strongly interacts with cholesterol, which the Al protein does not (Fig. 8). Competition experiments between the two proteins lend further support to the concept of specificity in lipid-protein interactions. For example, if the Folch-Lees proteolipid is first allowed to interact with cholesterol, the basic protein is unable to displace the proteolipid, whereas the proteolipid does displace the basic protein. This type of observation strongly supports the existence of distinct regions within membrane proteins having affinities for specific lipids.

Although such studies of the specificity of lipid-protein interactions in biological membranes is rapidly becoming a rewarding area of research, particularly when coupled with studies of enzymatically active systems, it must be emphasized that a detailed understanding of the physical properties of lipid-protein association requires the use of reasonably simple model systems.

THE SPECIFICITY OF LIPID-PROTEIN INTERACTIONS:

Guido Guidotti

The most convincing evidence for the importance of protein-lipid interactions to protein function has come from demonstrations that lipid removal abolishes a specific protein function, and that subsequent replacement of the lipid restores that function. A lipid requirement has been shown in this way for the phosphotransferase enzyme of *E. coli* (Kundig and Roseman, 1971), the galactosyl transferase system of *S. typhimurium* (Romeo, Hinckley, and Rothfield, 1970), and the betahydroxybutyrate system of mitochondria (Menzel and Hammes, 1973). In addition, the normal function of several proteins has been shown to be dependent on the presence of quite specific lipid moieties. For example, the antibiotic amphotericin B is ineffective unless sterol is a membrane constituent (De Kruijff and Demel, 1974).

The free energy (G) of any protein-lipid interaction is dependent on both polar and nonpolar factors:

$$G = G_p + G_{np}$$

As limiting cases, membrane proteins might have only polar or only nonpolar interactions with the surrounding lipid. The former would represent an interaction limited to the external, hydrophilic polar head groups of the lipid bilayer, while the latter would be limited to the interior, hydrophobic nonpolar chain regions. All intermediates between these two extremes are possible, including proteins that extend through the bilayer to link the cell cytoplasm with its external milieu. The surface of such proteins would possess both hydrophobic and hydrophilic regions.

Several such proteins have now been characterized, including the 130,000-dalton Na^+-K^+ ATPase system of the dog kidney. The ATPase molecule is structurally and functionally polarized within the membrane; only that part of the protein exposed to the outer surface reacts with the ATPase inhibitor ouabain, and ATP hydrolysis takes place only on the inner surface.

As also noted by Singer, the bulk effects of lipid on a membrane protein may be analogous to the solvent effects of water on the properties of a soluble protein. It is therefore not surprising that alterations in the lipid milieu should alter the properties of a lipid-soluble protein, in the same way that alterations in ionic strength and other properties of an aqueous solution alter the activity of a water-soluble protein.

There is only one type of water, but many types of lipid molecules, and this wide spectrum of lipid molecules makes possible a wide variety of specific interactions with membrane proteins. Membrane proteins can thus be considered as having both a surface with a higher affinity for a nonpolar environment than for water and a specific requirement for certain lipid molecules, involving either the polar head group or the nonpolar side chain. A specific interaction between the surface of a protein and specific lipid molecules would represent a coding or recognition mechanism specified by the conformation of the protein, which is in turn governed by its genetically determined amino acid sequence. It would thus differ significantly from the nonspecific water of hydration surrounding an aqueous protein. Whether such specific recognition sites do in fact exist has not yet been determined.

Given these two types of lipid-protein interactions, one basic method for distinguishing between them is a determination of the transit time of a given lipid species within the plane of the membrane, since lateral movement will be restricted for any lipid molecule that is tightly bound to a specific protein; this approach is described by Metcalfe in Chapter 3.

The surface of a specific protein must first be characterized in order to confirm the existence of specific lipid recognition sites. This has been attempted for the erythrocyte membrane protein Component A (Berg, 1969; Bretscher, 1971), which has a molecular weight of 150,000, contains 5 to 7% carbohydrate, spans the bilayer, and is involved in the transport of anions across the membrane.

The protein surface was characterized by its ability to bind the detergent Triton X-100 (Fig. 12; Clarke, *personal communication*), whose structure resembles that of phospholipid. Detergent was used rather than lipid because the critical micellar concentration of useful phospholipid is approximately 10^{-10} M. The extent of Triton X-100 binding is a function of nonpolar surface area. This effect is highly specific, as is indicated by the differential

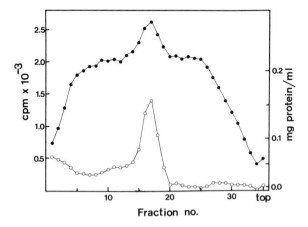

FIG. 12. The binding of ³H-Triton X-100 by an RBC extract after sucrose density gradient centrifugation. (Courtesy of S. Clarke.)

binding of labeled detergent by aqueous and membrane-bound proteins (Table 2; Clarke and Farber, 1974). The percent of a molecule's surface that is hydrophobic can be calculated from the Stoke's radius, molecular weight, sedimentation velocity in sucrose density gradients, and amount of detergent bound per mole (Table 3).

TABLE 2. *³H-Triton X-100 Binding to Proteins*

Material	Source	mg Triton bound/ mg protein
Alcohol dehydrogenase (deH)	Horse liver	<0.02
Aldolase	Rabbit muscle	<0.005
Catalase	Bovine liver	<0.01
Cytochrome c	Horse heart	<0.02
Glyceraldehyde 3-P deH	Rabbit muscle	<0.02
Hemoglobin	Human	<0.01
Lysozyme	Hen egg white	<0.02
Ovalbunin	Hen egg white	<0.01
Calsequestrin	Rabbit muscle	<0.07
Serum albumin	Bovine	0.025
Na⁺/K⁺ ATPase	Canine renal medulla	0.21
Ca²⁺ ATPase	Rabbit muscle	0.20
Minor glycoprotein	Human rbc	0.77
Rhodopsin	Frog retina	1.10
Sarcoplasmic reticulum	Rat muscle	0.20
Inner membrane + matrix	Rat liver mitochondria	
Low salt-Triton extract		0.07
High salt-Triton extract		0.27
Walking leg nerve	*Cancer*	1.00

TABLE 3. *Hydrophobic Sites on Membrane Proteins Determined by Triton X-100 Binding**

Protein	Stoke's radius (Å)	Surface area (Å)	Moles Triton/ mole protein	Percent of surface covered
Red cell				
minor glycoprotein	36	16,300 A^2	165	50
Rhodopsin	23	6,600	63	48
Na$^+$/K$^+$ ATPase	39	19,100	63	16
165,000 M.W.				
component from				
rat liver mitos	36	16,300	<23	<7

* Area occupied by Triton X-100 molecule as a surface film = 50 Å^2.

Of primary interest is a determination of the number of phospholipid molecules that would be attached to each protein molecule within a bilayer. Each Triton molecule in a monolayer occupies an area of 50 Å^2. A model cylindrical protein 80 Å in diameter and 50 Å in length should be surrounded by a minimum of 56 phospholipid molecules. It has been calculated that approximately one-sixth of the phospholipid molecules in the erythrocyte membrane may be involved in such linkages. Since the membrane also contains cholesterol and glycolipids, 6 to 7% of the entire membrane lipid may be tightly bound to specific proteins.

Is this essentially the same as saying that approximately 40% of the surface of the hemoglobin molecule interacts with water? At least in part, such binding does derive simply from the hydrophobic nature of the surface. However, there is a strong probability that quite specific interactions do occur, and such interactions may actually impart specificity to the protein. This type of specificity would make it possible to regulate enzyme activity by altering its associated lipid, without requiring genetic modification of the protein. Such interactions may impart the membrane characteristics that underlie a variety of functional linkages of the type described in subsequent chapters.

LIPID-PROTEIN INTERACTIONS IN BIOLOGICAL SYSTEMS:

Lawrence I. Rothfield

The behavior of an integral membrane protein in a model lipid system indicates the kinds of interactions that may occur within biological membranes. However, unless an assay for the function of the protein is available or its conformation can be shown to be the same as *in vivo,* such data may bear no relation to the interaction of the protein with membrane lipid components *in situ.*

Many functional membrane systems probably involve more than one protein or polypeptide chain and more than one lipid, resulting in more complicated interactions than those between a single protein and a single lipid species. In addition to interactions between proteins and lipids and between different proteins, there is also the possibility for interactions between unlike species of lipid.

Rothfield has characterized an enzyme system from Gram-negative bacteria that consists of two purified membrane proteins that are part of a functionally linked system, phosphatidylethanolamine (PE), and a specific lipopolysaccharide (LPS) that is both a structural element of the membrane and the substrate for the enzyme system (Rothfield, Romeo, and Hinckley, 1972). The two enzymes, with molecular weights of approximately 20,000, are enzymes 1 and 2 of a multienzyme system that catalyzes a series of glycosyl transferase reactions (Fig. 13). When reconstituted under appropriate conditions, the characteristics of the system are indistinguishable from those seen *in situ* with regard to K_M's, turnover numbers, and other reaction parameters. It is therefore reasonable to assume that the conformation of these proteins and their association with each other and with the lipids at least approximates that in the native membrane system.

This system is an excellent model in which to examine the molecular mechanisms involved in the proper assembly of protein and lipid components. One series of questions that can be asked is: (1) Does reassembly of this two-protein, two-lipid system utilize a concerted mechanism in which all four components must be present simultaneously, or is a sequential mechanism involved; (2) if a sequential mechanism is involved, is a specific order of reassembly required; and (3) how does reassembly occur—do the two enzymes enter the membrane together, must one precede the other, does one provide a binding site for the second, etc.?

These problems were examined using the technique of monolayer penetration (Fig. 14), in which reassembly takes place within a monomolecular

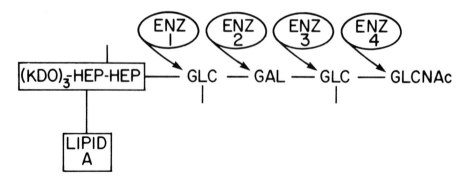

FIG. 13. Membrane-bound transferase system. Enzymes 1 and 2 are a glucosyl- and galactosyltransferase, respectively. The enzymes are part of a membrane-bound series of glycosyl transferases (Enz 1, 2, 3, 4). The sugar constituents are indicated (KDO = 2-keto-3-deoxyoctonysyl; HEP = heptosyl; GLC = glucosyl; GAL = galactosyl; GLCNAc = N-acetylglucosaminyl). (From Rothfield et al., 1972.)

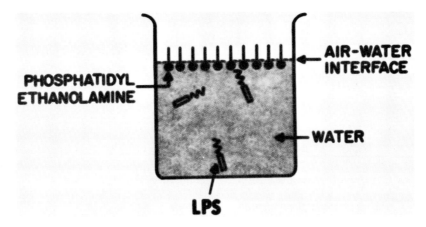

FIG. 14. Monolayer technique. A monomolecular film is formed with PE, and additional components are added to the subsolution.

film. The penetration of a substance from the subsolution into an array of lipid molecules can be measured as an increase in pressure (Fig. 15), and the activity of the coupled enzyme system can be assayed to demonstrate that function has been restored and that the characteristics of the system do have some biological meaning.

The reassembled system contained approximately one protein molecule for 5 to 10 LPS molecules, or one mole of protein to 100 moles of phospholipid. The reassembly process had an absolute requirement for a divalent

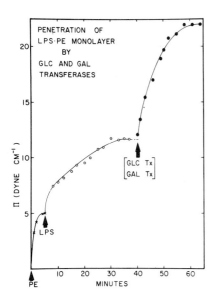

FIG. 15. Penetration of LPS-PE monolayer by GLC and GAL transferases, as shown by an increase in monolayer pressure. Π $\pm$ surface pressure; PE = phosphatidylethanolamine; LPS = lipopolysaccharide; GLC Tx = glucosyltransferase; Gal Tx = galactosyl transferase. The arrows indicate the time of addition of the components. (From Rothfield et al., 1972.)

cation, preferably Mg^{2+}. Neither enzyme penetrated the mixed lipid film in the absence of Mg^{2+}, and no enzymatic function could be restored. The function of Mg^{2+} is not yet known; it might (1) alter the conformation of the protein such that it can bind to the LPS, (2) alter the conformation or fluidity of the film, or (3) act as a ligand to bind the protein to either the PL or LPS.

The proteins interacted with the mixed lipopolysaccharide-phospholipid film differently than with a film composed solely of phospholipid. For example, Mg^{2+} was not required for penetration of the pure phospholipid monolayer. Of greater significance, there was a marked difference in the surface potential when the proteins interacted with the PL film, while only a minor or negligible change occurred with the mixed film, indicating that these are quite different types of interactions in terms of their effect on the PL. The interaction of a small number of protein molecules with the pure PL film blocked the subsequent access of lipopolysaccharide to the film, whereas lipopolysaccharide continued to penetrate the film when a similar amount of protein was placed in a mixed film. This indicates that the protein conformation differs in the two situations and that the protein may mask the polar groups of the PL when it interacts with the pure PL film.

Since membranes are a mosaic of many different lipids, and the lipid composition of various membrane regions may differ significantly, this observation suggests that membrane proteins can exist in different conformational states within the membrane, depending on the local lipid composition.

Alterations in protein conformation and enzymatic activity might serve as a regulatory mechanism to keep membrane proteins in a nonfunctional state until needed, at which time they could be activated by modifying the surrounding lipid. This type of regulatory mechanism would restrict all components to the membrane, and would not require insertion and removal of new protein molecules whenever an increase or decrease in activity was desired.

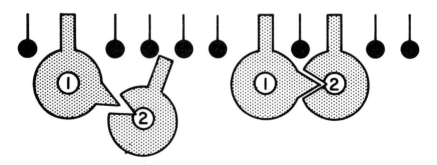

FIG. 16. Sequential assembly of a linked, two-enzyme system.

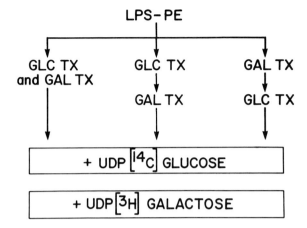

FIG. 17. Experimental design for testing whether a concerted, sequential, or independent entry mechanism is utilized by the glucosyl- and galactosyltransferases. The arrows indicate the points at which the monolayer or bilayer suspension was reisolated prior to addition of the next component. (From Hinckley, Müller, and Rothfield, 1972.)

Figure 16 illustrates one mode of assembly that might be used for proteins that catalyze linked reactions. This model postulates that assembly may be linked as well as function, an assumption that is generally made for membrane-bound multienzyme systems. It also assumes that only one

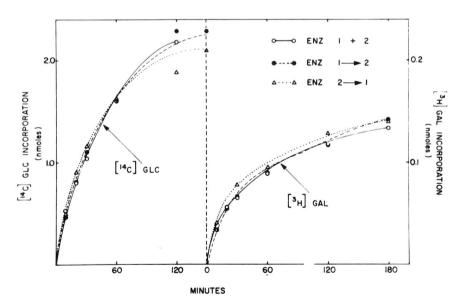

FIG. 18. Sequential activity of glucosyl- and galactosyltransferases in reconstituted systems prepared by three different modes of reassembly (see Fig. 17).

TABLE 4. *The specific activity of enzymes 1 and 2 in transferase mutants of Salmonella typhimurium**

	GlcTx	GalTx
Wild type	+	+
Spec. act.	(1.0)	(1.0)
SL3656 (Amber)	0	+
Spec. act.	(0.05)	(1.4)
SL3657 (Amber)	+	0
Spec. Act.	(1.1)	(0.06)

* Specific activities are shown in parentheses, relative to specific activity of wild type.

protein has a specific binding site and must therefore precede the other into the membrane. Several proteins that must be located adjacent to each other might also enter the membrane as a complex, or they might enter independently. This last possibility was found to be correct (Fig. 17 and 18); the entry of the two proteins into either a monolayer or a bilayer suspension occurred independently, with no preferred order of insertion and no requirement for a protein-protein intermediate at the time of assembly.

The insertion process was also examined *in vivo* in bacterial amber mutants lacking either enzyme 1 or 2 (Kuo and Stocker, 1970). These studies confirmed the *in vitro* results; mutants lacking the glucosyl transferase were able to insert the galactosyl transferase into the cell membrane, and vice versa (Table 4).

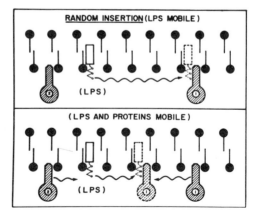

FIG. 19. A permissive model of membrane assembly. Proteins and LPS are randomly inserted into the bilayer, and the required functional association is achieved by subsequent migration within the plane of the membrane.

The lack of coupling in the initial assembly of these functionally linked proteins suggests that we must alter some of our concepts concerning the organization of multiprotein membrane-bound systems. For example, they might not always be in contact with each other, as in the electron-transfer chain. Although such proteins *may* be in physical contact with each other, they do not *have* to be. The most permissive model of assembly, and one that might evolutionarily be most probable, is one in which proteins can independently enter a region of a membrane and reorganize themselves within the plane of the membrane when necessary (Fig. 19).

REFERENCES

Benson, A. A. (1966): On the orientation of lipids in chloroplast and cell membranes. *J. Amer. Oil Chem. Soc.,* 43:265–270.
Berg, H. C. (1969): Sufanilic acid diazonium salt: A label for the outside of the human erythrocyte membrane. *Biochim. Biophys. Acta,* 183:65–78.
Bretscher, M. S. (1971): A major protein which spans the human erythrocyte membrane. *J. Mol. Biol.,* 59:351–357.
Clarke, S., and Farber, J. (1974): *Comparative Biochemistry and Physiology of Transport.* Amsterdam: North Holland Publishing Co. (*in press*).
Cramer, W. A., and Phillips, S. K. (1970): Response of an *Escherichia coli*-bound fluorescent probe to colicin El. *J. Bacteriol.,* 104:819–825.
Cramer, W. A., Phillips, S. K., and Keenan, T. W. (1973): On the role of membrane phase in the transmission mechanism of colicin El. *Biochemistry,* 12:1177–1181.
Davson, H., and Danielli, J. F. (1952): *The Permeability of Natural Membranes,* 2nd ed. Cambridge: Cambridge University Press.
De Kruijff, B., and Demel, R. A. (1974): *Biochim. Biophys. Acta,* 339:57–70.
Demel, R. A., Guerts Van Kessel, W. S. M., Vossenberg, F. G. A., and van Deenen, L. L. M. (1973): The specific interaction of myelin basic protein with lipids at the air-water interface. *Biochim. Biophys. Acta,*311:507–519.
Hinckley, A., Müller, E., and Rothfield, L. (1972): Reassembly of a membrane-bound multi-enzyme system. I. Formation of a particle containing phosphatidylethanolamine, lipopolysaccharide, and two glycosyltransferase enzymes. *J. Biol. Chem.,* 247:2623–2628.
Jost, P. C., Griffith, O. H., Capaldi, R. A., and Vanderkooi, G. (1973): Evidence for boundary lipid in membrane. *Proc. Nat. Acad. Sci.,* 70:480–484.
Kundig, W., and Roseman, S. (1971): Sugar transport. II. Characterization of constitutive membrane-bound enzymes II of the *Escherichia coli* phosphotransferase system. *J. Biol. Chem.,* 246:1407–1418.
Kuo, T., and Stocker, B. A. D. (1970): *Personal communication.*
London, Y., Demel, R. A., Guerts, Van Kessel, W. S. M., Vossenberg, F. G. A., and van Deenen, L. L. M. (1973): The protection of A_1 myelin basic protein against the action of proteolytic enzymes after interaction of the protein with lipids at the air-water interface. *Biochim. Biophys. Acta,* 311:520–530.
Menzel, H. M., and Hammes, G. G. (1973): Purification and characterization of a lecithin-D (−)-β-hydroxybutyrate dehydrogenase complex. *J. Biol. Chem.,* 248:4885–4889.
Romeo, D., Hinckley, A., and Rothfield, L. (1970): Reconstitution of a functional membrane enzyme system in a monomolecular film. II. Formation of a functional ternary film of lipopolysaccharide, phospholipid and transferase enzyme. *J. Mol. Biol.,*53:491–501.
Rothfield, L., Romeo, D., and Hinckley, A. (1972): Reassembly of purified bacterial membrane components. *Fed. Proc.,* 31:12–17.
Singer, S. J. (1971): The molecular organization of biological membranes. In: *Structure and Function of Biological Membranes,* edited by L. Rothfield, pp. 145–222. New York: Academic Press.
Singer, S. J., and Nicolson, G. L. (1972): The fluid mosaic model of the structure of cell membranes. *Science,* 175:720–731.

Triggle, D. J. (1970): Some aspects of the role of lipids in lipid-protein interactions and cell membrane structure and function. *Recent Prog. Surface Sci.,* 3:273–290.

Verkleij, A. J., Zwaal, R. F. A., Roelofsen, B., Comfurius, P., Kastelijn, D., and van Deenen, L. L. M. (1973): The asymmetric distribution of phospholipids in the human red cell membrane. A combined study using phospholipases and freeze-etch electron microscopy. *Biochim. Biophys. Acta,* 323:178–193.

Functional Linkage in Biomolecular Systems, edited by
F. O. Schmitt, D. M. Schneider, and D. M. Crothers.
Raven Press, New York © 1975.

Chapter 5

Lateral Molecular Motions in Membranes

COUPLING BETWEEN LATERAL AND PERPENDICULAR
MOTION IN BIOLOGICAL MEMBRANES:

Harden M. McConnell

The lateral distributions and lateral mobilities of membrane components
are features of membrane structure that probably play significant roles in
cellular functions. It is also probable that the lateral distribution and mobility of surface antigens are important in immunological events such as
complement fixation and immune lysis (Rapp and Borsos, 1970; Nicolson,
1972b; Raff and de Petris, 1973; Humphries and McConnell, *to be published*). This discussion considers one aspect of this problem, that of the
coupling between lateral and perpendicular motions in biological membranes; the "perpendicular motion" considered is the transport of molecules
across membranes, and the lateral motion is that of phospholipids.

Phase transitions of pure phospholipids, of the type described by Träuble
in Chapter 3, can be studied using spin-label techniques and paramagnetic
resonance (Hubbell and McConnell, 1971). Pure phospholipids such as
dipalmitoylphosphatidylcholine (DPPC) show quite sharp transitions,
with widths of ~1 to 2°C. Figure 1 illustrates typical paramagnetic resonance data, which clearly show the main "chain-melting" transition in
dipalmitoylphosphatidylcholine at 42°C (Shimshick and McConnell,
1973a,b). Such chain-melting transition temperatures depend strongly on
chain length, the nature of the polar head group, and the degree of unsaturation of the hydrocarbon chains (Phillips, Ladbrooke, and Chapman, 1970;
Fig. 2). Because biological membranes contain mixtures of phospholipids, it
is helpful to examine the properties of binary mixtures of pure phospholipids.
The rates of fission and fusion of phospholipid vesicles are very low, on
the order of hours^{-1}, and the rates of transmembrane flipping ("flip-flop")
are equally low (Kornberg and McConnell, 1971a; McConnell and Taupin,
1972). In contrast, the lateral diffusion rates of phospholipids are quite
high; a single lipid molecule can move a distance of ~1 μ in 1 sec when the
temperature is above the hydrocarbon chain-melting temperature (Kornberg and McConnell, 1971b; Scandella, Devaux, and McConnell, 1972;
Träuble and Sackmann, 1972; Devaux and McConnell, 1973).

Under these conditions, binary mixtures of phospholipids exhibit lateral

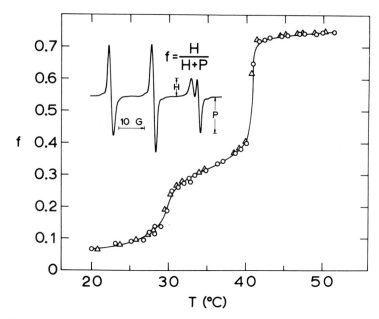

FIG. 1. Temperature-induced phase transitions for dipalmitoyl phosphatidylcholine and related phospholipids, determined by the paramagnetic resonance of the spin label TEMPO (2,2,6,6,-tetramethylpiperidine-1-oxyl), whose solubility increases in the fluid state (Shimshick and McConnell, 1973a,b).

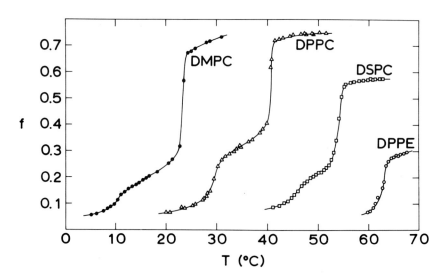

FIG. 2. Transition temperature as a function of chain length. The T_t increases with increasing length. DMPC = dimyristoyl lecithin; DPPC = dipalmitoyl lecithin; DSPC = distearoyl lecithin; DPPE = dipalmitoyl phosphatidylethanolamine.

phase separations in the plane of the membrane (Shimshick and McConnell, 1973a). These lateral phase separations can be described by means of phase diagrams such as the one shown in Fig. 3 (Shimshick and McConnell, 1973a,b). In the temperature-composition domain designated F, all the hydrocarbon chains are in their "melted" or "fluid" state, the rate of lateral diffusion is high, and there is a homogeneous mixture of phospholipid molecules in the plane of the membrane. In the temperature-composition region designated S, all the hydrocarbon chains are relatively rigid and extended, the rate of lateral diffusion is low, and there is still a homogeneous mixture of the two types of lipid molecules in the plane of the membrane.

In the region of the phase diagram designated F + S, the "fluid" and "solid" domains coexist; the fluid domain is richer in the lower-melting phospholipid, while the solid component domain is richer in the higher-melting one (Fig. 4).

Lateral phase separations in lipid mixtures differ from phase transitions of pure phospholipids in a number of important respects. For example, lateral phase separations require long-range molecular motion, over many molecular distances, in the plane of the membrane, and the molecules must segregate with respect to composition. In addition, a lateral phase separation typically takes place over a large temperature range (relative to the transition temperature width of a pure phospholipid). Lateral phase separations described by phase diagrams such as the one illustrated in Fig. 3 can be characterized by two temperatures, t_h and t_l, that define two points, one on the *fluidus* curve, and one on the *solidus* curve. The phase diagram shown in Fig. 3 represents only one type of phase behavior. Other lipid mixtures exhibit solid phase immiscibility (Shimshick and McConnell, 1973b), and some also exhibit fluid phase immiscibility (Wu and McConnell, *to be published*).

It is sometimes possible to visualize coexisting solid and fluid domains in lipid mixtures by freeze-fracture electron microscopy (Shimshick, Klee-

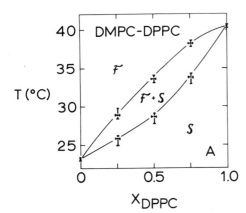

FIG. 3. Phase diagram of fluid-solid composition as a function of temperature for a mixture of two phospholipids, dimyristoyl lecithin (DMPC) and dipalmitoyl lecithin (DPPC). The diagram is constructed from TEMPO spectra (Fig. 1) of a series of phospholipid mixtures.

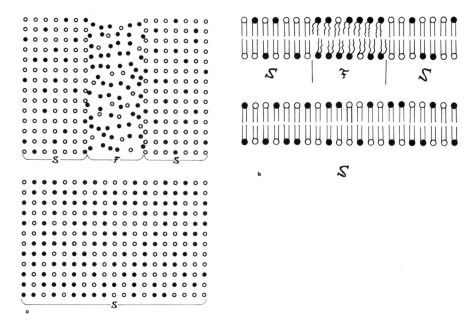

FIG. 4. In the temperature range where the F + S phase exists, it is possible to develop a differential composition between adjacent membrane regions. (a) A membrane surface view of such a phase separation. (b) A phase separation viewed in cross section.

mann, Hubbell, and McConnell, 1973). Figure 5 is from an early study in which a binary mixture of phospholipids was prepared at a temperature and composition such that, according to a phase diagram analogous to that shown in Fig. 3, approximately equal proportions of lipid in the solid and fluid phase were expected to be present. The sample was then rapidly frozen and the electron microscope replica prepared. In this particular sample, the fluid and solid domains could be readily distinguished by the strongly banded character of the solid domains. (For more recent quantitative studies, see Grant, Wu, and McConnell, 1974; Kleemann, Grant, and McConnell, 1974; for early evidence of domain structures see Ververgaert, Elbers, Luitingh, and van den Berg, 1972.) Similar features in freeze-fracture microphotographs have also been seen in biological membranes (Branton, Elgsaeter, and James, 1972; James, Branton, Wisnieski, and Keith, 1972; Ververgaert, Verkleij, Verhoeven, and Elbers, 1973). However, additional studies are required to demonstrate conclusively that these features do represent phase separations.

Further support for the existence of phase separations in biological membranes has been obtained in fatty acid auxotrophs of *E. coli* (Kleemann and McConnell, 1974) (Fig. 6 and 7). Curves of the binding of a spin label to phospholipids isolated from *E. coli* cell membranes as a function of temperature contain a region suggestive of the F + S state. This same

FIG. 5. Electron microphotograph of a mixture of two phospholipids following freeze-fracture.

pattern is seen for the intact membrane, but over a slightly smaller temperature range (Fig. 6).

Figure 7 shows galactoside uptake by the same *E. coli* cells (grown at 37°C before the transport assay) used to obtain the data in Fig. 6 (Linden, Wright, McConnell, and Fox, 1973). There is a close correlation between the temperature corresponding to the onset of the lateral phase separation of the lipids (37.3 to 37.7°C), and that at which there is an apparent discontinuity in galactoside transport (38.0 to 38.8°C). There is also a reason-

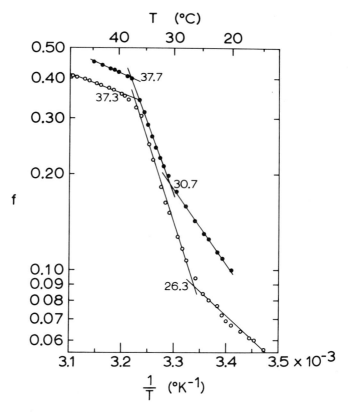

FIG. 6. The binding of spin label to both cell membranes and a mixture of phospholipids obtained from fatty acid auxotrophs of *E. coli* grown in medium containing elaidic acid. (From Linden et al., 1973.)

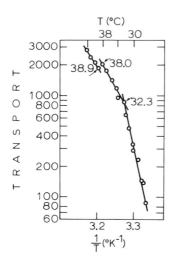

FIG. 7. Glucoside transport in *E. coli* as a function of temperature. The normal growth temperature is 37°C.

ably good correlation between the temperature at which there is a discontinuous change in the slope of β-galactoside (32.3°C) and that corresponding to the completion of the lateral phase separation of the membrane phospholipids (30.7°C). (For further discussion of these studies on *E. coli* mutants, see the following discussion by C. Fred Fox.) In these cells, grown on elaidic acid, the temperature for the onset of the lateral phase separation is close to the growth temperature.

The plasma membranes of these same *E. coli* fatty acid auxotrophs have been studied by freeze-fracture electron microscopy (Kleemann and McConnell, 1974). As shown in Fig. 8, the photomicrographs obtained from these cells are markedly different, depending on the ambient temperature at the instant they are rapidly frozen. Cell membranes maintained at 43°C before quick-freezing display a net-like distribution of membrane "particles" (proteins), whereas those maintained at 37°C before quick-freezing show large areas from which these membrane particles are excluded. For reasons that are discussed in detail elsewhere (Kleemann and McConnell, 1974), it is felt that these patterns do not accurately reflect the membrane particle distributions at 43°C and 37°C, but rather reflect particle distributions appropriate to lower temperatures. Unlike the binary mixtures of phospholipids discussed above, the rate of cooling of these membranes appears to be too slow, or the rate of lipid crystallization too high, to preserve the particle distribution on rapid freezing. The photomicrographs in Fig. 8 do exhibit the expected effect — as the ambient temperature is reduced, the particles redistribute themselves so as to be excluded from the domains of solid or crystalline lipids. The relative size of the solid domains increases as the ambient temperature is decreased. The exclusion of membrane proteins from solid phase regions of binary lipid mixtures has been clearly documented in a number of experiments involving reconstituted membranes (Kleemann et al., 1974). In these *E. coli* membranes, the particle distribution is believed to be essentially uniform at temperatures above 37 to 38°C, and to be maximally condensed at temperatures below ~31°C, the temperature indicated by the spin-label data to represent the completion of the lateral phase separation.

In the study by Linden et al. (1973), it was suggested that the marked enhancement of β-galactoside and β-glucoside transport in *E. coli* observed when the temperature was reduced in the vicinity of the onset of the lateral phase separation is related to the expected enhanced lateral compressibility of the membrane lipids at this temperature. Theoretically, enhanced lateral compressibility is associated with enhanced density fluctuations, and it is these enhanced lipid density fluctuations that may be directly involved in the enhanced sugar transport. This coupling between lateral motions of the lipids and the "perpendicular" transport of sugars may involve expansion-contraction cycles of the membrane proteins and/or changes in the depth of penetration of protein into the bilayer. Some of these ideas can be

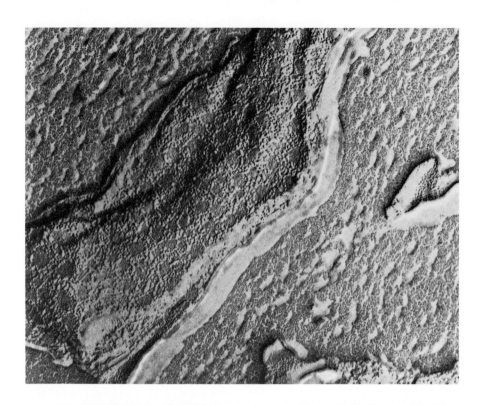
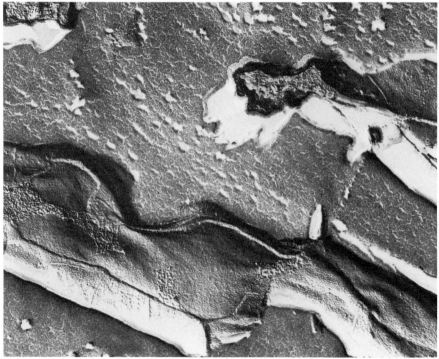

tested by a variety of physicochemical experiments, especially those that are sensitive to the dynamic aspects of lipid-protein interactions.

These studies in selected cell types raise several interesting general questions. For example, can regulation of membrane fluidity — specifically phospholipid fluidity — serve as a regulatory control mechanism, especially in cells of higher organisms? Isothermal changes in lateral pressure brought about by contractile proteins, or other lipid-protein interactions, could also modulate the "fluidity" of biological membranes, and thus their rates of perpendicular transport. In this connection, it is interesting to mention briefly the effects of a number of hormones and neurotransmitters on the "fluidity" of erythrocyte membranes. For example, prostaglandins PGE_1 and PGE_2 produce changes in the lipid fluidity of erythrocyte membranes when present at concentrations of the order of 1 to 3 molecules/cell (Kury, Ramwell, and McConnell, 1974). PGE_1 produces a more "fluid" membrane, and PGE_2 produces a more "rigid" membrane. These very specific effects of the prostaglandins are probably mediated by their role in the production of cyclic AMP (and/or cyclic GMP) in the cell, and the subsequent phosphorylation of microfilaments or microfilament-associated components of the red cell membrane. The neurotransmitter-like substances carbamyl choline and epinephrine have also been shown to affect the fluidity of the erythrocyte membrane (Huestis and McConnell, 1974). Such changes in membrane fluidity (phospholipid fluidity) might affect a number of other seemingly independent membrane-associated transport systems in these cells.

ASSEMBLY OF THE *E. COLI* MEMBRANE:

C. Fred Fox

The insertion of hydrophobic proteins into membrane presents problems that are not necessarily encountered in the assembly of supramolecular entities that contain no lipid, such as ribosomes and certain viruses. Of particular interest is the mechanism by which a hydrophobic protein is transported from its site of synthesis on the ribosome to its site of deposition in a membrane. This problem is particularly acute in procaryotes, where there is no convincing evidence for functional association of ribosomes with membranes.

One form in which an integral membrane protein might be transported from ribosome to membrane is as a lipoprotein complex, in which the

---

FIG. 8. Microphotographs of *E. coli* membranes from fatty acid auxotrophs following freeze-fracture. (Top) Cells grown in elaidic acid above the temperature at which the onset of lateral phase separation occurs. (Bottom) Cells quenched below the transition temperature.

hydrophobic areas of protein would interact with the hydrocarbon chains of phospholipids. One possible corollary of such a transport mechanism is the availability of lipid to protein at the time of its folding, during and/or subsequent to synthesis. The availability of lipid at this time could promote the proper folding of a protein having largely nonpolar surface areas. Zilversmitt (1972) has described a class of carrier proteins that can catalyze the transport of lipids from one organelle to another in eukaryotes. One of the major lipid biosynthetic enzymes is ribosome-associated in a strain of *E. coli* B (Raetz and Kennedy, 1972) and is evenly distributed between the cytoplasmic and membrane fractions in extracts of *E. coli* K12 (Machtiger and Fox, 1973). If this enzyme were involved in the transport of lipids from their site of synthesis to the sites of protein synthesis, it is conceivable that newly synthesized proteins might be inserted into membrane with newly synthesized lipids. This possibility led Fox and his colleague to look for a preferential association of newly synthesized membrane lipids and proteins in *E. coli*.

Initial studies were based on observations (Schairer and Overath, 1969; Wilson, Rose, and Fox, 1970) that unsaturated fatty acid auxotrophs of *E. coli*, which can be grown in media supplemented with a wide variety of fatty acids, incorporate into their membrane lipids only the unsaturated fatty acid that is provided in the medium. It is thus possible to use unsaturated fatty acid auxotrophs to "construct" membranes with different melting properties. As noted by McConnell, membrane lipids of an auxotroph grown with any one of a number of supplements melt over a temperature range bounded by unique upper and lower characteristic temperatures. In collaborative studies with McConnell, Fox has shown that transport is in most cases affected at both the upper and lower characteristic temperatures of the lipid phase transition (Linden et al., 1973). However, the following discussion is concerned only with the events that occur at the lower characteristic temperature, that is, the temperature at which all the membrane lipids assume the frozen state.

The induction of the lactose transport system of *E. coli* has been studied at temperatures below and above the lower characteristic temperature of the lipid phase transition (Tsukagoshi and Fox, 1973a). When the lactose operon is induced below the lower characteristic temperature (the "membrane lipid freezing point"), soluble enzyme products of genes that map on either side of the transport protein are synthesized in the same ratio as when induction proceeds above the membrane lipid freezing point. Below the membrane lipid freezing point, however, the induction of lactose transport is abortive, indicating that some post-translational step in the formation of the transport system requires a fluid membrane. Induction of transport proceeded normally when cells were first incubated below the freezing point of the membrane lipids derived from the fatty acid supplement, and transport induction was monitored when the growth medium was subsequently supplemented with a second unsaturated fatty acid that gave rise to lipids that were themselves fluid at the induction temperature (Tsukagoshi and Fox, 1973b). This suggested that the transport protein might be influenced preferentially by the newly synthesized lipids. This hypothesis was tested directly by measuring the effects of temperature on the transport rate after the same manipulations of fatty acid supplements.

Cells were first grown with the fatty acid supplement elaidic acid, which gives rise to lipids having a freezing point of 30°C, and then shifted to a medium containing oleic acid, which gives rise to membrane lipids having a freezing point of 14°C. Transport was induced during the second growth period. When induction proceeded at 37°C (above the freezing points of lipids derived from both supplements), effects on transport of only one lower characteristic temperature of the phase transition were observed; this lower characteristic temperature was intermediate between those of cells grown with either supplement (Fig. 9a). Therefore, the new and old lipids appear to randomize, probably by a lateral diffusion process, when transport system assembly occurs under conditions where the culture temperature is above the freezing point of all the membrane lipids. This result is in agreement with studies by Overath, Hill, and Lamnek-Hirsch (1971). In contrast, transport induced at 25°C (below the freezing temperature of the membrane lipids derived from elaidic acid, so that the lateral diffusion of membrane components should be slowed dramatically) was prominently affected by the lower characteristic temperature of the newly synthesized lipids, that is, those derived from oleic acid (Fig. 9b). The transport system formed under this condition may have also been affected by the lower characteristic temperature of the preexisting membrane lipids, since a second characteristic temperature for transport was observed near 30°C. This observation indicates that (1) lipids at some newly formed transport sites may have mixed, giving rise to mixtures in which the preexisting lipids predominated, or (2) only one of the two membrane monolayers at the transport site contain newly synthesized lipids. The latter could arise either as a consequence of or subsequent to assembly of the transport sites. When cells with the transport characteristics shown in Fig. 9b were incubated above 30°C (the freezing point of membrane lipid derived from either fatty acid supplement) prior to assay of transport at the indicated temperatures, the transport system appeared to be affected by a mixed lipid phase (Fig. 9c). This further supported the conclusion that the transport system formed under the conditions of Fig. 9b is affected by newly synthesized lipids rather than by a mixed lipid phase. The conclusions from these experiments are summarized schematically in Fig. 10.

These experiments indicated the mode of assembly only for the lactose transport system. It was therefore of interest to determine whether this system is unique or is representative of a more general mechanism. Subsequent studies utilized both an unsaturated fatty acid auxotroph and bromo-

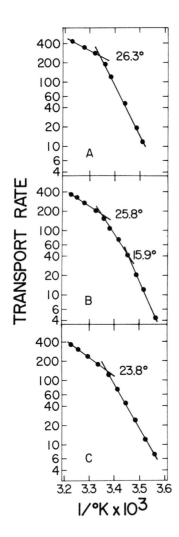

FIG. 9. The influence of growth temperature on transport induced after shifting from growth with one fatty acid supplement (elaidic acid) to growth with a second (oleic acid). The experimental details are described in the text.

stearic acid, a density-labeled fatty acid supplement (Fox, Law, Tuskagoshi, and Wilson, 1970); this made it possible to separate membranes enriched for the density-labeled fatty acid during growth on this supplement from the less dense membranes formed during growth in the presence of a "light" fatty acid supplement. Membranes were fragmented prior to separation on the basis of density, since nonfragmented membranes cannot be separated into fractions that are enriched in lipids containing either the light or density-labeled lipid precursors (Tsukagoshi, Fielding, and Fox, 1971).

Cells of the unsaturated fatty acid auxotroph grown in medium containing ^{3}H-bromostearic acid synthesize membrane lipids that become totally frozen at 22°C. Cells grown with this supplement were then washed free of bromo-stearic acid and suspended in fresh medium containing ^{14}C-oleic acid, which

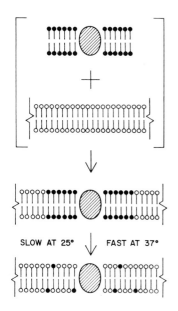

FIG. 10. Proposed mechanism for the insertion of the β-galactoside transport protein into membrane (Tsukagoshi and Fox, 1973b). Head groups of lipids formed prior to induction of the transport protein are represented as solid circles; head groups of lipids formed during induction of the transport protein are represented as open circles; and the transport protein is represented as a cross-hatched ellipse. The notations "slow at 25°" and "fast at 37°" refer to the consequences of the specific conditions described in Fig. 9, where the lipids synthesized prior to transport-system induction have a freezing temperature (lower characteristic temperature of the phase transition) of 30°C, and the lipids formed during transport-system induction have a freezing point of less than 25°C.

gives rise to lipids that are totally frozen at 14°C. The culture was then divided into two portions; one was grown at 37°C, a temperature above the freezing point of lipids derived from both fatty acid supplements, while the second was grown at 20°C, a temperature above the freezing point of lipids derived from oleic acid but below the freezing point of lipids derived from bromostearic acid.

After growth, the cells grown under these conditions were processed to remove extraneous labeled fatty acid, disrupted, and the membranes fragmented in a single sonication step. A fraction containing the membrane that separates the cytosol from its extracellular surroundings was then prepared and subjected to gel filtration on Agarose 150m (Fig. 11) to separate membrane fragments on the basis of particle size. Four pooled fractions were prepared; these are termed A, B, C, D, respectively, in order of decreasing particle size (A $\geq$ 1,600 Å; D $\leq$ 600 Å). Each of these pooled fractions was then concentrated, applied to a preformed linear sucrose density gradient, and centrifuged to equilibrium density. The ratio of $^{14}C/^{3}H$ was determined for each of 20 fractions from this gradient (Fig. 12).

The $^{14}C/^{3}H$ ratio of the membrane fragments prepared from cells grown at 37°C after the density shift was fairly uniform, and little difference in ratio was detected between the low- and high-density fragments. This would be expected if the lipids formed prior to and after the density shift had randomized. In contrast, membrane fragments prepared from cells grown at 20°C showed a significant increase in $^{14}C/^{3}H$ ratio with deceasing density. This is the result predicted by the hypothesis described schematically (and no doubt in oversimplified form) in Fig. 10. These experiments are

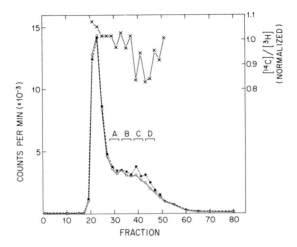

FIG. 11. Gel filtration chromatography of sonicated membrane fragments obtained from cells subjected to a density shift. The cells were grown initially in medium containing ³H-bromostearic acid and were shifted to growth in medium containing ¹⁴C-oleic acid. Four portions of the column eluates were pooled, concentrated, and subjected to equilibrium density gradient centrifugation in linear preformed sucrose density gradients.

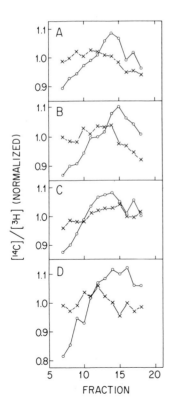

FIG. 12. Distribution of light and density-labeled membrane fragments from the column eluate described in Fig. 11. The most dense fraction is fraction 1. Isotope ratios of fragments obtained from cells grown at 37°C after the density shift (crosses). Isotope ratios of fragments obtained from cells grown at 20°C after the density shift (circles).

thus consistent with a model in which new membrane regions are formed and inserted as a unit into preexisting membrane. However, the data also support a model in which the membrane components are inserted at many, but nevertheless unique points, but in which the coordinated incorporation of newly synthesized protein and lipid is fortuitous. The mechanism of membrane assembly indicated by these experiments does not produce any permanent separation of "new" from "old" membrane under normal physiological conditions, since membrane lipids formed prior to and after the density shift can and do mix at temperatures above the membrane lipid freezing point.

More recent studies from this laboratory have utilized cultured animal cell systems, which present many membrane problems of potential interest that cannot be examined in bacteria. It is possible to modify the membrane lipid fatty acid composition to produce cells with membranes that have physical characteristics different from those of cells grown under "ordinary" conditions (Wisnieski, Williams, and Fox, 1973; Williams, Wisnieski, Rittenhouse, and Fox, 1974). The effects of the physical properties of membrane lipid on the display and function of cell surface receptors is now being investigated (Rittenhouse and Fox, 1974; Rittenhouse, Williams, Wisnieski, and Fox, 1974a; Rittenhouse, Williams, and Fox, 1974b).

RESTRICTIONS ON THE LATERAL MOBILITY OF CELL MEMBRANE COMPONENTS:

Garth L. Nicolson

Specific cell-membrane components are now known to possess varying degrees of mobility within the plane of the membrane. Estimates of phospholipid planar diffusion calculated from nuclear magnetic resonance and electron paramagnetic resonance spin-label studies indicate a rapid motion of these components ($D = 10^{-8}$ cm sec^{-1}) (Hubbell and McConnell, 1968; Keith, Waggoner, and Griffith, 1970; Tourtellotte, Branton, and Keith, 1970; Kornberg and McConnell, 1971a,b; Scandella et al., 1972; Jost, Griffith, Capaldi, and Vanderkooi, 1973; Lee, Birdsall, and Metcalfe, 1973), but little or no "flip-flop" or rotation from one side of the membrane to the other (Kornberg and McConnell, 1971b).

Certain protein membrane components also appear to diffuse rapidly, but much less rapidly than phospholipids. After Sendai virus-induced fusion of two unlike (from different species) cells to form a heterokaryon, Frye and Edidin (1970) demonstrated that about 30 to 40 min at 37°C are required for the complete intermixing of two specific surface antigens, and uncharacterized human antigens and H-2 histocompatibility antigens were shown to diffuse laterally at different rates. In several studies, antibody-induced antigen aggregation and "capping" of H-2 and surface immunoglobulin were utilized to follow the fate of antigen-antibody complexes on lymphoid cell surfaces (Taylor, Duffus, Raff, and de Petris, 1971; Davis, 1972; Edidin and Weiss, 1972; Kourilsky, Silvestre, Neauport-Sautes, Loosfelt, and Dausset, 1972; de Petris and Raff, 1972). Using fluorescent-antibody techniques, Edidin and Fambrough (1973) estimated the diffusion constant for certain antigens on muscle fibers to be approximately $D = 10^{-9}$ cm sec^{-1}. This is in good agreement with Cone's (1972) estimates of the diffusion constant of rhodopsin in the retinal disc membranes, calculated following flash photolysis. Oligosaccharides that are probably attached to membrane glycoproteins can also be quickly aggregated with lectins on certain cells, but not on others (Comoglio and Guglielmone, 1972; Nicolson, 1972*b*, 1973*b*, 1974*a;* Inbar and Sachs, 1973; Rosenblith, Ukena, Yin, Berlin, and Karnovsky, 1973; Comoglio and Filogamo, 1973; Loor, 1973).

It is therefore apparent that different membrane components may move laterally at quite different rates, from very fast to very slow or undetectable, depending on the fluidity of the membrane or other types of restraints applied from outside and/or inside the cell. In a modified, dynamic version of the Fluid Mosaic Membrane Model (Fig. 13; Nicolson, 1974*a,b,c*), the phospholipids are suggested to diffuse laterally at a high rate in the membrane and to intermix rapidly. Certain integral proteins and glycoproteins are postulated to move laterally at a rate slower than that of the phospholipids, although considerably faster than some integral glycoproteins and proteins that are *relatively* "frozen" by either external restraints (such as cell-to-cell coupling in gap junctions) or internal cytoplasmic restraints acting at the inner surface (such as the attachment of an extensive network of membrane-associated components).

Plasma membrane-associated components, such as energy-driven filamentous or contractile structures (microtubule/microfilament systems), may under certain conditions be involved in either impeding lateral motion or inducing motion in energy-dependent systems. Such systems may control processes such as those subsequent to antibody- and lectin-induced aggregation, which leads to cap formation of receptors on lymphocytes (Taylor et al., 1971; de Petris and Raff, 1972; Loor, Forni, and Pernis, 1972; Yahara and Edelman, 1972), cell motility and endocytosis (Berlin, 1972; Unanue, Perkins, and Karnovsky, 1972). However, the lateral mobilities of certain linked integral proteins and glycoproteins might be very low under resting conditions, in the absence of contraction of membrane-associated contractile systems.

As an example, consider the restraints that might be responsible for the different rates of lectin-induced lateral movement of lectin receptors on normal and oncogenic virus-transformed cells (Inbar and Sachs, 1973; Nicolson, 1973*b*, 1974*a;* Rosenblith et al., 1973). Lectin receptors for concanavalin A and *Ricinus communis* agglutinin on transformed fibroblasts

T₁ T₂

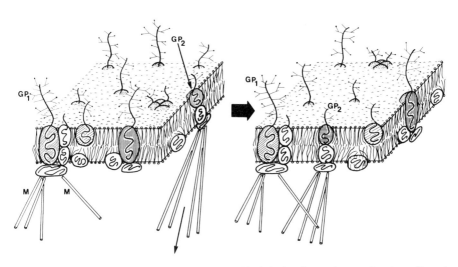

FIG. 13. Modified version of the Fluid Mosaic Model of cell membrane structure. T_1 and T_2 represent different points in time. Certain hypothetical integral membrane glycoprotein components are free to diffuse laterally in the membrane plane formed by a lipid bilayer, while others such as the integral glycoprotein-peripheral protein macromolecular complex (GP_1) are impeded by membrane-associated components (M). Under certain conditions some membrane macromolecular complexes (GP_2) can be laterally displaced by membrane-associated contractile components in an energy-dependent process. (From Nicolson, 1974a,b.)

such as SV40 and polyoma-transformed 3T3 cells can be easily aggregated by first labeling with lectins at low temperature (0 to 4°C), then elevating the temperature to 20 to 37°C for 10 min. This aggregation does not appear to occur when normal 3T3 cells are labeled in a similar way (Nicolson, 1973b; Rosenblith et al., 1973), indicating a lower *relative* mobility of lectin sites on normal cells; however, there is one report that claims the contrary (de Petris, Raff, and Mallucci, 1973). Experiments on the intermixing of antigenic sites after fusion of mouse and human normal and transformed cells also indicate a lower relative mobility of receptors on normal cells. Edidin and Weiss (1972, 1974) could not demonstrate capping of antigens on normal fibroblasts, but they obtained rapid capping on transformed cells. They found low rates of antigen intermixing when normal cells were fused to form normal-normal heterokaryons, high rates were obtained with transformed-transformed heterokaryons, and intermediate rates were observed in normal-transformed heterokaryons (Edidin and Weiss, 1974).

Recent evidence suggests that cytoplasmic membrane-associated alkaloid-binding components are involved in regulating the mobility of the surface

receptors for concanavalin A on mouse fibroblasts. Incubation of fibroblasts with colchicine or vinblastine sulfate, which disrupt microtubules,
modifies cell agglutination by concanavalin A (Yin, Ukena, and Berlin,
1972; Berlin and Ukena, 1972). In normal fibroblasts, structures such as
subplasma membrane networks of microfilaments appear to be associated
with a population of relatively immobilized concanavalin A surface receptors. An extensive microfilament system forms beneath the plasma
membrane after cell-to-cell contact of normal murine 3T3 cells, but not
their virus-transformed counterparts (McNutt, Culp, and Black, 1971).
Labeling of confluent 3T3 cells with ferritin-concanavalin A at 4°C, followed
by washing and elevating the temperature to 37°C for 15 min, does not
produce receptor aggregation in regions immediately over the microfilament
networks, but it does in regions that do not have these membrane-associated
structures. This suggests that there are concanavalin A receptors with
differing mobilities after 3T3 cells contact. Transformed cells do not
appear to have different classes of concanavalin A receptors; rather, all
have a high mobility (Nicolson, 1974b).

Normal cells have also been shown to undergo density-dependent surface
changes that seem to be associated with cell-to-cell contact. Certain glycolipids increase at the time of cell-to-cell contact in normal hamster fibroblasts, but this response is lost after transformation (Hakomori, 1970;
Robbins and Macpherson, 1971). Forssman and hematoside glycolipids
increase at the early stages of cell contact in hamster NIL cells (Hakomori
and Kijimoto, 1972; Kijimoto and Hakomori, 1972). Lectin-binding sites
such as those for *Ricinus communis* agglutinin also increase in number at
the time of cell contact in 3T3 cells, but not in virus- or spontaneously
transformed 3T3 lines (Nicolson and Lacorbiere, 1973).

The restriction of mobility of plasma membrane components and their
segregation into distinct membrane domains has been studied in mammalian
sperm. These haploid cells, surrounded by a single plasma membrane,
contain distinct binding sites for colloidal iron hydroxide particles (Yanagimachi, Noda, Fujimoto, and Nicolson, 1972) and certain lectins (Nicolson
and Yanagimachi, 1972, 1974). For example, rabbit spermatozoa contain a
high density of colloidal iron hydroxide-binding sites on the tail regions,
but the tail middle-piece is only lightly labeled and the head regions are
unlabeled (Yanagimachi et al., 1972). When these cells were labeled with
ferritin-conjugated *R. communis* agglutinin at room temperature, head and
acrosomal (but not postacrosomal) regions were labeled, as were the tail
regions (Nicolson and Yanagimachi, 1974).

This restricted localization of membrane components within specific
regions of a single plasma membrane indicates that a cellular mechanism
must exist that "fixes" specific membrane components in place. One
possible mechanism for anchoring cell membrane components has been
suggested by electron microscopic studies of 3T3 cells (McNutt et al.,

1971) that revealed the formation of extensive microfilament networks just beneath the cell membrane and in regions of contact whenever the cells made contact with a surface. Similar structures may also be present in rabbit sperm tails, in which Shelanski and Taylor (1968) have found colchicine-binding components. These observations clearly suggest that the submembrane microfilament/microtubule network in some way controls the mobility of molecules within the plane of the membrane.

Not all cell lines have microfilaments or microtubule networks beneath the cell membrane, but those that do appear to be colchicine-sensitive. It has been proposed that microtubules may be attached to the cell membrane through microfilament networks and that colchicine could affect the membrane through these networks. Such a network may be present in the immune system, in which a colchicine-binding protein has been found beneath the cell surface, as described by Edelman in Chapter 8. Cone also suggested that rhodopsin might be restricted to the plasma membrane of the outer segment in rod cells by a microtubular "fence" at the constriction between outer and inner segments.

The concept that the mobility of certain surface membrane components may be restricted in this fashion recently received experimental support (Nicolson and Painter, 1973). The human erythrocyte glycoprotein, glycophorin (Kathan and Winzler, 1963; Marchesi and Steers, 1968; Winzler, 1970; Marchesi, Tillock, Jackson, Segrest, and Scott, 1972), is known to span the lipid bilayer and can be chemically modified from both sides of the membrane (Bretscher, 1971; Segrest, Kahane, Jackson, and Marchesi, 1973). The molecule is a 203 amino acid residue glycoprotein, and possesses most of the characteristic surface-binding properties of the erythrocyte membrane, with binding sites for the blood-group antigens, influenza virus, colloidal iron hydroxide, and other ligands (Winzler, 1969; Nicolson, 1973a; Segrest et al., 1973). The major human erythrocyte protein spectrin, which represents 20% by weight of the total membrane protein (Marchesi and Steers, 1968), is found exclusively on the inner membrane surface and does not react with reagents presented to the outside surface (Singer and Nicolson, 1971; Nicolson, Marchesi, and Singer, 1971). When Nicolson and Painter (1973) sequestered affinity-purified antibodies against spectrin on the inside surface of human erythrocyte ghosts by mild hemolysis, and then incubated for 30 min at 37°C, they observed a dense aggregation of iron-binding glycoprotein (glycophorin) sites on the outside of the membrane. That this effect was indeed due to an aggregation of spectrin induced by divalent antibody was indicated by the concentration dependence of the response, and by the lack of any effect when noncrosslinking Fab monovalent fragments of antispectrin were used. No redistribution occurred at 0°C, when the lateral movement of membrane components would be very slow, or at 37°C when the membrane was pretreated with glutaraldehyde. Also, spectrin could be aggregated by a transmembrane effect when the

Ricinus communis receptors were aggregated on the cell surface (Ji and Nicolson, 1974).

These observations suggest that internally located peripheral membrane proteins may exert a transmembrane control of external components. Such linkages between the cytoplasm and cell membrane could be involved in the control of receptor-site localization and in the attachment of contractile proteins involved in processes such as cellular motility and endocytosis (Fig. 13). In the nervous system, preliminary evidence (Cotman and Taylor, 1974; Fig. 14). indicates that dense ferritin-concanavalin A binding, indicative of α-mannopyranosyl-like carbohydrate groups, occurs predominantly at the postsynaptic region and does not extend to the adjacent cell membrane, implying a considerable restriction on the mobility of the components, possibly glycoproteins, that bind concanavalin A. Membrane components analogous to spectrin might be located immediately below the postsynaptic membrane region, which shows a characteristic dense staining in electron micrographs. These components might restrict the movement of proteins such as the acetylcholine receptor, which is known to be localized to the postsynaptic region. It would be of particular interest to examine the neuromuscular junction for microfilaments during development, since acetylcholine receptors are initially distributed over the cell surface and later congregate. The induction of a filament system by the formation of a synapse might resemble the process that occurs in 3T3 cells when cell contact occurs.

A related mechanism by which membrane components might be anchored in place was suggested by Singer. Membranes may contain regular arrays of components whose motion is restricted by submembrane "scaffolding." For example, the gap junction contains a protein which appears to form a regular crystalline array, and 20% of the membrane surface of purple bacteria consists of a rigid two-dimensional crystalline array that appears to function as a proton pump.

In support of this proposal, Träuble noted that the Stokes-Einstein equation does not really apply to the diffusion of aggregates in proteins:

Stokes-Einstein:

$$\text{diffusion} = \sqrt{\frac{F_{\text{lipid}}}{F_{\text{protein}}} \times V_{\text{lipid}}}$$

Actual:

$$\text{diffusion}_{\text{protein}} = \frac{F_{\text{lipid}}}{F_{\text{protein}}} \times V_{\text{lipid}}$$

This means that a large membrane aggregate can, as the result of its size, prevent the aggregation or movement of other components.

The restriction of mobility of certain plasma membrane components may be an essential step in cell recognition and development. Concentrating

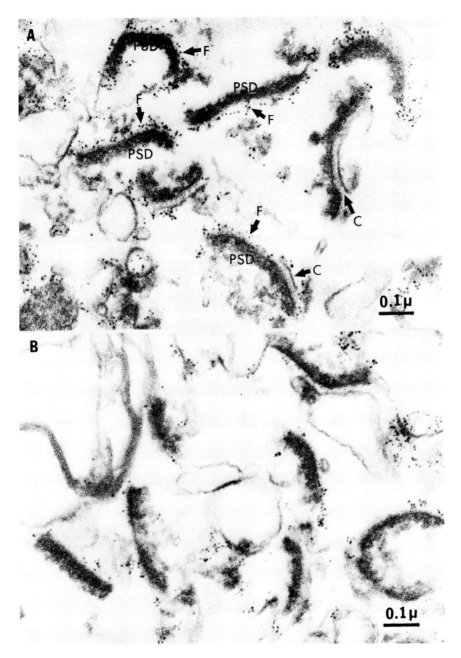

FIG. 14. (a) Localization of concanavalin A-binding sites to the synaptic clefts (C) of purified synaptic membrane complexes utilizing ferritin-conjuaged concanavalin A. In those complexes where the cleft is open, exposing the outer surface of the postsynaptic membrane, the ferritin molecules are seen localized on the external surface of the post-synaptic membrane (F) overlying the postsynaptic density (PSD). Ferritin-conjugated concanavalin A does not bind to the PSD and is excluded from closed clefts. (C). (b) Saccharide inhibitor (α-methyl-ᴅ-glucoside) inhibits binding to the postsynaptic membrane surface. (From Cotman and Taylor, 1974.)

certain receptors in specific cell-surface regions may provide a necessary "molecular pattern" for the recognition of localized regions of multiple receptors to permit successful cell interactions after contact. Such interactions would include both neuromuscular junction and synapse formation.

REFERENCES

Berlin, R. D. (1972): Effect of concanavalin A on phagocytosis. *Nature New Biol.,* 235:44–45.

Berlin, R. D., and Ukena, T. E. (1972): Effect of colchicine and vinblastine on the agglutination of polymorphonuclear leucocytes by concanavalin A. *Nature New Biol.,* 238:120–122.

Branton, D., Elgsaeter, A., and James, R. (1972): Freeze-etch Studies of membrane organization and reorganization. In: *Mitochondrion/Biomembranes,* pp. 165–183. Amsterdam: North Holland Publishing Co.

Bretscher, M. S. (1971): Major human erythrocyte glycoprotein spans the cell membrane. *Nature New Biol.,* 231:229–232.

Comoglio, P. M., and Filogama, G. (1973): Plasma membrane fluidity and surface motility of mouse C-1300 neuroblastoma cells. *J. Cell Sci.,* 13:415–420.

Comoglio, P. M., and Guglielmone, R. (1972): Two dimensional distribution of concanavalin-A receptor molecules on fibroblast and lymphocyte plasma membranes. *FEBS Letters,* 27:256–258.

Cone, R. A. (1972): Rotational diffusion of rhodopsin in the visual receptor membrane. *Nature New Biol.,* 236:39–43.

Cotman, C., and Taylor, D. (1974): Localization and characterization of concanavalin A receptors in the synaptic cleft. *J. Cell Biol.,* 62:236–242.

Davis, W. C. (1972): H-2 antigen on cell membranes: An explanation for the alteration of distribution by indirect labeling techniques. *Science,* 175:1006–1008.

de Petris, S., and Raff, M. C. (1972): Distribution of immunoglobulin on the surface of mouse lymphoid cells as determined by immunoferritin electron microscopy. Antibody-induced, temperature-dependent redistribution and its implications for membrane structure. *Eur. J. Immunol.,* 2:523–535.

de Petris, S., Raff, M. C., and Mallucci, L. (1973): Ligand-induced redistribution of concanavalin A receptors on normal, trypsinized and transformed fibroblasts. *Nature New Biol.,* 244:275–278.

Devaux, P., and McConnell, H. M. (1973): Equality of the rates of lateral diffusion of phosphatidylethanolamine and phosphatidylcholine spin labels in rabbit sarcoplasmic reticulum. *Ann. N.Y. Acad. Sci.,* 222:489–498.

Edidin, M., and Fambrough, D. (1973): Fluidity of the surface of cultured muscle fibers. Rapid lateral diffusion of marked surface antigens. *J. Cell Biol.,* 57:27–37.

Edidin, M., and Weiss, A. (1972): Antigen cap formation in cultured fibroblasts: A reflection of membrane fluidity and of cell motility. *Proc. Nat. Acad. Sci.,* 69:2456–2459.

Edidin, M., and Weiss, A. (1974): Restriction of antigen mobility in the plasma membranes of some cultured fibroblasts. In: *Control of Proliferation in Animal Cells,* edited by B. Clarkson and R. Baserga, pp. 213–220. New York: Cold Spring Harbor Laboratory.

Fox, C. F., Law, J. H., Tuskagoshi, N., and Wilson, G. (1970): A density label for membranes. *Proc. Nat. Acad. Sci.,* 67:598–605.

Frye, L. D., and Edidin, M. (1970): The rapid intermixing of cell surface antigens after formation of mouse-human heterokaryons. *J. Cell Sci.,* 7:319–335.

Grant, C. W. M., Wu, S. H. W., and McConnell, H. M. (1974): Lateral phase separations in binary lipid mixtures: Correlation between spin label and freeze-fracture electron microscopic studies. *Biochim. Biophys. Acta,* 363:151–158.

Hakomori, S. I. (1970): Cell density-dependent changes of glycolipid concentrations in fibroblasts, and loss of this response in virus-transformed cells. *Proc. Nat. Acad. Sci.,* 67:1741–1747.

Hakomori, S. I., and Kijimoto, S. (1972): Forssman reactivity and cell contacts in cultured hamster cells. *Nature New Biol.,* 239:87–88.

Hubbell, W. L., and McConnell, H. M. (1968): Spin-label studies of the excitable membranes of nerve and muscle. *Proc. Nat. Acad. Sci.,* 61:12–16.

Hubbell, W. L., and McConnell, H. M. (1971): *J. Amer. Chem. Soc.,* 94:4475.

Huestis, W. H., and McConnell, H. M. (1974): A functional acetylcholine receptor in the human erythrocyte. *Biochem. Biophys. Res. Commun.,* 57:726–732.

Inbar, M., and Sachs, L. (1973): Mobility of carbohydrate containing sites on the surface membrane in relation to the control of cell growth. *FEBS Letters,* 32:124–128.

James, R., Branton, D., Wisnieski, B., and Keith, A. (1972): Composition, structure and phase transition in yeast fatty acid auxotroph membranes: Spin labels and freeze-fracture. *J. Supramol. Struct.,* 1:38–49.

Ji, T. H., and Nicolson, G. L. (1974): Lectin binding and perturbation of the cell membrane outer surface induces a transmembrane organization alteration at the inner surface. *Proc. Nat. Acad. Sci.,* 71:2212–2216.

Jost, P. C., Griffith, O. H., Capaldi, R. A., and Vanderkooi, G. (1973): Evidence for boundary lipid in membranes. *Proc. Nat. Acad. Sci.,* 70:480–484.

Kathan, R. H., and Winzler, R. J. (1963): Structure studies on the myxovirus hemagglutination inhibitor of human erythrocytes. *J. Biol. Chem.,* ⨿38:21–25.

Keith, A. D., Waggoner, A. S., and Griffith, O. H. (1970): Spin-labeled mitochondria lipids in *Neurospora crassa. Proc. Nat. Acad. Sci.,* 61:819–826.

Kijimoto, S., and Hakomori, S. I. (1972): Contact-dependent enhancement of net synthesis of forssman glycolipid antigen and hematoside in nil cells at the early stage of cell-to-cell contact. *FEBS Letters,* 25:38–42.

Kleeman, W., Grant, C. W. M., and McConnell, H. M. (1974): Lipid phase separations and protein distribution in membranes. *J. Supramol. Struct. (in press).*

Kleemann, W., and McConnell, H. M. (1974): Lateral phase separations in *Escherichia coli* membranes. *Biochim. Biophys. Acta,* 345:220–230.

Kornberg, R. D., and McConnell, H. M. (1971*a*): Inside-outside transitions of phospholipids in vesicle membranes. *Biochemistry,* 10:1111–1120.

Kornberg, R. D., and McConnell, H. M. (1971*b*): Lateral diffusion of phospholipids in a vesicle membrane. *Proc. Nat. Acad. Sci.,* 68:2564–2568.

Kourilsky, F. M., Silvestre, C., Neauport-Sautes, C., Loosfelt, Y., and Dausset, J. (1972): Antibody-induced redistribution of HL-A antigens at the cell surface. *Eur. J. Immunol.,* 2:249–257.

Kury, P. G., Ramwell, P. W., and McConnell, H. M. (1974): The effect of prostaglandins E_1 and E_2 on the human erythrocyte as monitored by spin labels. *Biochem. Biophys. Res. Commun.,* 56:478–483.

Lee, A. G., Birdsall, N. J. M., and Metcalfe, J. C. (1973): Measurement of fast lateral diffusion of lipids in vesicles and in biological membranes by ¹H nuclear magnetic resonance. *Biochemistry,* 12:1650–1659.

Linden, C. D., Wright, K., McConnell, H. M., and Fox, C. F. (1973): Lateral phase separations in membrane lipids and the mechanism of sugar transport in *Escherichia coli. Proc. Nat. Acad. Sci.,* 70:2271–2275.

Loor, F. (1973): Lectin-induced lymphocyte agglutination. An active cellular process? *Exp. Cell Res.,* 82:415–425.

Loor, F., Forni, L., and Pernis, B. (1972): The dynamic state of the lymphocyte membrane. Factors affecting the distribution and turnover of surface immunoglobulins. *Eur. J. Immunol.,* 2:203–212.

Machtiger, N. A. and Fox, C. F. (1973): *J. Supramol. Struct.,* 1:545–564.

Marchesi, V. T., and Steers, E., Jr. (1968): Selective solubilization of a protein component of the red cell membrane. *Science,* 159:203–204.

Marchesi, V. T., Tillack, T. W., Jackson, R. L., Segrest, J. P., and Scott, R. E. (1972): Chemical characterization and surface orientation of the major glycoprotein of the human erythrocyte membrane. *Proc. Nat. Acad. Sci.,* 69:1445–1449.

McNutt, N. S., Culp, L. A., and Black, P. H. (1971): Contact-inhibited revertant cell lines isolated from SV40-transformed cells. II. Ultrastructural study. *J. Cell Biol.,* 50:691–706.

Nicolson, G. L. (1972*a*): Topological studies on the structure of cell membranes. In: *Membrane Research,* edited by C. F. Fox, pp. 53–70. New York: Academic Press.

Nicolson, G. L. (1972*b*): Topography of membrane concanavalin A sites modified by proteolysis. *Nature New Biol.,* 239:193–197.

Nicolson, G. L. (1973*a*): Anionic sites of human erythrocyte membranes. I. Effects of trypsin, phospholipase C, and pH on the topography of bound positively charged colloidal particles. *J. Cell Biol.*, 57:373–387.

Nicolson, G. L. (1973*b*): Temperature-dependent mobility of concanavalin A sites on tumour cell surfaces. *Nature New Biol.*, 243:218–220.

Nicolson, G. L. (1974*a*): Factors influencing the dynamic display of lectin binding sites on normal and transformed cell surfaces. In: *Control of Proliferation in Animal Cells*, edited by B. Clarkson and R. Baserga, pp. 251–270. New York: Cold Spring Harbor Laboratory.

Nicolson, G. L. (1974*b*): Cell-contact and transformation-induced changes in the dynamic organization of normal and neoplastic cell plasma membranes and their role in lectin-mediated toxicity toward tumor cells. In: *Biology and Chemistry of Eucaryotic Cell Surfaces, Proceedings of the Sixth Miami Winter Symposium*, edited by E. Y. C. Lee and E. E. Smith, pp. 103–124. New York: Academic Press.

Nicolson, G. L. (1974*c*): The interactions of lectins with animal cell surfaces. *Int. Rev. Cytol.*, 39:89–190.

Nicolson, G. L., and Lacorbiere, M. (1973): Cell contact-dependent increase in membrane D-galactopyranosyl-like residues on normal, but not virus-or spontaneously-transformed murine fibroblasts. *Proc. Nat. Acad. Sci.*, 70:1672–1676.

Nicolson, G. L., Marchesi, V. T., and Singer, S. J. (1971): The localization of spectrin on the inner surface of human red blood cell membranes by ferritin-conjugated antibodies. *J. Cell Biol.*, 51:265–272.

Nicolson, G. L., and Painter, R. G. (1973): Anionic sites of human erythrocyte membranes. II. Antispectrin-induced transmembrane aggregation of the binding sites for positively charged colloidal particles. *J. Cell Biol.*, 59:395–406.

Nicolson, G. L., and Yanagimachi, R. (1972): Terminal saccharides on sperm plasma membranes: Identification by specific agglutinins. *Science,* 177:276–279.

Nicolson, G. L., and Yanagimachi, R. (1974): Mobility and the restriction of mobility of plasma membrane lectin-binding components. *Science,* 184:1294–1296.

Overath, P., Hill, F. F., and Lamnek-Hirsch, I. (1971): Biogenesis of *E. coli* membrane: Evidence for randomization of lipid phase. *Nature New Biol.*, 234:264–267.

Phillips, M. C., Ladbrooke, B. D., and Chapman, D. (1970): *Biochim. Biophys. Acta,* 196:35.

Raetz, C. R. H., and Kennedy, E. P. (1972): The association of phosphatidylserine synthetase with ribosomes in extracts of *Escherichia coli. J. Biol. Chem.,* 247:2008–2014.

Raff, M. C., and de Petris, S. (1973): Movement of lymphocyte surface antigens and receptors: The fluid nature of the lymphocyte plasma membrane and its immunological significance. *Fed. Proc.,* 32:48–54.

Rapp, H. J., and Borsos, T. (1970): *Molecular Basis of Complement Action.* New York: Appleton-Century-Crofts.

Rittenhouse, H. G., and Fox, C. F. (1974): Concanavalin A mediated hemagglutination and binding properties of LM cells. *Biochem. Biophys. Res. Commun.,* 57:323–331.

Rittenhouse, H. G., Williams, R. E., and Fox, C. F. (1974*a*): *J. Supramol. Struct. (in press).*

Rittenhouse, H. G., Williams, R. E., Wisnieski, B. J., and Fox, C. F. (1974*b*): Alterations of characteristic temperatures for lectin interactions in LM cells with altered lipid composition. *Biochem. Biophys. Res. Commun.,* 58:222–228.

Robbins, P. W., and Macpherson, I. A. (1971): Glycolipid synthesis in normal and transformed animal cells. *Proc. Roy. Soc. B,* 177:49–58.

Rosenblith, J. Z., Ukena, T. E., Yin, H. H., Berlin, R. D., and Karnovsky, M. J. (1973): A comparative evaluation of the distribution of concanavalin A-binding sites on the surfaces of normal, virally-transformed, and protease-treated fibroblasts. *Proc. Nat. Acad. Sci.,* 70:1625–1629.

Scandella, C. J., Devaux, P., and McConnell, H. M. (1972): Rapid lateral diffusion of phospholipids in rabbit sarcoplasmic reticulum. *Proc. Nat. Acad. Sci.,* 69:2056–2060.

Schairer, H. U., and Overath, P. (1969): Lipids containing *trans*-unsaturated fatty acids change the temperature characteristic of thiomethylgalactoside accumulation in *Escherichia coli. J. Mol. Biol.,* 44:209–214.

Segrest, J. P., Kahane, I., Jackson, R. L., and Marchesi, V. T. (1973): Major glycoprotein of the human erythrocyte membrane: Evidence for an amphipathic molecular structure. *Arch. Biochem. Biophys.,* 155:167–183.

Shelanski, M. L., and Taylor, E. W. (1968): Properties of the protein subunit of central-pair and outer-doublet microtubules of sea urchin flagella. *J. Cell Biol.*, 38:304–315.

Shimshik, E. J., Kleemann, W., Hubbell, W. L., and McConnell, H. M. (1973): Lateral phase separations in membranes. *J. Supramol. Struct.*, 1:285–294.

Shimshick, E. J., and McConnell, H. M. (1973a): Lateral phase separation in phospholipid membranes. *Biochemistry*, 12:2351–2360.

Shimshick, E. J., and McConnell, H. M. (1973b): Lateral phase separations in binary mixtures of cholesterol and phospholipids. *Biochem. Biophys. Res. Commun.*, 53:446–451.

Singer, S. J., and Nicolson, G. L. (1971): The structure and chemistry of mammalian cell membranes. *Amer. J. Pathol.*, 65:427–438.

Taupin, C., and McConnell, H. M. (1972): Membrane fusion. In: *Mitochondria: Biogenesis and Bioenergetics. Biomembranes: Molecular Arrangements and Transport Mechanisms. Volume 28.* Federation of European Biochemical Societies, Eighth Meeting, Amsterdam, 1972, pp. 219–229. Amsterdam: North Holland/American Elsevier.

Taylor, R. B., Duffus, W. P., Raff, M. C., and de Petris, S. (1971): Redistribution and pinocytosis of lymphocyte surface immunoglobulin molecules induced by anti-immunoglobulin antibody. *Nature New Biol.*, 233:225–229.

Tourtellotte, M. E., Branton, D., and Keith, A. (1970): Membrane structure: Spin labeling and freeze etching of *Mycoplasma laidlawii*. *Proc. Nat Acad Sci.*, 66:909–916.

Träuble, H., and Sackmann, E. (1972): Studies of the crystalline-liquid crystalline phase transection of lipid model membranes. III. Structure of a steroid-lecithin system below and above the lipid phase transition. *S. Amer. Chem. Soc.*, 94:4499–4510.

Tsukagoshi, N., Fielding, P., and Fox, C. F. (1971): Membrane assembly in *Escherichia coli*. I. Segregation of preformed and newly formed membrane into daughter cells. *Biochem. Biophys. Res. Commun.*, 44:497–502.

Tsukagoshi, N., and Fox, C. F. (1973a): Abortive assembly of the lactose transport system in *Escherichia coli. Biochemistry*, 12:2816–2822.

Tsukagoshi, N., and Fox, C. F. (1973b): Transport system assembly and the mobility of membrane lipids on *Escherichia coli. Biochemistry*, 12:2822–2829.

Unanue, E. R., Perkins, W. D., and Karnovsky, M. J. (1972): Endocytosis by lymphocytes of complexes of anti-Ig with membrane-bound Ig[1]. *J. Immunol.*, 108:569–576.

Ververgaert, P. H. J., Elbers, P. F., Luitingh, A. J., and van den Berg, H. J. (1972): *Cytobiology*, 6:86.

Ververgaert, P. H. J. Th., Verkleij., J. J., Verhoeven, J. J., and Elbers, P. F. (1973): Sprayfreezing of liposomes. *Biochim. Biophys. Acta*, 311:651–654.

Williams, R. E., Wisnieski, B. J., Rittenhouse, H. G., and Fox, C. F. (1974): Utilization of fatty acid supplements by cultured animal cells. *Biochemistry*, 13:1969–1977.

Wilson, G., Rose, S. P., and Fox, C. F. (1970): The effect of membrane lipid unsaturation on glycoside transport. *Biochem. Biophys. Res. Commun.*, 38:617–623.

Winzler, R. (1969): In: *The Red Cell Membrane: Structure and Function,* edited by G. A. Jamieson and T. J. Greenwalt, pp. 157–171. Philadelphia: Lippincott.

Winzler, R. (1970): Carbohydrates in cell surfaces. *Int. Rev. Cytol.*, 29:77–125.

Wisnieski, B. J., Williams, R. E., and Fox, C. F. (1973): Manipulation of fatty acid composition in animal cells grown in culture. *Proc. Nat. Acad. Sci.*, 70:3669–3673.

Yahara, I., and Edelman, G. M. (1972): Restriction of the mobility of lymphocyte immunoglobulin receptors by concanavalin A. *Proc. Nat. Acad. Sci.*, 69:608–612.

Yanagimachi, R., Noda, Y. D., Fujimoto, M., and Nicolson, G. L. (1972): The distribution of negative surface charges on mammalian spermatozoa. *Amer. J. Anat.*, 135:497–520.

Yin, H. H., Ukena, T. E., and Berlin, R. D. (1972): Effect of colchicine, colcemid, and vinblastine on the agglutination, by concanavalin A, of transformed cells. *Science*, 178:867–868.

Functional Linkage in Biomolecular Systems, edited by
F. O. Schmitt, D. M. Schneider, and D. M. Crothers.
Raven Press, New York © 1975.

Chapter 6

Linkage in Transmembrane Transport

THERMODYNAMIC AND KINETIC ANALYSIS OF FUNCTIONAL
LINKAGE IN TRANSMEMBRANE TRANSPORT:

Robert Blumenthal

Blumenthal presented two examples of the application of irreversible thermodynamics to the analysis of "functional linkage." The first was based on a linearized formalism originally developed by Onsager (1931) for chemical reactions and extended to membrane transport by Staverman (1951), Schlögl (1956), Kedem and Katchalsky (1958), and many others (see Katchalsky and Curran, 1965). The second was an extension of chemodiffusional coupling to the nonlinear range, which gives rise to dynamic patterns. The latter approach originated in a paper by Türing (1952) on the chemical basis of morphogenesis, and has been discussed extensively by Gmitro and Scriven (1966), Prigogine (1969), and Katchalsky (see Katchalsky, Rowland, and Blumenthal, 1974).

Chemodiffusional Coupling in the Linear Range

If a chemical reaction is constrained to occur within an asymmetric structure—for example, by the presence of bound or otherwise trapped enzyme—it becomes possible to couple the reaction to the flow of one or more solutes or to the flow of electric current. Such a system has been devised by Blumenthal, Caplan, and Kedem (1967), and functions as a model in which transport can be "driven" by a chemical reaction. The processes involved are in this respect analogous to active transport, although the molecular mechanisms may be quite different from those that occur in nature. The simple arrangement that has been studied is a composite membrane consisting of two synthetic ion-exchange membranes having opposite fixed charge, separated by an intermediate layer of solution containing the enzyme papain, with two large outside chambers that can be regarded as infinite reservoirs. The reaction-diffusion scheme is shown in Fig. 1.

In this system, the uncharged substrate (N-acetyl-L-glutamic acid diamide) diffuses freely across the membrane, whereas the hydrolysis product (ammonium salt of N-acetyl-L-glutamine) is charged and will therefore be retained by the fixed-charge cation- and anion-exchange membranes (in-

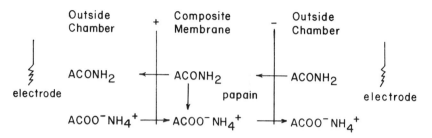

FIG. 1. Reaction-diffusion scheme. The two ion-exchange membranes are separated by a solution containing the enzyme papain, which catalyzes the hydrolysis of N-acetyl-L-glutamic acid diamide (A stands for $NH_2CO(CH_2)_2(CH_3(ONH)CH-)$ to the ammonium salt of N-acetyl-L-glutamine.

dicated by + and −, respectively in Fig. 1). This produces a potential difference that can be measured by the introduction of electrodes. It can readily be seen that the splitting of uncharged molecules within the sandwiched layer gives rise to an electrical potential even though *identical* electrodes are introduced into *identical* solutions on either side. Current can be drawn from the system when the electrodes are connected, and in this sense the model is an enzymatic fuel cell.

In the stationary state, the system is determined by two thermodynamic forces, the electrical potential (E) and the free energy of the reaction (ΔG_r), and two conjugate flows, the electric current (I) and the rate of the reaction (J_r), respectively; these are represented by equation (1):

$$E = R_{11}I + R_{12}J_r$$
$$\Delta G_r = R_{21}I + R_{22}J_r \tag{1}$$

The forces are related to their conjugate flows through the straight coefficients R_{11} and R_{22}, which are essentially resistences to ion flow and reaction flow, respectively. As the result of stationary-state coupling, the electric potential is related to the rate of reaction by the cross-coefficient R_{12}; that is, an electrical potential can be built up in the absence of current when the reaction is proceeding, and conversely, the free energy is related to the electrical current by the cross-coefficient R_{21}.

In order to test the Onsager reciprocity relationship, which requires that $R_{12} = R_{21}$ in equation (1), Blumenthal et al. (1967) carried out two independent sets of measurements on their model active transport system.

When given values for the external free energy of the reaction (ΔG_r) were set by fixing the external concentrations of substrate and product and by subsequently measuring the electrical potential to which the system built up at zero current, the relationship between the steady-state electrical potential and the free energy of the reaction is linear over the experimental range of free energies up to 3 kcal/mole (Fig. 2a). From equation (1) it can be seen that the slope represents $(E/\Delta G_r)_{I=0} = R_{12}/R_{22}$.

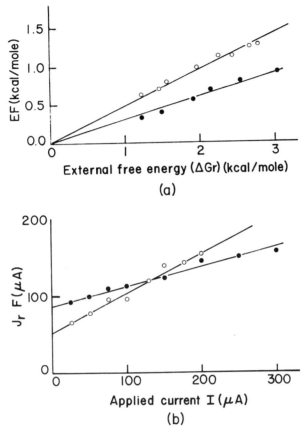

FIG. 2. Behavior of a model active transport system (see text). (a) Steady-state reaction flow versus electrical current at a given free energy of 2.6 kcal/mole. The open and filled circles represent the same membranes for the two sets of experiments, respectively. The electrical potential and the reaction flow multiplied by the Faraday constant (*F*) yield the dimensions corresponding to the independent variables (ΔG_r and *I*, respectively). After Blumenthal et al. (1967).

When the free energy of the reaction was held constant and the influence of a constant electric current on the rate of reaction was monitored, the relationship between the reaction rate and electrical current was linear over a wide range (Fig. 2*b*). From equation (1) it is seen that the slope represents $-(\delta J_r/\delta I)_{\Delta G_r} = R_{21}/R_{22}$. Equality of the slopes in the two sets of experiments on the same membrane established the validity of the Onsager reciprocity relationship over a wide experimental range of free energies. This is the first case in which the Onsager reciprocity relationship was tested for the coupling of a chemical reaction to a vectorial flow.

The approach outlined by the model study of Blumenthal et al. (1967) has since been applied to an analysis of the energetics of active sodium transport in frog skin (Vieira, Caplan, and Essig, 1972) and to the mechanism of energy-dependent ion transport in mitochondria (Rottenberg, 1973a). The application of nonequilibrium thermodynamics to bioenergetics has been reviewed by Caplan (1971).

The nonequilibrium thermodynamic analysis of coupled flows is based on linear relationships between the forces and flows, as shown in equation (1). Theoretically, such linear relationships obtain only in a region close to equilibrium. Experimentally, however, linearity can be maintained in a region further away from equilibrium than expected by considering the theoretical relation between reaction rate and the free energy of the reaction (Blumenthal et al., 1967; Caplan, 1971, Vieira et al., 1972; Rottenberg, 1973b).

Although linear irreversible thermodynamics seems adequate for the description of phenomenological flows, it is extremely useful to consider nonlinear relationships between forces and flows; these arise in many biological systems, such as excitable membranes, and broaden a living cell's repertoire of regulatory controls.

Linkage of Nonlinear Flows

Excitable membranes exhibit a repertoire of nonlinear regenerative phenomena, including the initiation and propagation of a nerve impulse, sustained oscillations, and multiple steady-state transitions, that is, long-lasting all-or-none responses to small stimuli. In an excitable membrane, a small stimulus applied to a few localized points on the membrane surface produces a global response over a large portion of the membrane. The response of an excitable membrane to an electrical or nonelectrical stimulus is usually expressed in terms of a membrane potential or current. However, membrane excitability need not be limited to electrical events; it may also be expressed in terms of the flow and chemical potential difference of a transported species across a membrane (Blumenthal, Changeux, and Lefever, 1970). Propagation may occur by means of "chemical waves" over the membrane surface, such as those observed in a purely artificial system by Zaikin and Zhabotinsky (1970; see also Winfree, 1974).

Several observations suggest that such chemical waves do exist in biological systems. Coleman, Coleman, Griffin, Weltman, and Chapman (1972) observed a series of self-propagating waves in chicken muscle fibers developing in culture. Under phase contrast, these appeared as wide light bands at intervals of 10 μm, and traveled at speeds of 60 μm/sec. They are not accompanied by changes in membrane potential. The underlying mechanism might be a regenerative calcium release-uptake mechanism, such as that described by Lehninger for the mitochondrion. Another example is that of bacterial taxis, in which an excited state induced by the interaction of light or a chemical agent with a membrane receptor is transmitted to locomotor areas to produce a coordinated motor response (see Chapter 13). The phototactic behaviour of *Rhodospirillum rubrum* (Clayton, 1958) has many properties in common with nerve excitability, including "all-or-none" responses to stimuli, accommodation refractiveness, rhythmicity, reciprocity of strength and duration, and summation of subliminal stimuli. The transmission mechanism appears to be mediated by a transient concentration wave of a metabolite (Clayton, 1958). A similar transmission mechanism might operate between the receptor site and the flagella of bacteria. Because chemotaxis can occur under widely different ionic conditions, and even in distilled water (see Adler, Chapter 13), the signal is unlikely to be transmitted by an electrical spike generating mechanism. The attachment of colicin E_1 to membranes of *E. coli* also causes a reversible change at the receptor site that spreads over the entire membrane (see Singer, Chapter 4).

Other manifestations of excitable membranes are also found in nonelectrical systems, including multiple steady-state transitions and sustained oscillations. Such processes include the response of cellular cyclic AMP levels to a transient hormone signal (see Chapter 9), state changes in steady-state oxidation-reduction flows in the respiratory control of mitochondria that can be induced by ADP, inorganic phosphate, oxygen, or substrate (see Lehninger, Chapter 7) and the release of calcium from the sarcoplasmic reticulum of muscle cells in response to calcium (see Chapter 14). With regard to sustained nonelectrical oscillations, membrane transport has been suggested to be the controlling pacemaker of glycolysis (Becker and Betz, 1972), and periodic waves of cyclic AMP are released by *Dictyostelium discoideum* during aggregation and morphogenesis (Robertson, Drage, and Cohen, 1971). In the latter case, the membrane is certain to play a role in the oscillatory mechanism, because the cyclic AMP system is membrane-bound (see Rodbell, Chapter 9).

Excitable membrane phenomena have been related to a highly cooperative membrane structure (Adam, 1968; Tasaki, 1968; Blumenthal et al., 1970; Hill and Chen, 1970). However, recent observations concerning membrane structure (see Singer, Chapter 4) have demonstrated the bilayer nature of membranes, and have ruled out the earlier repeating lipoprotein subunit model. Thus, cooperative processes within membranes do not appear to result from a repetitive membrane structure. Electrical excitability may have its physical basis in voltage-dependent ionic channels (Hille, 1970). These are sparsely distributed over the membrane surface (10–100 channels/μm^2), and are believed to be single discrete units (Ehrenstein, Blumenthal, Latorre, and Lecar, 1974) that respond to the electric field by a conformational change from "closed" to "open" states. No structural interaction between the ionic channels need be involved in the production of an action potential; in fact, structural cooperativity is inconsistent with the data for kinetics of voltage-dependent opening of potassium channels in the giant squid axon

(Hill and Chen, 1971). The all-or-none nature of the phenomenon depends on a delicate balance between the small threshold sodium current and the oppositely directed currents that drive the system back to the resting state.

Similar mechanisms are probably involved in the other apparently co-operative membrane phenomena mentioned above. Blumenthal (1973) has developed a model with sparsely distributed discrete oligomeric transport sites to demonstrate that chemical waves need not be mediated by a highly cooperative membrane structure, in contrast to the assumptions of a previous model (Blumenthal et al., 1970). In this current model, the "excitable" phenomena are the result of transitions in the steady-state solutions for the system of nonlinear flow equations. The structural changes of the membrane that cause these nonlinearities are very slight, and are probably not detectable by presently known physical techniques. In the model of Blumenthal et al. (1970), membrane transport mediated by transport units arranged in an infinite lattice exhibited negative slope permeability and multiple steady-state transitions. These same phenomena could be reproduced by sparsely distributed discrete oligomeric transport sites. The oligomeric transport model can also generate limit cycle oscillations, pattern formation of the transported species on the membrane surface, and chemical wave propagation. The model is developed for a system of passive facilitated transport.

The Model

The membrane proteins that mediate transport are assumed to be oligomers, that is, to consist of a number (n) of subunits (Fig. 3). The oligomer is assumed to undergo a "concerted" conformational change (see Hammes, Chapter 2) from an inactive form to one that can bind and translocate the permeant.[1] Each subunit in the oligomer contains two specific recognition sites for the permeant, located on the inner and outer surfaces of the membrane. The translocation of the permeant from the inner to outer sites within a subunit occurs via a jump transition mechanism. If the arrangement of the oligomer in the membrane is asymmetrical, the inner and outer sites will not have identical dissociation constants, and the forward and backward intrasubunit transition rate constant will be different due to microscopic reversibility.

This model is "exclusive" (see Hammes, Chapter 2); that is, the inactive form does not bind the permeant.[1] In the absence of permeant, the equilibrium constant for the conformational change between the inactive and active form of the oligomer is 10,000; that is, the oligomer is predominantly inactive. The binding of permeant shifts the conformational equilibrium to the active form and thus activates the transport process. The

---

[1] The exclusive, concerted model was chosen for its simplicity. The same conclusions are also valid for more general sequential cooperative models (see Chapter 2).

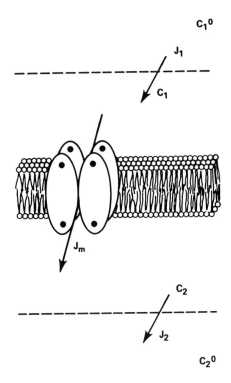

$c_1{}^0$

J_1

C_1

J_m

FIG. 3. A tetrameric transport protein embedded in a lipid matrix. J_m is the tetramer-mediated flow, J_1 and J_2 are exchange flows or enzymatic turnover, C_1 and C_2 are local concentrations of transported species in the neighborhood of the membrane, and $C_1{}^0$ and $C_2{}^0$ are fixed concentrations of the transported species in the bulk solution.

C_2

J_2

$c_2{}^0$

process is cooperative, since the binding to one subunit stabilizes the active conformation of n subunits. The total oligomer concentration in the membrane is indicated by M. The rate of transport (J_m) through the model membrane as a function of the local concentrations (C_1) and (C_2) of transported species adjacent to the membrane is given by

$$J_m = R(C_1 - C_2) \tag{2}$$

where the permeability rate constant R is a function of the local concentrations C_1 and C_2.

In Fig. 4, J_m and R are plotted as a function of C_1, with $n = 4$ (tetramer) for a constant $C_2 = 23$ mM. The parameter values given in the legend of Fig. 3 correspond to 100 transport sites/μm^2 and a forward rate constant of 1,000/sec. These values are in agreement with data on biological membranes concerning transport site density and carrier-mediated transport turnover number.

In the case represented in Fig. 3, however, the absolute value of the flow *increases* at decreasing absolute values of the concentration gradient up to $C_1 = 8$ mM. In other words, J_m exhibits a negative slope permeability characteristic.

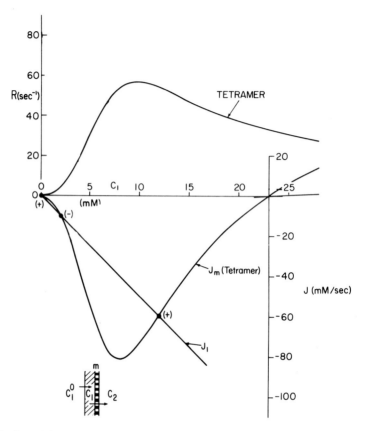

FIG. 4. J_m, R, and J_1 as a function of internal concentration C_1 at constant C_2 according to equations (1) and (2). In the inset the flows are shown: J_m is the flow through the membrane and J_1 from C_1^0 to C_1. Scales for the flows on the right, for the permeability on the left. Steady states are intersections between J_1 and J_m. Stability indicated by (+) and instability by (−).

Multiple Steady States

If C_1 is the concentration of transported species in an unstirred layer adjacent to the membrane, its level will change due to the oligomer-mediated flow J_m and to an exchange flow (j_1) between the unstirred layer and the bulk solution (see inset, Fig. 3). The latter flow is given by

$$J_1 = P_1(C_1^0 - C_1) \tag{3}$$

where C_1^0 is the concentration in the bulk solution and P_1 is the rate constant for the exchange.

The rate of change in the unstirred layer is given by

$$\frac{dC_1}{dt} = -J_m + J_1 \tag{4a}$$

and at steady state

$$J_m^s - J_1^s = 0 \tag{4b}$$

where the superscripts indicate steady state.

For the particular parameter values of Fig. 4, equation (4b) yields three solutions for C_1^s, given by the three intersections of J_m and J_1 in Fig. 4, the "singular" points. The stability of the steady state can be tested by linearizing equation (4a) at the singularity, reexpressing the original equations in terms of fluctuations, and showing that the perturbations grow in time.

This system will be unstable if the eigenvalue is positive. As shown in Fig. 4, this occurs for the center singularity indicated by (−). The other two singularities, indicated by (+), yield negative eigenvalues, and the steady states at those points are therefore stable.

The model thus acts as a bistable trigger or switch that can be set off by a transient signal (hormone, neurotransmitter). For example, the binding of a hormone to its receptor stimulates adenylate cyclase, producing a high level of cyclic AMP in the cell. Removal of the hormone would in principle return the adenylate cyclase activity to its basal level and decrease the cellular concentration of cyclic AMP. In this model, however, the cellular cyclic AMP concentration remains high after removal of the hormone, because the system is "switched" to a new stable steady state.

Transport mediated by discrete oligomeric units that undergo cooperative conformational transitions thus exhibits a negative slope permeability characteristic. The system displays multiple steady-state transitions when such a nonlinear membrane transport process is kinetically coupled to rate processes in the unstirred layers adjacent to the membrane—such as diffusion or enzymatic conversion. This analysis has been carried further to show that under certain conditions the system exhibits action potential-like overshoots in metabolite concentration levels and limit cycle oscillations (Blumenthal, 1974). Moreover, when the transported species undergoes two-dimensional lateral diffusion over the membrane surface (Adam and Delbrück, 1968), the system exhibits spatial pattern formation over the membrane surface and chemical wave propagation.

Applications to Membrane Dynamics

In this model, "messenger" molecules transmit information over a membrane surface by generating a chemical wave, rather than by two-dimensional random diffusion, as proposed by Adam and Delbrück (1968). The messenger might be a water-soluble substance such as calcium, cyclic AMP, or an uncharged metabolite. In the latter case, it would be difficult to detect a chemical wave mechanism. If it can be shown that a particular metabolite exhibits a negative slope permeability, then its generation of a chemical wave is a real possibility.

The messenger might also be the membrane phospholipid, which has been shown to undergo rapid lateral diffusion over the membrane surface (see McConnell, Chapter 5). However, random diffusion does not seem to be an adequate mechanism for information transmission, because it is an equilibrium situation and a small perturbation will not produce a global effect. Alternatively, Träuble (Chapter 3) has suggested that phase transitions of the phospholipid are involved in excitable membrane phenomena. This seems unlikely, because the excitable phenomena could then occur only in a narrow temperature range close to the phase-transition temperature of the membrane phospholipid. However, electrical excitability is maintained in the squid axon over a wide range of temperatures.

One alternative to the random diffusion or phase transition of lipids is their involvement in "pressure" waves (Singer, 1971), local areas of transient lipid compression-decompression that are transmitted through the membrane and connected with its "breathing" motions. The mechanism for such pressure waves immediately follows from the model, if the transported species is a certain membrane phospholipid and C_1 and C_2 are concentrations of that lipid on the two sides *in* the bilayer. J_m then represents the rate of mediated phospholipid translocation by a putative flip-flop enzyme, J_1 the rate of incorporation of lipids into the bilayer from the cytoplasmic side, possibly mediated by a phospholipid exchange protein (see Van Deenen, Chapter 4), and J_2 the breakdown of the phospholipid by an external phospholipase. Membrane structure could then be subject to a much more subtle control mechanism than expected from equilibrium considerations.

LINKAGE EFFECTS ON TRANSMEMBRANE MOVEMENTS:

Jared M. Diamond

Diamond described several ways in which transmembrane fluxes of solute are linked with other solute fluxes (cf. phenomenological treatment by Blumenthal in the preceding section) and with membrane structure.

Varying the hydrogen ion concentration alters ionic movements across biological membranes in several ways (cf. discussion of pH effects by Lehninger in Chapter 7). First, some biological membranes behave as ion exchangers in which the concentration of permeating ions is a function of the pH-controlled degree of dissociation of acidic or basic groups in the membrane (Wright and Diamond, 1968). Second, H^+ similarly controls the degree of dissociation of surface charges, which skew ion concentrations in the aqueous phase within a few Debye lengths of the membrane and hence

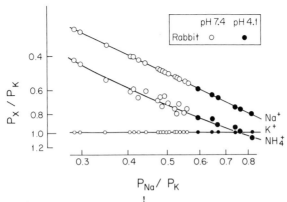

FIG. 5. NH_4^+, Na^+, and K^+ "selectivity isotherms" for ion permeation across junctional membranes of rabbit gall bladder. This graph demonstrates that the permeabilities of K^+, Na^+, and NH_4^+ are controlled by the same electrostatic forces, and that these forces vary between membranes from different animals and as a function of pH. The permeabilities of three ions were determined by an electrical method based on biionic potentials. The abscissa gives P_{Na}/P_K values measured in the gall bladders of each of 20 individual rabbits, while the ordinate gives P_X/P_K values in the same gallbladder, where X may be either NH_4^+, Na^+, or K^+. The scales are logarithmic. Thus, sets of permeability coefficients are determined for the three ions in a single animal. The K^+ points automatically fall along the horizontal line $P_X/P_K = 1.0$, and the Na^+ points automatically fall along the line of identity. Note that the NH_4^+ points cluster closely about the second-order polynomial fitted through them by least mean squares, the NH_4^+ isotherm. That this is the case, rather than that the NH_4^+ points scatter at random, means that P_{NH4}/P_K and P_{Na}/P_K are closely correlated (e.g., because both are determined by the same physical variable). Open and filled circles were measured at pH 7.4 and 4.1, respectively. From Moreno and Diamond, 1974.

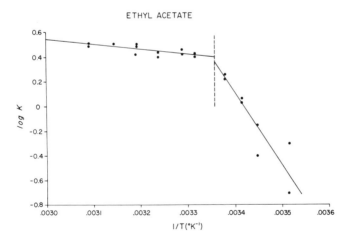

FIG. 6. Experimental measurements of partition coefficients (ordinate, log K) for the solute ethyl acetate between dimyristoyl lecithin liposomes and water, as a function of temperature (abscissa, $1/T$ in reciprocal degrees Kelvin). The slope gives the enthalpy of partition. The dashed line is the phase-transition temperature of this lecithin. Note that as one "freezes" lecithin (i.e., moves to the right across the transition), the slope (enthalpy of partition) becomes much steeper, and there is a modest jump downward in K corresponding to freezing out of solute. From Katz and Diamond, 1974.

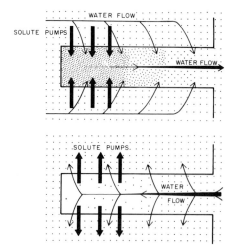

FIG. 7. Example of how membrane geometry affects linkage of transmembrane fluxes: the standing-gradient flow systems of epithelia. Epithelia are sheets of cells (as in the intestine, kidney, liver, etc.) separated by long and narrow lateral intercellular spaces terminated at one end (left in the figure) by so-called tight junctions. Because of the geometry of these spaces, active solute transport into the spaces is osmotically coupled to water transport. The channels of epithelia are oriented either "forward" (above: water flow toward the open end) or "backward" (water flow into the open end). The density of dots indicates the solute concentration. Forward operation (top): solute is actively transported into the channel across its walls, making the channel fluid hypertonic. As solute diffuses down its concentration gradient toward the open mouth, more and more water enters the channel across its walls due to the osmotic gradient. In the steady state a standing osmotic gradient will be maintained in the channel by active solute transport, with the osmolarity decreasing progressively from the closed end to the open end; and a fluid of fixed osmolarity (isotonic or hypertonic, depending upon the values of such parameters as radius, length, and water permeability) will constantly emerge from the mouth. Backward operation (bottom): solute is actively transported out of the channel across its walls, making the channel fluid hypotonic. As solute diffuses down its concentration gradient toward the closed end, more and more water leaves the channel across its walls owing to the osmotic gradient. In the steady state a standing osmotic gradient will be maintained in the channel by active solute transport, with the osmolarity decreasing progressively from the open end to the closed end; and a fluid of fixed osmolarity (isotonic or hypertonic, depending upon the parameters of the system) will constantly enter the channel mouth and be secreted across its walls. Solute pumps are depicted only at the bottom of the channels for illustrative purposes, but may have different distributions along the channel. From Diamond and Bossert, 1968.

within the membrane itself (McLaughlin, Szabo, Eisenman, and Ciani, 1970). Finally, H^+ also alters permeability ratios of other cations. For instance, Fig. 5 shows that a shift to a more acidic pH increases both the Na^+/K^+ and NH_4^+/K^+ permeability ratios across gall bladder tight junctions. These changes in selectivity result from changes in the partial charge of membrane sites that bind ions and hence in electrostatic binding forces (Eisenman, 1962; Moreno and Diamond, 1974).

A solute's membrane:water partition coefficient may be defined as the equilibrium ratio of the solute's concentration in the membrane to that in water. Measurements of the temperature dependence of partition yield the enthalpy of partition, as the slope of a graph of log K vs. $1/T$ (Fig. 6). This changes dramatically as a bilayer "freezes" (Dix, Diamond, and Kivelson, 1974; Katz and Diamond, 1974; see also discussions by McConnell (Chapter 5) and by Träuble (Chapter 3). For example, when a bilayer of dimyristoyl lecithin freezes, the (positive) enthalpy of partition for the solute ethyl acetate increases 15-fold, and the (positive) entropy of partition 12-fold. The enthalpy changes reflect the increased work needed to insert a solute molecule between closely packed hydrocarbon chains, while the entropy changes reflect the disruption of a highly ordered structure. Since the enthalpy and entropy changes affect K in opposite directions, the freezing out of solute at the transition temperature itself is modest.

Membrane configuration at the macroscopic level is also important in the coupling of transmembrane fluxes. For example, the geometrical arrangement of cell membranes in the cell sheets called epithelia results in an osmotic coupling between water movement and ATP-driven solute transport, such that 300 or more water molecules can be transported for each solute molecule (Fig. 7; Diamond and Bossert, 1968).

REFERENCES

Adam, G. (1968): *Z. Naturforsh.*, 23b:181.

Adam, G., and Delbrück, M. (1968): Reduction of dimensionality in biological diffusion processes. In: *Structural Chemistry and Molecular Biology,* edited by N. Davidson and A. Rich, pp. 198–215. San Francisco: W. H. Freeman and Co.

Becker, J.-U., and Betz, A. (1972): Membrane transport as controlling pacemaker of glycolysis in *Saccharomyces carlsbergensis. Biochim. Biophys. Acta*, 274:584–597.

Blumenthal, R. (1973): Dynamic patterns in active transport. *Israel J. Chem.*, 11:341–355.

Blumenthal, R. (1974): Instabilities, oscillations and chemical waves in an oligomeric model for membrane transport. *J. Theor. Biol. (in press).*

Blumenthal, R., Caplan, S. R., and Kedem, O. (1967): The coupling of an enzymatic reaction to transmembrane flow of electric current in a synthetic "active transport" system. *Biophys. J.,* 7:735–757.

Blumenthal, R., Changeux, J-P., and Lefever, R. (1970): Membrane excitability and dissipative instabilities. *J. Membr. Biol.,* 2:351–374.

Caplan, S. R. (1971): In: *Current Topics in Bioenergetics,* Vol. 4, edited by R. Sanadi, p. 1. New York: Academic Press.

Clayton, R. K. (1958): *Arch. Microbiol.,* 29:189.

Coleman, A. W., Coleman, J. R., Griffin, J. D., Weltman, J. K., and Chapman, K. M. (1972): Methylxanthine-induced escalation: A propagated wave phenomenon observed in skeletal muscle developing in culture. *Proc. Nat. Acad. Sci.,* 69:613–616.

Diamond, J. M., and Bossert, W. H. (1968): Functional consequences of ultrastructural geometry in "backwards" fluid-transporting epithelia. *J. Cell Biol.*, 37:694–702.

Dix, J. A., Diamond, J. M., and Kivelson, D. (1974): Translational diffusion coefficient and partition coefficient of a spin-labeled solute in lecithin bilayer membranes. *Proc. Nat. Acad. Sci.*, 71:474–478.

Dmitrov, J. I., and Scriven, L. E. (1966): A physicochemical basis for pattern and rhythm. In: *Intracellular Transport*, edited by K. B. Warren, pp. 221–225. New York: Academic Press.

Ehrenstein, G., Blumenthal, R., Latorre, R., and Lecar, H. (1974): *J. Gen. Physiol.*, 63:707.

Eisenman, G., (1962): Cation selective glass electrodes and their mode of operation. *Biophys. J.*, 2:259–323.

Hill, T. L., and Chen, Y. (1970): Cooperative effects in models of steady-state transport across membranes, I. *Proc. Nat. Acad. Sci.*, 65:1069–1076.

Hill, T. L., and Chen, Y. (1971): On the theory of ion transport across the nerve membrane, II. Potassium ion kinetics and cooperativity (with $x = 4$). *Proc. Nat. Acad. Sci.*, 68:1711–1715.

Hille, B. (1970): Ionic channels in nerve membranes. *Progr. Biophys. Mol. Biol.*, 21:1–32.

Katchalsky, A., and Curran, P. F. (1965): *Nonequilibrium Thermodynamics in Biophysics.* Cambridge, Mass.: Harvard University Press.

Katchalsky, A., Rowland, V., and Blumenthal, R. P. (1974): Dynamic Patterns of Brain Cell Assemblies. *Neurosci. Res. Prog. Bull.*, 12:1–187.

Katz, Y., and Diamond, J. M. (1974): Thermodynamic constants for non-electrolyte partition between dimyristoyl lecithin and water. *J. Membr. Biol.*, 17:101–120.

Kedem, O., and Katchalsky, A. (1958): Thermodynamic analysis of the permeability of biological membranes to non-electrolytes. *Biochim. Biophys. Acta*, 27:229–246.

McLaughlin, S. G. A., Szabo, G., Eisenman, G., and Ciani, S. M. (1970): Surface charge and the conductance of phospholipid membranes. *Proc. Nat. Acad. Sci.*, 67:1268–1275.

Moreno, J. H., and Diamond, J. M. (1974): Discrimination of monovalent inorganic cations by "tight" junctions of gall-bladder epithelium. *J. Membr. Biol.*, 15:277–318.

Onsager, L. (1931): Reciprocal relations in irreversible processes. I. *Phys. Rev.*, 37:408–426. Reciprocal relations in irreversible processes. II. *Phys. Rev.*, 38:2265–2279.

Prigogine, I. (1969): In: *Theoretical Physics and Biology*, edited by M. Marois, pp. 23–52. Amsterdam: North-Holland.

Robertson, A., Drage, D. J., and Cohen, M. H. (1971): Control of aggregation in *Dictyostelium discoideum* by an external periodic pulse of cyclic adenosine monophosphate. *Science*, 175:333–335.

Rottenberg, H. (1973a): The mechanism of energy-dependent ion transport in mitochondria. *J. Membr. Biol.*, 11:117–137.

Rottenberg, H. (1973b): The thermodynamic description of enzyme-catalyzed reactions. The linear relation between the reaction rate and the affinity. *Biophys. J.*, 13:503–511.

Schlögl, R. (1956): The significance of convection in transport processes across porous membranes. *Disc. Far. Soc.*, 21:46–52.

Singer, S. J. (1971): The molecular organization of biological membranes. In: *Structure and Function of Biological Membranes*, edited by L. Rothfield, pp. 145–222. New York: Academic Press.

Staverman, A. J. (1951): The theory of measurement of osmotic pressure. *Rec. Trav. Chim.*, 70:344–352.

Tasaki, I. (1968): *Nerve Excitation: A Macromolecular Approach.* Springfield, Ill.: Charles C Thomas.

Türing, A. M. (1952): The chemical basis of morphogenesis. *Phil. Trans. Roy. Soc. B*, 237:37–72.

Vieira, F. L., Caplan, S. R., and Essig, A. (1972a): Energetics of sodium transport in frog skin. I. Oxygen consumption in the short-circuited state. *J. Gen. Physiol.*, 59:60–76.

Winfree, A. (1974): Rotating chemical reactions. *Sci. Amer.*, 230:82–95.

Wright, E. M., and Diamond, J. M. (1968): Effects of pH and polyvalent cations on the selective permeability of gall-bladder epithelium to monovalent ions. *Biochim. Biophys. Acta*, 163:57–74.

Zaikin, A. N., and Zhabotinsky, A. M. (1970): Concentration wave propagation in two-dimensional liquid-phase self-oscillating system. *Nature*, 225:535–537.

Functional Linkage in Biomolecular Systems, edited by
F. O. Schmitt, D. M. Schneider, and D. M. Crothers.
Raven Press, New York © 1975.

LINKED FUNCTIONS IN BIOLOGICAL MEMBRANES

This section could be characterized as a theme and variations: The theme is the binding of a biodynamic ligand by a membrane-borne receptor which, through functional linkage, profoundly alters the function for which the organelle, cell, or tissue is differentiated; the variations are the receptor-effector complex characteristic of each case, of which four are considered in this section.

The binding of small amounts of ADP to the mitochondrial membrane, which represents a message that the store of the high-energy compound ATP is low and needs replenishment, shifts the entire organelle from a state of low activity to one in which a variety of metabolic processes are activated. This shift is the result of a highly cooperative structural change in the entire organelle, which alters the linkage between components of major metabolic pathways. State changes can also be induced by slight alterations in pH, similar to those shown in Chapter 3 to induce phase transitions in lipid bilayers. Calcium ions play a major role in the cooperative control of mitochondrial structure and function.

In the immune system, the binding of antigen molecules to specific cell surface receptors produces cell division by virtue of as yet unidentified linked reactions. The initial step in this complex series of events appears to be a disruption of the linkage between the membrane proteins and a colchicine-binding protein located immediately below the membrane surface.

Several steps in the series of reactions that intervene between the binding of certain hormone or neurotransmitter molecules at the surface of their target cells and intracellular effector processes have recently been clarified and are described in Chapter 9. The binding of certain hormones or transmitters alters the relationship between the receptor and adenylate cyclase so as to activate the cyclase enzyme, probably by inducing a conformational change in the receptor protein. The cyclic AMP produced by this activation in turn stimulates a series of cell-specific protein kinases, which then increase the phosphorylation of their substrates. Cell-specific kinases make it possible for a relatively small number of activators to elicit a variety of responses, determined by their preset enzyme composition.

The postsynaptic membrane of neurons that responds to the neurotransmitter acetylcholine (ACh) couples allosteric alterations in the receptor, produced by ACh binding, to the processes that control ionic transport across the neuronal or muscle membrane to produce depolarization; this in turn initiates an action potential wave in the axon or muscle fiber. This system is of particular interest because it is one of the few cases in which it has been possible thus far to isolate and characterize a receptor protein.

Functional Linkage in Biomolecular Systems, edited by
F. O. Schmitt, D. M. Schneider, and D. M. Crothers.
Raven Press, New York © 1975.

Chapter 7

Linked Transport and Binding Functions in the Mitochondrial Membrane

Albert L. Lehninger

The preceding chapters have considered linked functions and cooperativity in relatively simple macromolecular systems. In this chapter, these concepts are extended to a far more complex system, the inner mitochondrial membrane, in which a number of molecular events across and within the plane of the membrane are linked or coupled.

It is well known that mitochondria are the power plants of the cell, generating ATP at the expense of electron transport to oxygen. However, the full complexity of mitochondrial functions and activities is not generally appreciated. Recent research has shown that there is a complex set of transport processes and regulatory activities that are energetically coupled to electron transport in the mitochondrial membrane. These include the transmembrane transport of H^+ and K^+, the transport of various organic metabolites, conformational transitions of the mitochondrial membrane and matrix, and changes in membrane permeability. These events take place in the inner mitochondrial membrane, which is perhaps the most complex of all biological membranes, since it contains some 70 or more enzymes and transport systems.

When we consider large supramolecular systems at the level of organelles, it is not always possible to observe and quantitate cooperativity and the coupling of functions with the same criteria and measurements possible in simpler systems. Thus we cannot always produce nicely sigmoidal plots or calculate Hill coefficients with precision. Nevertheless, certain hallmarks of cooperativity are clearly evident in mitochondria and can be demonstrated at least semiquantitatively. This discussion assumes a more general and qualitative definition of cooperativity as a relationship between two or more functions or properties in which the occurrence of one event greatly increases the probability of others. It is also assumed that all-or-none phenomena are indicative of highly cooperative systems. Indeed, there are instances in which the binding of a relatively small number of ligand molecules to the mitochondrial membrane produces profound long-range effects over the entire membrane surface.

The mitochondrion consists of two membranes. The inner membrane, which invaginates into the mitochondrial matrix to form the cristae, is the

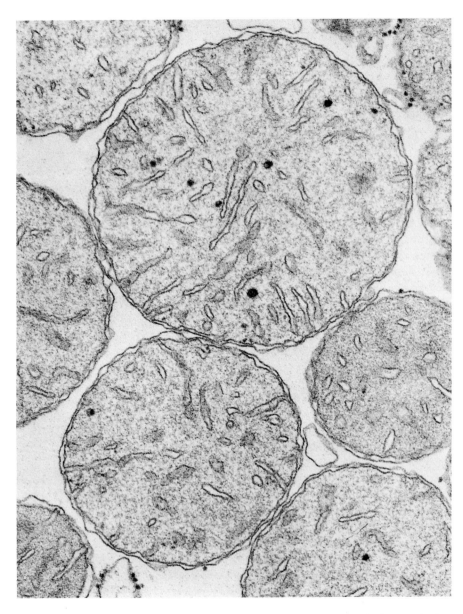

FIG. 1. Ultrastructural transitions of mitochondria. Mitochondria can exist in two physiologically important respiratory states. The orthodox state (*left*) is characteristic of state 4,
the "off" state of respiration, in which no ATP is produced, while the condensed state

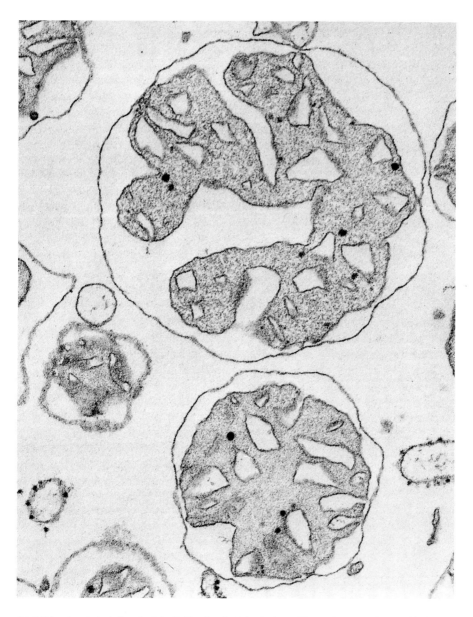

(*right*) is characteristic of state 3, the "on" state, induced by an increase in the ADP/ATP ratio. From Hackenbrock, 1968*a,b*.

true permeability barrier; the outer membrane is freely permeable even to rather large solute molecules.

The two mitochondrial membrane systems differ significantly in their chemical composition and physical properties. The outer membrane contains approximately 50% protein and 50% lipid, while the inner membrane contains 80% protein and only about 20% lipid. The latter is the site of the electron transport and energy-transducing systems. The inner membrane is chemically and functionally asymmetric and has a specific vectorial organization. It is intrinsically impermeable to H^+, OH^-, Cl^-, and most other simple anions and cations, but has a highly selective permeability for specific metabolites and certain mineral ions because of the presence of specific transport systems. Many of the metabolites and intermediates within the mitochondrial matrix are functionally distinct from their counterparts in the cytosol. Their compartmentation is reflected by large concentration differences between the cytoplasm and the matrix, which are the consequence of the activity of specific enzymes and transport systems in the inner membrane.

The mitochondrial matrix possesses a complete genetic apparatus, including a distinctive DNA and DNA polymerase, a set of enzymes—distinct from those of the nucleus—for making messenger RNA and certain transfer RNAs, and their own type of ribosomes, usually localized on the inner surface of the inner membrane. As in bacterial cells, a nuclear zone containing the single DNA molecule or chromosome can be observed in some types of mitochondria.

The mitochondrial matrix also contains a highly organized reticular network of protein; it is capable of undergoing a reversible aggregation-disaggregation process depending on the respiratory state of the mitochondrion. In the "idling" but energized respiratory state (state 4), in the absence of ADP as acceptor, the mitochondria show the "orthodox" conformation commonly pictured in textbooks (Fig. 1), in which the matrix proteins form a loose reticular network that is physically connected with the inner membrane (Hackenbrock, 1966, 1968*a,b*). However, when the mitochondria are stimulated to respire and phosphorylate by the addition of ADP (i.e., respiratory state 3), the entire matrix is transformed into the "condensed" state, in which the inner membrane is highly convoluted and the volume is reduced to about one-half its original size. This process greatly increases the protein concentration of the matrix, and there are profound differences in the properties and activity of certain enzymes and transport systems in these two respiratory states.

POSSIBLE MECHANISMS FOR THE TRANSDUCTION OF ELECTRICAL TO CHEMICAL ENERGY IN THE MITOCHONDRION

We shall first review the basic energy source and the mechanism of transduction of the energy of electron transport into the chemical energy of ATP. There are three major hypotheses for converting oxidation-reduction energy into ATP energy in mitochondria: the chemical, conformational, and chemiosmotic coupling hypotheses.

The chemical coupling hypothesis invokes the general mechanism of energy coupling found in most other metabolic pathways in the cell, which proceed by sequential reactions in which an intermediate common to two successive enzyme-catalyzed steps is the vehicle for the transfer of free energy from the first to the second reaction (Lehninger, 1964). This hypothesis requires a high-energy covalent intermediate that is formed by electron transport and then utilized to make ATP. This intermediate, if it exists, must have a free energy of hydrolysis of about -15 kcal mol^{-1}. No such intermediate has ever been detected or isolated, despite more than 25 years of search. This fact, as well as the fact that oxidative phosphorylation requires that the inner membrane be intact, is incompatible with the chemical coupling hypothesis.

The conformational coupling hypothesis (Boyer, Cross, and Momsen, 1973) postulates that free energy is transferred from the oxido-reduction to the synthesis of ATP via a conformational change in a macromolecule, presumably a protein. In this hypothesis, the vehicle for energy transfer is thought to be a number of relatively weak bonds in the protein, presumably hydrogen bonds and hydrophobic interactions rather than a single covalent bond as in the chemical coupling hypothesis. Although conformational or phase changes appear to occur in the inner membrane during electron transport, there is little concrete evidence to support the hypothesis that these changes are obligatory intermediate states responsible for energy transfer from electron transport to ATP formation.

The chemiosmotic hypothesis of Mitchell (1966, 1968) is today the best-supported mechanism. It proposes that the electron transport chain functions as a proton pump to generate a negative-inside electrochemical gradient of H$^+$ across the inner membrane. This gradient is proposed to be the vehicle (i.e., the intermediate high-energy state) for transfer of the energy of electron transport to the synthesis of ATP from ADP and phosphate by the action of a vectorial ATP-synthetase in the membrane. The inner membrane is further proposed to be impermeable to H$^+$ ions, a feature that is essential for chemiosmotic energy transduction.

It is now well established that the electron transport chain does have the capacity to function as a proton pump and that the inner membrane is impermeable to H$^+$. Moreover, ATP formation can occur only when the mitochondrial membrane is intact. Although it is clear that a proton gradient can in fact be generated across the inner membrane by electron transport and that this gradient can drive the formation of ATP from ADP and phosphate, it is not yet certain whether a proton gradient is an *obligatory* step in the transduction of electron transport energy into the chemical energy of ATP. It is still possible that the observed proton gradient is not an obligatory intermediate state but is the consequence of side reactions that

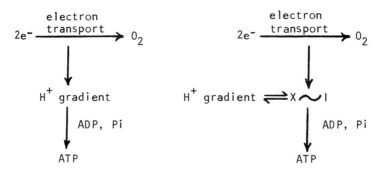

FIG. 2. The "mitochondriac's" dilemma (1973). The proton gradient generated by electron transport might be an obligatory intermediate in the generation of ATP (*a*), or it might lie on a side pathway (*b*).

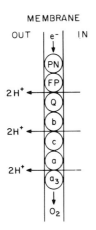

FIG. 3. The mitochondrion can function as a proton pump. At least two protons can be pumped at each of three energy-conserving sites in the electron transport chain.

are in equilibrium with a covalent high-energy intermediate generated by electron transport (Fig. 2). Most available evidence indicates that two H^+ ions are pumped at each of the three energy-conserving sites in the electron transport chain (Fig. 3), although some studies with mitochondria and chloroplasts have suggested that each of these sites may pump as many as four H^+.

TRANSPORT MECHANISMS IN MITOCHONDRIA

Mitochondria participate in many metabolic processes in addition to electron transport and oxidative phosphorylation, particularly in metabolically flexible tissues such as the liver (Lehninger, 1971). In such cells there is a constant flow of metabolites across the mitochondrial membrane in both directions, a flow that is constantly regulated. For example, citrate generated by the tricarboxylic acid cycle within the mitochondrion must pass into the cytoplasm to be utilized as a precursor of acetyl-CoA for extra-mitochondrial fatty acid synthesis. Similarly, malate generated within the mitochondrion is a precursor in extramitochondrial gluconeogenesis. More-over, many reactions of amino acid metabolism take place within the mitochondria; for example, glutamate enters the mitochondria to be deami-nated and α-ketoglutarate, the product of the deamination reaction, must leave. In addition, some enzyme systems, such as the urea cycle, are divided between the cytoplasm and the mitochondrial compartment. Of particular importance is the transport of Ca^{2+} across the mitochondrial membrane. Mitochondria help to maintain the delicately balanced, steady-state level of Ca^{2+} in the cell cytosol by energy-coupled segregation of Ca^{2+} and by a regulated, passive release (Fig. 4). This balance of Ca^{2+} between cytosol and mitochondria is involved in the regulation of many different Ca^{2+}-dependent activities in vertebrate cells (Lehninger, 1970). All these move-ments of ions and metabolites across the mitochondrial membrane are highly selective, highly integrated, and promoted by specific transport systems. At least a dozen different transport systems for specific metabolites have been demonstrated in the mitochondrial inner membrane (Fig. 5).

These transport systems also participate, jointly with allosteric regulation of metabolic cycles, in the control and compartmentation of metabolism. Allosteric mechanisms control a number of multienzyme systems within the mitochondrion and in the cytoplasm. Inside the mitochondrial matrix, feedback inhibition occurs at crucial points in the tricarboxylic acid (TCA) cycle (Fig. 6). ATP and NADH are feedback inhibitors of isocitrate de-hydrogenase, succinyl-CoA inhibits the formation of citrate from oxalo-acetate, and oxaloacetate is an inhibitor of succinate oxidation. Moreover, the pyruvate dehydrogenase complex in the matrix is also regulated through the steady-state levels of ATP and ADP in the mitochondria. These allo-

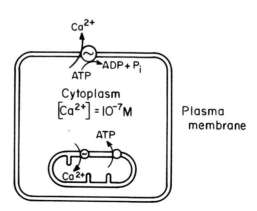

FIG. 4. The Ca^{2+} carrier system.

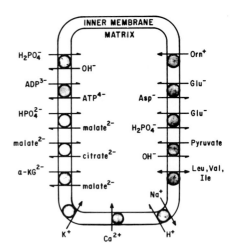

FIG. 5. Mitochondrial transport systems.

steric mechanisms thus control the flow of metabolites through the tricarboxylic acid cycle. Outside the mitochondria, in the cytosol, many different allosteric enzymes participate in regulation of glycolysis and various biosynthetic pathways.

Some of the allosteric effectors that modulate mitochondrial and cytoplasmic reactions may cross the mitochondrial membrane; their transport across the membrane may thus regulate events in both cell compartments. For example, the activity of phosphofructokinase in the cytosol is allosterically regulated by citrate and by ATP generated within the mitochondrion (Fig. 6). Conversely, some of the metabolites generated in the cytosol must enter the mitochondrion in their function as modulators of various enzymatic reactions in the matrix. We can therefore identify two levels of metabolic regulation by the mitochondrion. One is the set of classical allosteric mechanisms for regulation of the multienzyme systems that catalyze the tricarboxylic acid cycle within the mitochondrial compartment. The other is a set of mechanisms that regulate the rate of transport of metabolites and allosteric modulators across the membrane (Lehninger, 1971).

The membrane transport systems of the mitochondrion are highly integrated in their activity; they frequently show precise stoichiometric relationships. For example, in the urea cycle, which is divided between the mitochondria and cytosol, one molecule of citrulline must leave the mitochondrion for each ornithine molecule that enters from the cytosol (Gamble and Lehninger, 1973). Thus the mitochondrial membrane transport processes must often maintain precise stoichiometry between incoming and leaving metabolites to produce a smooth integration of those metabolic systems that are partitioned between the cytosol and mitochondria. We must therefore also inquire into the mechanisms by which the mitochondrial membrane

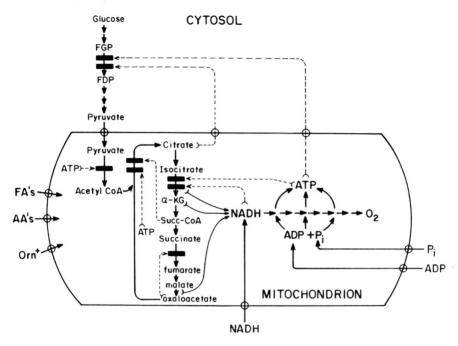

FIG. 6. Allosteric regulatory mechanisms within the TCA cycle. Feedback relationships are indicated by dashed lines.

transport systems are regulated so as to maintain the required stoichiometric relationships between the two major metabolic compartments of cells.

The mitochondrial transport systems (Fig. 5) can be subdivided into several classes. Some are uniport systems (Mitchell, 1967), which transport a molecule of a metabolite across the membrane without necessarily having to transport another in the reverse direction in exchange. The mitochondrial transport systems for K^+, Ca^{2+}, and ornithine$^+$ operate in this way; that for Ca^{2+} operates in both directions, while ornithine can be transported only into the mitochondrion. These are electrogenic systems.

The second class consists of antiport or exchange diffusion systems, which exchange one specific ion or metabolite for another. For example, a molecule of ADP that enters is exchanged for a molecule of ATP by the ADP-ATP translocase (Chappell, 1968; Klingenberg, 1970; Lehninger, 1971), while a molecule of phosphate is exchanged for one of malate (Chappell, 1968). Some of the antiport systems are electrogenic, such as the ADP-ATP system, which exchanges external ADP^{3-} for internal ATP^{4-} (Klingenberg, 1970). Other antiport systems are electrically neutral, such as the phosphate-hydroxide, phosphate-malate, and malate-citrate systems (Chappell, 1968; Lehninger, 1971).

All the transport systems shown in Fig. 5 are passive; none is directly coupled to ATP hydrolysis in the same way that the transport of Na^+ and K^+ is coupled to ATP hydrolysis by the classical Na^+,K^+-ATPase of the erythrocyte membrane. The passive transport systems of the mitochondria respond either to a concentration gradient of their ligands across the membrane, to a potential difference across the membrane, or, as will be shown later, to a pH gradient.

Some of the mitochondrial carrier systems have extremely high affinities for their ligands. For example, the mitochondrial Ca^{2+} carrier helps maintain the cytosol Ca^{2+} concentration at about 10^{-7} M against intramitochondrial concentrations of about 10^{-3} M Ca^{2+} (Fig. 4), a 10,000-fold gradient (Lehninger, 1970).

The membrane transport systems of mitochondria are genetically determined (Chappell, 1968; Lehninger, 1971). Mitochondria that serve a purely respiratory function, such as those in flight muscle of the adult blowfly, apparently possess only three transport systems, for pyruvate, for phosphate, and for ADP-ATP. In contrast, liver mitochondria contain over a dozen different transport systems, consonant with the much more complex metabolic activities of this organ.

All the different mitochondrial membrane transport systems are ultimately coupled to electron transport. The vehicle of coupling is the pH gradient generated by the electron transport chain (Fig. 3), which can be converted into a transmembrane electrical potential through the phosphate-hydroxide transport system (Fig. 7). This system makes possible the exchange of excess OH^- generated within the mitochondrion by electron transport for external $H_2PO_4^-$; as a result, the internal compartment becomes relatively electronegative in relation to the outside compartment (Chappell, 1968; Klingenberg, 1970; Lehninger, 1974). This transport system thus converts a pH gradient into a neutral (from the standpoint

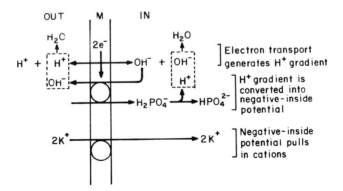

FIG. 7. The coupling of the H^+ gradient generated by electron transport to K^+ accumulation by the production of a negative-inside potential.

of pH) negative-inside potential gradient across the membrane, which can in turn be used to drive other transport activities. For example, the negative-inside potential can be used to transport cations such as K^+ into the matrix, thus relieving the electrical imbalance (Fig. 7). In the same way, inward transport of other cations such as Ca^{2+} and ornithine can be coupled to the negative-inside membrane potential generated by electron transport acting via the phosphate-hydroxide antiporter.

This negative-inside membrane potential can also be utilized to bring about inward transport of certain anions (Fig. 8). For example, malate^{2-} can be transported inward in exchange for HPO_4^{2-} by the dicarboxylate carrier. An internal accumulation of malate^{2-} can in turn cause an influx of citrate^{2-} via the tricarboxylate carrier, which promotes the exit of malate^{2-} in equimolar exchange with citrate^{2-} from outside (Chappell, 1968; Klingenberg, 1970; Lehninger, 1974).

Thus, all the transport systems of the mitochondrial membrane are integrated in their action by coupling of flows across the membrane, flows of either electric charge or mass. Ultimately, all transmembrane movements are energetically coupled to the proton gradient generated by electron transport. The phosphate-hydroxide antiporter is crucial to all aspects of metabolite transport by mitochondria (Lehninger, 1974), since it is the mediator for converting the primary pH gradient into a negative-inside membrane potential (Fig. 9).

The many different energy-dependent activities taking place in the mitochondrion do not compete equally for the respiratory energy generated by electron transport. The activity taking precedence over all others is the accumulation of Ca^{2+}, which can even preempt the proton gradient from being used for the phosphorylation of ADP (Lehninger, 1970). Oxidative phosphorylation has second priority, followed by the accumulation of certain anions and other activities such as reversed electron flow. These priorities appear to be controlled in part by the relative Michaelis constants

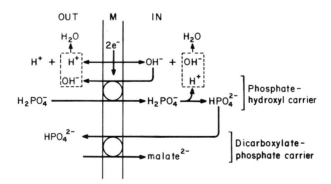

FIG. 8. Coupling of an anionic metabolite transport system to the proton pump.

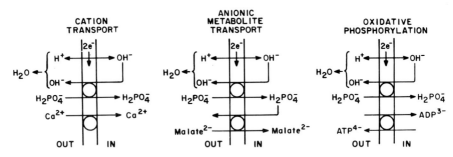

FIG. 9. The central role of the phosphate-hydroxyl antiport in transport processes coupled to the electron transport system.

or ligand affinities of the various transport systems. The carrier for Ca^{2+} has an extraordinarily high affinity, with a K_M of approximately 0.1 μM, that for ADP influx is about 2 μM, and the carriers for the transport of citrate and malate are in the range 100 to 500 μM (Chappell, 1968; Klingenberg, 1970; Lehninger, 1970, 1974). The coupling of transmembrane flows thus forms the basis of a highly integrated set of metabolite transport processes.

At least two of the mitochondrial transport systems, those for ADP and for Ca^{2+}, show evidence of cooperativity in their transport activity. The Ca^{2+} carrier shows a sigmoidal relationship between Ca^{2+} concentration and transmembrane transport (Bygrave, Reed, and Spencer, 1971). The ADP carrier has binding sites with different affinities for ADP on the outside and inside of the mitochondrial membrane (Heldt, Klingenberg, and Milovancev, 1972; Vignais, Vignais, Lauquin, and Morel, 1973). Some recent evidence suggests that ADP may act both as a transported ligand and as stimulatory modulator of ADP transport. Such adaptations apparently increase the efficiency of ADP-ATP exchange when rapid formation of ATP is required.

ULTRASTRUCTURAL AND CONFORMATIONAL TRANSITIONS IN MITOCHONDRIA AS A FUNCTION OF METABOLIC STATE

There is yet another level of linked functions in mitochondria. Respiring mitochondria undergo sharp transitions in their ultrastructure as a function of the external ATP/ADP ratio. When this ratio is high and there is no need for ATP synthesis, respiration is turned off and we have "idling" or state 4 respiration. When the rate of cytoplasmic ATP dephosphorylation increases, with a concomitant decrease in the cytoplasmic ATP/ADP ratio, respiration is turned on and we have "active" or state 3 respiration. The most extreme example of the difference in rates of states 3 and 4 respiration is the housefly,

in which the rate of respiration increases over 100-fold in the transition from
rest to flight.

As noted earlier, mitochondria exist in two conformational or ultrastructural states corresponding to these respiratory states (Fig. 10). The structure
corresponding to state 4 respiration is called the "orthodox" conformation.
In state 3 the inner compartment shrinks and the inner membrane folds
to yield the "condensed" configuration (Hackenbrock, 1966, 1968*a,b*).

There are a number of functional differences between these two states
of mitochondria. For example, the permeability of the inner membrane to
K^+ is much greater in state 4 than in state 3, in which K^+ is practically
impermeant in the absence of an ionophore (Hansford and Lehninger, 1972).
The inward transport of ornithine$^+$ cation is also greatly diminished in state 3
(Gamble and Lehninger, 1973).

Moreover, other experiments have shown that certain polar and nonpolar
groups on the mitochondrial membrane appear to undergo changes in
polarity during the state 4-state 3 transition, as indicated by fluorescent
probes (Azzi, 1969; Azzi, Chance, Radda, and Lee, 1969). Moreover, it
has also been shown that cooperative binding of small amounts of Ca^{2+}
to the membrane of state 4 mitochondria also causes a release of protons
from the membrane as respiration is stimulated (Azzi, 1969; Colonna,
Dell'Atone, and Azzone, 1970; Reynafarje and Lehninger, 1974*a,b*). This
has been called a "membrane Bohr effect," analogous to the decrease in
pK of certain protonated groups on the hemoglobin molecule caused by
cooperative oxygen binding.

Until recently, it was tacitly assumed that the ultrastructural transitions
of mitochondria from orthodox to condensed were a reflection of conformational transitions of the electron carrier molecules of the respiratory chains

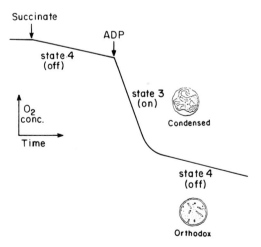

FIG. 10. The conformational states of liver mitochondria in relation to respiratory state.

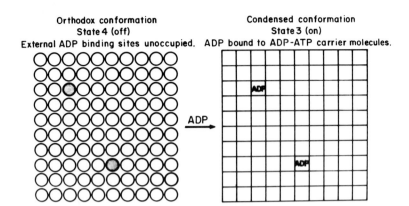

FIG. 11. Schematic representation of the apparently cooperative conformational change of the inner membrane on binding a small number of ADP molecules to their carrier sites.

in the inner membrane, from relatively reduced to relatively oxidized states. However, the ultrastructural transitions have recently been found to be induced by the binding of ADP to the ADP translocase molecules in the inner mitochondrial membrane (Weber, 1972; Stoner and Sirak, 1973; Scherer and Klingenberg, 1974). The ADP-induced ultrastructural transition does not occur in the presence of atractyloside, which specifically prevents the binding of ADP to the carrier. No events other than binding of small amounts of ADP appear to be required for the induction of this profound structural transition of the matrix (Fig. 11). Since the ADP carrier molecules occupy only a very small fraction of the inner membrane surface, and since the transition of a single mitochondrion can be triggered by the binding of a small number of ADP molecules, the profound structural and functional transition of the entire organelle suggests that the coupling between the ADP binding sites and the mitochondrial membrane and matrix is very highly cooperative, since the effect is essentially all-or-none (Hackenbrock, 1966; 1968*a*,*b*).

SUMMARY

The mitochondrial inner membrane has been shown to exhibit a number of coupled or linked functions. Across the plane of the membrane there is a coupling of flows of mass and electric charge, in the form of a variety of specific metabolites and mineral ions. These flows are energetically coupled to the generation of a proton gradient across the membrane by the electron transport chain. Such coupling of flows across the membrane is stoichiometric and adjusted to the metabolic needs in the mitochondrial and cytosol compartments. These metabolite movements are sequentially coupled, so that the occurrence of one primary event, that is, the pumping of protons across the membrane, increases the probability of the subsequent transport events. A second level of cooperative behavior of the mitochondrial membrane is superimposed on the first, namely, functional and structural changes occurring in the plane of the membrane by the occurrence of electron transport. These changes, which are triggered in an all-or-none or cooperative fashion, result in altered activity of certain of the transmembrane transport processes. Thus we have a complex interplay of cooperative coupled processes taking place across and within the mitochondrial membrane, which serve to regulate and adjust the metabolic events in the mitochondrial and cytoplasmic compartments of the cell.

REFERENCES

Azzi, A. (1969): Redistribution of the electrical charge of the mitochondrial membrane during energy conservation. *Biochem. Biophys. Res. Commun.,* 37:254–260.

Azzi, A., Chance, B., Radda, G. K., and Lee, C. P. (1969): A fluorescence probe of energy-dependent structure changes in fragmented membranes. *Proc. Nat. Acad. Sci.,* 62:612–619.

Boyer, P. D., Cross, R. L., and Momsen, W. (1973): A new concept for energy coupling in oxidative phosphorylation based on a molecular explanation of the oxygen exchange reactions. *Proc. Nat. Acad. Sci.,* 70:2837–2839.

Bygrave, F. L., Reed, K. C., and Spencer, T. (1971): Cooperative interactions in energy-dependent accumulation of Ca^{2+} by isolated rat liver mitochondria. *Nature New Biol.,* 230:89.

Chappell, J. B. (1968): Systems for the transport of substances into mitochondria. *Br. Med. Bull.,* 24:150–157.

Colonna, R., Dell'Antone, P., and Azzone, G. F. (1970): Nucleophilic sites in energized mitochondrial membranes. *FEBS Letters,* 10:13–16.

Gamble, J. G., and Lehninger, A. L. (1973): Transport of ornithine and citrulline across the mitochondrial membrane. *J. Biol. Chem.,* 248:610–618.

Hackenbrock, C. R. (1966): Ultrastructural bases for metabolically linked mechanical activity in mitochondria. I. Reversible ultrastructural changes with change in metabolic steady state in isolated liver mitochondria. *J. Cell Biol.,* 30:269–297.

Hackenbrock, C. R. (1968a): Ultrastructural bases for metabolically linked mechanical activity in mitochondria. II. Electron transport-linked ultrastructural transformations in mitochondria. *J. Cell Biol.,* 37:345–369.

Hackenbrock, C. R. (1968b): Chemical and physical fixation of isolated mitochondria in low-energy and high-energy states. *Proc. Nat. Acad. Sci.,* 61:598–605.

Hansford, R. G., and Lehninger, A. L. (1972): The effect of the coupled oxidation of substrate upon the permeability of blowfly flight muscle mitochondria to potassium and other cations. *Biochem. J.,* 126:689–700.

Heldt, H. W., Klingenberg, M., and Milovancev, M. (1972): Differences between the ATP/ADP ratios in the mitochondrial matrix and in the extramitochondrial space. *Eur. J. Biochem.,* 30:434–440.

Klingenberg, M. (1970): Metabolite transport in mitochondria: An example for intracellular membrane function. *Essays Biochem.,* 6:119–159.

Lehninger, A. L. (1964): *The Mitochondrion.* Menlo Park, Calif.: W. A. Benjamin.

Lehninger, A. L. (1970): Mitochondria and calcium ion transport. The Fifth Jubilee Lecture. *Biochem. J.,* 119:129–138.

Lehninger, A. L. (1971): The transport systems of mitochondrial membranes. In: *Biomembranes,* Vol. 2 edited by L. A. Manson, pp. 147–164. New York: Plenum Press.

Lehninger, A. L. (1974): Role of phosphate and other proton-donating anions in respiration-coupled transport of Ca^{2+} by mitochondria. *Proc. Nat. Acad. Sci.,* 71:1520–1524.

Mitchell, P. (1966): Chemiosmotic coupling in oxidative and photosynthetic phosphorylation. *Biol. Rev.,* 41:445.

Mitchell, P. (1967): Translocations through natural membranes. *Adv. Enzymol.*, 29:33–87.

Mitchell, P. (1968): *Chemiosmotic Coupling and Energy Transduction.* Glynn Research Ltd. Bodmin.

Reynafarje, B., and Lehninger, A. L. (1974a): A quantitative analysis of superstoichiometric H^+ ejection and Ca^{2+} uptake in respiring rat liver mitochondria. *J. Biol. Chem.* (*in press*).

Reynafarje, B., and Lehninger, A. L. (1974b): The cause of superstoichiometric Ca^{2+} uptake and H^+ ejection in L1210 mouse ascites tumor mitochondria. *Biochem. Biophys. Res. Commun.*, 57:286–292.

Scherer, B., and Klingenberg, M. (1974): Demonstration of the relationship between the adenine nucleotide carrier and the structural changes of mitochondria as induced by adenosine 5′-diphosphate. *Biochemistry*, 13:161–170.

Stoner, C. D., and Sirak, H. D. (1973): Adenine nucleotide-induced contraction of the inner mitochondrial membrane. I. General characterization. II. Effect of bongkrekic acid. *J. Cell Biol.*, 56:51–64, 65–73.

Vignais, P. V., Vignais, P. M., Lauquin, G., and Morel, F. (1973): *Biochimie*, 55:763–778.

Weber, N. E. (1972): Ultrastructural studies of beef heart mitochondria. III. The inequality of gross morphological change and oxidative phosphorylation. *J. Cell Biol.*, 55:457–470.

Functional Linkage in Biomolecular Systems, edited by
F. O. Schmitt, D. M. Schneider, and D. M. Crothers.
Raven Press, New York © 1975.

Chapter 8

Cooperative Coupling in the Immune System

THE NATURE OF THE IMMUNE RESPONSE:

Gustav J. V. Nossal

Functional linkage is apparent at several levels within the immune system. The primary emphasis of this chapter will be on the linkage between the surface receptors of lymphoid cells and their antigens, an interaction that initiates the immune response. Another level of cooperativity is that shown by the three fundamental cell types of the immune system, the T (thymus-derived) and B (bone-marrow-derived) lymphocytes and the macrophage. This cellular interaction is now fairly well characterized, and it is known that an immune response cannot occur without the active participation of all three cell types.

Most immune responses have two components. *Humoral immunity* is produced by cells which synthesize and secrete antibody molecules into the bloodstream. The second type of response does not involve the secretion of antibodies; the effector that produces *cellular immunity* is a lymphocyte that migrates to the site of antigen deposition and there induces an inflammatory response. These two classes of immune response are produced by two families of cells, the T and B lymphocytes, derived from the thymus and bone marrow, respectively (Fig. 1). Lymphocytes exported from these tissues enter the peripheral lymphocyte compartment, comprising the lymph nodes, spleen, Peyer's patches, and so on. These tissues are the actual sites of antibody production, in which the lymphocytes encounter antigens and are stimulated to divide and to differentiate into immunological effector cells. The T lymphocytes are responsible for cell-mediated immunities, including the rejection of graft tissue and cancer cells, while the B lymphocytes give rise to antibody-forming cells. For many, and perhaps most, immune responses, these two systems must cooperate to produce an optimal response.

Not all lymphocytes express the same functional potential. Each cell of the B lymphocyte system expresses only one kind of receptor, that is, one kind of immunoglobulin molecule that has the capacity to recognize a specific antigen. It is probable that a similar situation occurs in the T

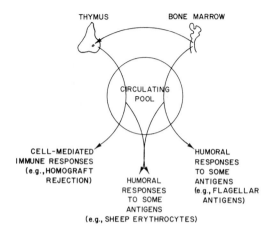

FIG. 1. The two classes of lymphocytes are derived from the thymus and bone marrow.

lymphocyte system, and that only one, or at the most a small number of receptors are expressed by each cell.

An antigen encounters these lymphocytes in the peripheral lymphoid compartment, where it essentially performs a genetic recognition process. The antigen does not bring any new information to the lymphocyte; it simply reacts with any cell having a preformed surface receptor whose conformation permits binding. This cell then undergoes what is essentially a process of dedifferentiation, changing from a small, nondividing cell into a large, rapidly dividing one. A series of mitotic divisions results in the creation of a family of cells, all possessing the specific surface antibody receptor (Fig. 2).

A variety of techniques now exist for studying these receptors, including electron microscopic radioautography. Such studies have proved the major tenet of the clonal selection theory: only one cell in 10,000 has the capacity to adsorb a given antigen, and only those cells which adsorb the antigen have the capacity to produce its specific antibody. The receptors of the B cell, which synthesize a specific kind of antibody referred to as IgM, are localized to the cell periphery. Receptors form patches after the binding of multivalent antigens rather than being distributed uniformly over the cell surface. This agrees with observations that receptor aggregation is one of the early events in the initiation of immune response, discussed at length in the following section.

Much less is known about the T lymphocytes. T cells *may* have a small amount of immunoglobulin on their surface, which may or may not function as a receptor; however, there is no consensus as to whether this Ig is synthesized by the T cells or passively adsorbed. The T cell might utilize a

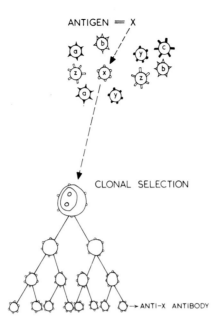

FIG. 2. Clonal selection in response to a specific antigen.

completely different kind of receptor; if this turns out to be correct, immunologists may have to learn to deal with an entirely new type of recognition mechanism.

T cells have two basic functions. They migrate to sites of antigen deposition, where they multiply, differentiate, and release their chemical products. Their second function, as yet only poorly understood, is to facilitate antigen synthesis by the B lymphocytes. Through an essentially cooperative phenomenon, that of recognizing an antigenic determinant different from that to which the B cell reacts, the T cell in some way focuses or aids the presentation of the antigen to the B cell.

Antibody production generally cannot occur in the absence of macrophages, scavenger cells which neither form antibodies nor possess specific receptors for antigen. These cells passively acquire receptors by adsorbing immunoglobulin synthesized by the B and T cells. Since this is a nonspecific process, any macrophage can respond to all antigens. These cells are involved in the collaboration between T and B lymphocytes and in the initiation of cellular immunity. The macrophage appears to secrete substances which lower the triggering threshold of the lymphocytes. Protein molecules derived from activated macrophages significantly alter the membrane reactivity of the lymphocytes; this has been most clearly shown for the B type.

THE REGULATION OF MACROMOLECULAR SYNTHESIS AND SECRETION IN THE IMMUNE SYSTEM:

Jonathan Uhr

Extensive regulation of macromolecules destined to be exteriorized occurs at the level of the plasma membrane. Such macromolecules may follow one of three distinct pathways. The pathway for conventional secretion is exemplified by the secretion of the polymeric form of IgM, or of IgG, the major class of circulating immunoglobulins. These molecules are secreted without a cell surface phase, and in their final molecular form. Other macromolecules are first inserted into the plasma membrane surface, then gradually shed with fragments of the membrane; this is the form in which the monomeric IgM receptor of the B lymphocyte is released. Still a third class of macromolecules is inserted into portions of the plasma membrane which are not readily shed. This group includes the H-2 alloantigens, now believed to be involved in the recognition that takes place on the lymphocytic surface during T-B cell cooperation.

Proteins destined for conventional secretion are synthesized on membrane-bound polyribosomes (Fig. 3), with the heavy and light chains synthesized separately. Assembly begins with the binding of completed light chains to nascent heavy chains to which some sugar residues have already been attached, and is completed in the cisterna of the rough endoplasmic reticulum (ER). The rough ER is thus one of the major sites for the

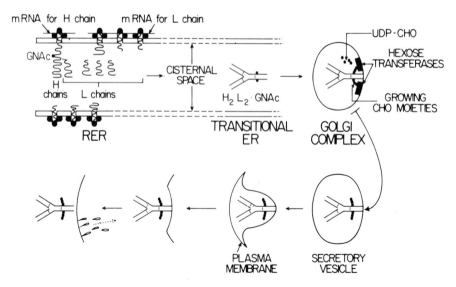

FIG. 3. Model of assembly, intracellular transport, and secretion of IgG (Uhr, 1970).

segregation of proteins destined to be exteriorized. The molecule is next transported to the Golgi complex for the addition of more sugar residues. It is presumed that this segregation from cytoplasmic proteins continues, and that the Ig molecules are transported to the plasma membrane to release their contents; this process is therefore essentially one of reverse pinocytosis.

Early studies with a lymphoma cell line, a neoplastic counterpart of the B lymphocyte that has IgM on its surface but does not secrete it, indicated that a similar biosynthetic pathway is involved as for conventional secretion. The simplest hypothesis that would explain the exteriorization of these cell surface receptors is that some of the Ig molecules are released into the vesicle, while others remain adherent to the vesicle membrane (Fig. 4). The free molecules would be secreted after merger of the vesicle with the plasma membrane, while those that were adhered would become surface molecules and would gradually be shed with portions of the membrane. Moreover, it was suggested that those molecules that remained bound to the Golgi membrane were incompletely glycosylated, and that release occurred following addition of the terminal sugar. The addition of carbohydrate would thus determine which of the two distinct pathways would be followed from the Golgi complex to exteriorization.

The IgM molecules remaining on the cell surface were examined by enzymatic radioiodination with lactoperoxidase of the surface of living lymphoid cells. Since only the cell surface molecules are labeled with this technique, the heavy and light chains can be easily distinguished from intracellular molecules following precipitation with an antiimmunoglobulin and subsequent electrophoresis (Fig. 5).

Since radioiodinated lymphocytes are viable, they could be used to trace the cell surface Ig during the shedding process. A 30 to 40% loss of the cell

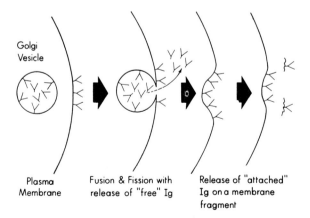

FIG. 4. Exteriorization of cell surface Ig destined to act as receptors on B lymphocytes.

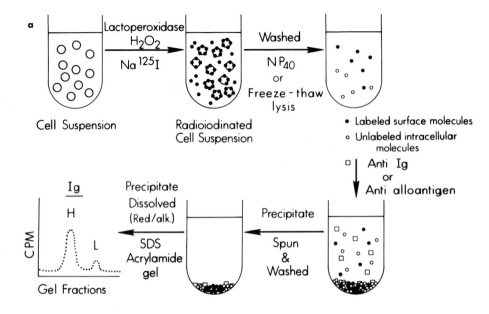

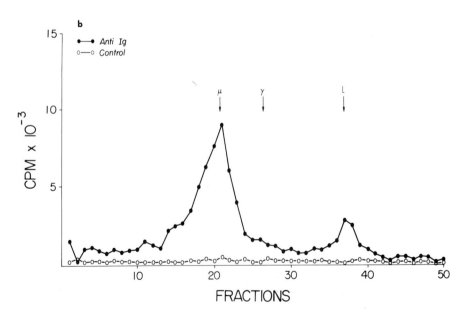

FIG. 5. (a) Isolation of cell surface Ig. (b) Gel electrophoresis pattern of Ig obtained from mouse lymphocytes and treated as in (a). The two peaks represent the H and L chains of the Ig molecule.

surface Ig was demonstrated following a 3-hr incubation. This loss could be quantitatively accounted for by the appearance of Ig in the incubation medium. No shedding of H-2 alloantigen could be demonstrated under the same conditions. H-2 alloantigens are present on all nucleated cells, and must therefore be retained by the same cells which rapidly shed Ig in association with membrane fragments. A similar selective release was observed in T-cells when the Thy-1 (formerly called Theta) antigen and H-2 alloantigen were compared.

What mechanisms might be responsible for the selective loss of macro-molecules from the cell surface, and how might they be related to the conventional secretion process? Since Ig or Thy-1 are released in associa-tion with plasma membrane fragments, certain membrane regions must have special characteristics that lead to their selective loss.

The biosynthetic pathway for the H-2 alloantigens is similar to that of Ig. All molecules destined to be exteriorized appear to be synthesized on the rough ER, then transported to the Golgi complex and plasma membrane.

Electron micrographs of lymphocytes to which antigens have been bound show an apparently nonrandom distribution on the cell surface, with many molecules localized in the region of microvilli. Figure 6 illustrates two models which might explain the phenomenon of shedding based on an association with microvilli.

The simplest model (Fig. 6*a*) is one in which microvilli form on the surface of lymphocytes. Molecules such as the Thy-1 antigen would be embedded only in the outer layer of the membrane bilayer, while those

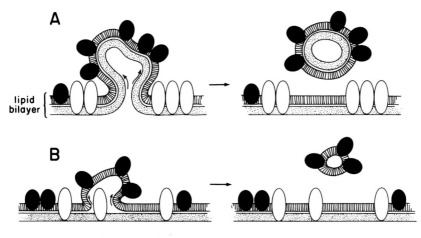

● Peripheral macromolecule such as THY-1 antigen
○ Integral macromolecule such as H-2 antigen

FIG. 6. Two possible mechanisms for the specific shedding of cell surface proteins.

such as the H-2 alloantigen would span the bilayer, possibly as the result of a large hydrophobic surface area. Only the former would be associated with the microvillus, and when shed it would contain only the peripheral proteins. It is also possible that those antigens that are not shed might be bound to the cell surface by association with a submembrane assembly similar to the colchicine-binding protein assembly described by Edelman in the next section. However, the Ig molecule must also be associated with other membrane proteins to relay information properly to the interior of the cell following its interaction with antigen.

A second, far less conventional possibility (Fig. 6b) is that the bilayers slip over each other, and that redundancy in the outer layer results in the release from a microvillus of a vesicle containing only a single layer.

What might be the biological function of this dynamic state of these surface recognition units on the plasma membrane, and the purpose of shedding pieces of membrane containing many molecules, including Ig? One possibility is that the membrane fragments have an affinity for the surface of the macrophage, the cell which may induce the proper positioning of the antigen for stimulation of the B and T lymphocytes. Such a mechanism would provide the macrophage with a sufficient density of "like" receptors for them to position antigen appropriately within the lymphoid organ to trigger the lymphocytes.

RECEPTOR INTERACTIONS AND MITOGENESIS IN LYMPHOID CELLS:

Gerald M. Edelman

Introduction

All of the information that an organism requires to recognize any antigen is present or potentially present within the cells of the immune system, without any requirement for information transfer from the structure of the antigen.

The basis for antigenic specificity lies in the variable region of the immunoglobulin molecule (Fig. 7). The Ig's are symmetrical molecules containing two types of polypeptide chains, light (L) and heavy (H) (Edelman, Cunningham, Reeke, Becker, Waxdal, and Wang, 1972). Ig molecules are folded into a series of domains, each of which appears to carry out a specific function. The variable (V) domains of the L and H chains form a combining site that is complementary to a specific antigenic structure. One of the fundamental problems in immunology is to determine the origin of the variability in the amino acid sequence of V regions, which leads to a three-dimensional structural variability great enough to provide a sufficiently extensive repertoire for the selective and specific binding of antigens.

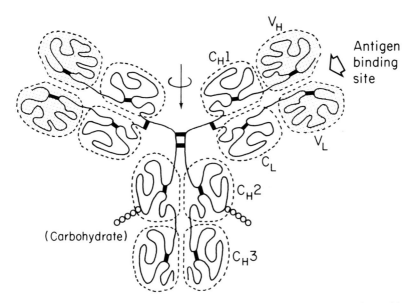

FIG. 7. A model of the structure of a human IgG molecule. The variable regions of heavy and light chains (V_H and V_L), the constant region of the light chain (C_L), and the homology regions in the constant region of heavy chain (C_H1, C_H2, and C_H3) are thought to fold into compact domains (delineated by dashed lines), but the exact conformation of the polypeptide chains has not been determined. The vertical arrow represents the twofold rotation axis through the two disulphide bonds linking the heavy chains. A single interchain disulphide bond is present in each domain. Carbohydrate prosthetic groups are attached to the C_H2 regions. From Gally and Edelman, 1972.

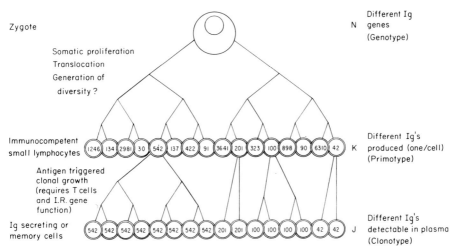

FIG. 8. A model of the somatic differentiation of antibody-producing cells according to the clonal selection theory. The number of immunoglobulin genes may increase during somatic growth so that in the immunologically mature animal, different lymphoid cells are formed, each committed to the synthesis of a structurally distinct receptor antibody (indicated by an Arabic numeral). A small proportion of these cells proliferate upon antigenic stimulation to form different clones of cells, each clone producing a different antibody. This model represents bone-marrow-derived (B) cells, but with minor modifications it is also applicable to thymus-derived (T) cells. From Gally and Edelman, 1972.

When an antigen is presented to the ensemble of lymphocytes, it will bind with more or less affinity to the surface of those cells whose surface Ig receptors have some degree of complementarity to that antigen. It appears that the extent of antigen-induced clonal growth will vary with the strength of antigen binding (Fig. 8), although the actual process of stimulation has many stages. Clearly the binding of antigen to the lymphocyte must be distinguished from the event which triggers cellular proliferation. Although the production of an immune response does require specific binding, the two events are not necessarily synonymous and are not coincidental. As discussed by Nossal, the triggering event probably requires more than one type of molecule, and more than one type of cell.

Ontogenetic Development of the Immune System

(See Spear, Wang, Rutishauser, and Edelman, 1973.)

In the mouse, T and B cells arise quite early during ontogeny; they are present by fetal day 15, only 2 to 3 days after the appearance of the spleen anlage. Their number increases rapidly until birth at 19 days, then plateaus until a subsequent increase of B cells occurs at 14 days postnatally (Fig. 9a). The number of antigen-binding cells (Fig. 9b) parallels the increase in B and T cells, with the ratio of various antigens remaining quite constant during development. The dispersion of receptor antibody binding constants

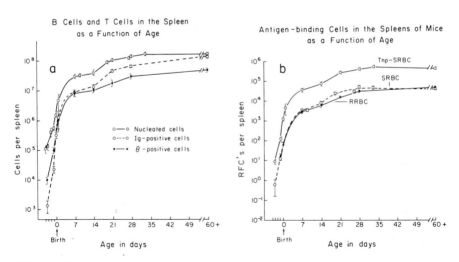

FIG. 9. (a) Number of nucleated cells, Ig-positive cells, and θ-positive cells per spleen in Swiss-L mice as a function of age. Numbers of nucleated cells were determined directly by counting spleen cell suspensions in hemocytometers. The number of animals at the same age used to prepare each spleen cell suspension ranged from 3 for adults to as many as 40 (four litters) for fetuses. (b) Numbers of RFC specific for Tnp-SRBC and RRBC in the spleens of Swiss-L mice as a function of age. From Spear, Wang, Rutishauser, and Edelman, 1973.

for the haptene trinitrophenol also remains fairly constant during maturation. One possible implication of the observations on early appearance of various antigen-binding capacities is that the diverse antibody receptors of the immune system are not likely to be generated by a process of somatic mutation and selection.

It should be noted, however, that the appearance of antigen-binding cells does not necessarily represent the capacity to produce an immune response. No response to an immune stimulus can be obtained until several weeks after birth, although antigen-binding cells are present much earlier. This appears to result from delayed T cell maturation, since the B cells seem to attain full functional capacity much earlier.

Generation of Immune Specificity

(See Haber, 1964; Siskind and Benacerraf, 1969; Edelman, Rutishauser, and Millette, 1971; Rutishauser and Edelman, 1972; Rutishauser, Millette, and Edelman, 1972; Rutishauser, D'Eustachio, and Edelman, 1973).

The generation of specificity in the immune system has been examined following the fractionation of immune cells on the basis of Ig receptor specificity (Edelman et al., 1971). Intact B cells having a specific antibody receptor were recovered and transferred into irradiated animals to reconstitute the immune response specified by the isolated cells.

Approximately 1% of the spleen lymphocytes bind to any given antigen (Table 1). Since there are many thousands of potential antigens, this suggests that lymphocytes must be capable of binding more than one antigen, and that the specificity of the binding sites of an ensemble of antibodies must be only relative. The necessary specificity appears to be generated in a hierarchical manner. A nonimmunized animal possesses cells which bind to a given antigen with a wide range of binding constants, with similar numbers of cells showing high and low affinities. An immune animal possesses approximately the same number of low-affinity cells, but shows a selective and large increase in high-affinity cells (Fig. 10).

Specificity must therefore arise through a series of sequential selection events, with the initial binding followed by a selective amplification and division of those cells having a high affinity for the antigen. This subpopula-

TABLE 1. *Percent of specific fiber binding cells in spleens of nonimmune mice*

Antigen	Percent
Dinitrophenol-bovine serum albumin (BSA)	1.1–1.5
Tosyl-BSA	0.6–0.8
BSA	0.4–0.6

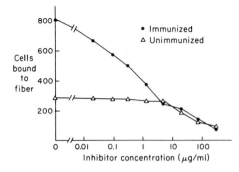

FIG. 10. Inhibition by free Dnp-BSA of spleen-cell binding to Dnp-BSA derivatized fibers. Cell numbers represent fiber edge counts for a 2.5-cm fiber segment. Spleens from immunized mice were removed at the height of a secondary response to Dnp-BGG and cells from several mice were pooled. From Rutishauser et al., 1972.

tion comprises only 1% of the 1% capable of binding the antigen, or no more than one in 10,000 cells, a proportion that generates the appropriate degree of specificity. The system is analogous to an amplifier with a high-pass filter on the input; specificity arises from the total properties of the system rather than simply from the properties of the antibody binding sites.

Activity of Mitogens

(See Frye and Edidin, 1970; Cooper, 1971; Fisher and Mueller, 1971; Novogrodsky and Katchalski, 1971; Taylor, Duffus, Raff, and de Petris, 1971; Edelman et al., 1972; Greaves and Bauminger, 1972; Hadden, Hadden, Haddox, and Goldberg, 1972; Sharon and Lis, 1972; Stobo, 1972; Unanue, Perkins, and Karnovsky, 1972; Yahara and Edelman, 1972, 1973a,b; Edelman, Yahara, and Wang, 1973; Gunther, Wang, Yahara, Cunningham, and Edelman, 1973).

Antigens that trigger only one in 10,000 cells cannot be used conveniently to probe the mechanism by which antigenic agents trigger cell division in lymphocytes, or to study how the triggering event is related to the distribution of receptors on the cell surface. It is possible, however, to induce maturation, division, and even immunoglobulin production by agents other than the antigens. One such group of mitogenic agents are the lectins, plant proteins that bind to cell surface glycoproteins through the sugar moiety. Lectins such as concanavalin A (Con A) stimulate a wide variety of lymphocytes, independent of their antigen-binding specificity.

There are a number of ways in which these mitogens could initiate cell division (Fig. 11): (1) directly, by binding to their glycoprotein receptor; (2) as the result of an allosteric change following binding; (3) by an interaction with internal structures following endocytosis; or (4) by perturbing the membrane structure through receptor cross-linking.

The Con A molecule (Fig. 12) is a tetramer whose subunits have a molecular weight of 26,000 and a size of 80 Å by 45 Å. It is a metalloprotein that contains both Mn^{2+} and Ca^{2+}. Each subunit has a binding site for sugars

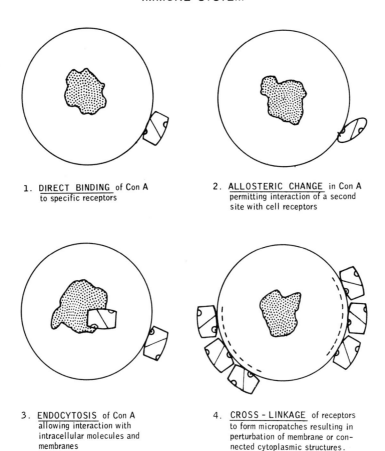

FIG. 11. Hypothesized alternative mechanisms for the mitogenic stimulation by Con A. From Cunningham, Wang, Gunther, Reeke, and Becker, 1974.

such as α-methyl mannoside. The molecular structure consists essentially of two dimers, with an antiparallel β-pleated sheet structure at the interface.

The interaction between various ligands and lymphocyte surface immunoglobulin receptors has been examined using fluorescein-labeled anti-immunoglobulin, following the process by fluorescence microscopy. Fluorescent patches appear over the entire cell surface within minutes following the combination of the antiimmunoglobulin with the surface Ig receptors (Fig. 13). These patches subsequently migrate to one pole of the cell, forming a cap that is either endocytosed or discarded. This suggests that the receptors are normally mobile and diffusely distributed. The phenomena of patch formation and subsequent capping are quite distinct; cap formation is dependent on cellular metabolism, and is inhibited by agents such as azide or dinitrophenol, while the initial formation of patches occurs independently of cellular metabolic processes.

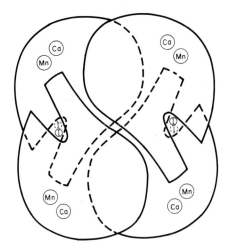

FIG. 12. Structure of Con A. Schematic view of the Con A tetramer showing the arrangement of the protomers and the proposed binding sites for the transition metal manganese (Mn), calcium (Ca), and β-IPG (I). From Reeke, Becker, Cunningham, Gunther, Wang, and Edelman, 1974.

These observations suggest the possibility that the patch and cap phenomena may somehow be related to the mechanism by which cell division is induced, and that receptor mobility might be modulated by a rather elaborate system capable both of anchoring the receptors and of modulating their movement.

The addition of 3 to 20 μg/ml Con A to lymphocytes at either 21°C or 37°C inhibits both patch and cap formation in response to anti-Ig (Fig. 13).

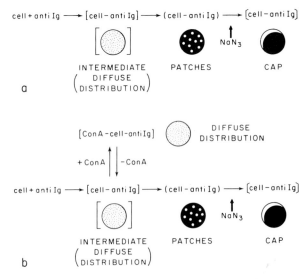

FIG. 13. (a) Schematic representation of patch and cap formation on lymphocytes obtained by the addition of fluorescein-labeled antiimmunoglobulin. (b) In the presence of Con A at 37°C, both patch and cap formation are inhibited and fl-anti Ig gives diffuse labeling of the cell. From Yahara and Edelman, 1972.

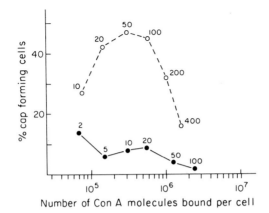

FIG. 14. Relation of cap formation to the number of Con A molecules bound to lymphoid cells at 4°C (open circles) and 37°C (filled circles). Numbers above each point refer to the concentrations of Con A used in micrograms per milliliter. From Yahara and Edelman, 1973a.

Inasmuch as the surface Con A receptors are not saturated under these conditions, the lectin must interact with structures involved in modulating the capacity to form patches, a process that appears to be a membrane-surface diffusional event (Taylor et al., 1971). That this inhibition is not the result of cellular damage is indicated by its reversibility; α-methylmannoside, a competitive inhibitor of Con A binding to the cell surface Ig, reverses the restriction of receptor mobility and permits patch and cap formation to occur.

When the identical binding experiment is carried out at 4°C and the temperature is then raised to 37°C, however (Fig. 14), the Con A receptors themselves patch and cap, and there is no inhibition of the patch and cap responses to other antigens. This phenomenon has been observed for the Ig receptors of B cells, the Theta receptor of T cells and thymocytes, and for H-2 antigen receptors. This phenomenon cannot be explained by differences in the number of molecules bound at the two temperatures (Fig. 14).

In order to examine the process by which Con A and other mitogenic lectins inhibit both their own patch formation and the formation of patches after binding of many other ligands, it is necessary first to determine the properties of the lectin molecule and of the lymphocyte that lead to this phenomenon.

It appears that the valence of the lectin may be of primary importance. Succinylation almost quantitatively dissociates the tetrameric Con A molecule to the dimeric form, with no alteration of the sugar specificity of the subunits (Fig. 15). Unlike the tetramer, dimeric succinyl-Con A does not cause cellular agglutination; it does not induce cap and patch formation by its own receptors under any reaction conditions, and it is incapable of

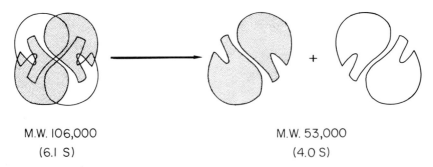

M.W. 106,000   M.W. 53,000

(6.1 S)   (4.0 S)

FIG. 15. Schematic drawing of the Con A molecule. Above pH 7, Con A consists of tetra-mers of the identical subunits arranged as shown on the left. Treatment with succinic anhydride yields a derivative which at pH 7.4 has half the molecular weight and half the valence of the untreated protein (right).

inhibiting the patch and cap formation of any other receptors (Fig. 16). These properties rapidly reappear if antibody to Con A is added to cells that have bound the succinyl-Con A dimer. This has led to the tentative conclusion that both the inhibition phenomenon and that of patch and cap formation are a function of the valence of the lectin molecule, although the net charge may also play a role.

The available data suggest that the cellular structures involved in the phenomena of inhibition are temperature-sensitive. Several explanations appear reasonable, including: (1) The membrane might undergo a phase transition or a phase separation in which the receptors "freeze" into one phase. To date, there is no evidence for such a radical change. (2) The cell

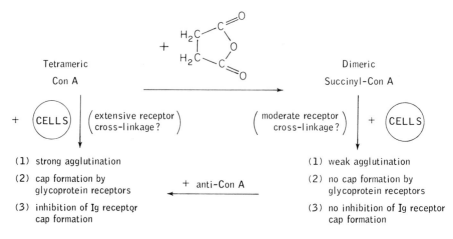

FIG. 16. Schematic comparison of the biological properties of native Con A and succinyl-Con A. The activities listed include those immediate cellular reactions mediated by the lectin. From Gunther et al., 1973.

membrane might contain barriers to the motion of different receptors. The extensive variety of receptors and the small amount of lectin required in comparison to the total number of receptors make this improbable. (3) There may be a system located on, in, or under the surface membrane of the cells that anchors the receptors and modulates their mobility.

Some suggestive evidence supports the third possibility. A variety of antimitotic drugs, including colchicine, colcemid, podophyllotoxin, vincristine, and vinblastine, all of which are thought to interact with microtubule systems, reverse the inhibition by Con A of patch formation and receptor mobility (Edelman et al., 1973; Table 2). This effect occurs at drug concentrations at least an order of magnitude higher than those required to inhibit mitosis. The effect is reversible, and the ability of Con A to inhibit patch and cap formation returns within a few hours after vinblastine is removed by washing. Low temperature, which also disrupts microtubular function, has an effect similar to that of the antimitotic drugs. Cytocholasin B, an agent that does not bind microtubules, neither has any effect of its own nor enhances that of the other agents.

The hypothesis that has been proposed to explain these effects bears directly on the topic of functional linkage. A subsurface protein capable of binding colchicine has been postulated to be in association-dissociation equilibrium directly or indirectly with certain cell receptors. Since it is not known whether this protein is tubulin or a related molecule, it is referred to simply as colchicine-binding protein (CBP). It is further proposed that the cross-linkage of external receptors by polyvalent ligands perturbs this cooperative structure, altering the entire cell surface, and that this perturbation is responsible for the modulation of cell surface receptor mobility. This

TABLE 2. *Effect of drugs on splenic lymphocytes*

Treatment	Percent cap-forming cells with fl-anti-Ig*	Percent cap-forming cells with fl-anti-Ig + Con A	Percent cap-forming cells with fl-Con A
Control	85	2	2
Colchicine (10^{-4} M)	87	22	31
Colcemid (10^{-4} M)	88	25	24
Vinblastine (10^{-4} M)	91	55	42
Vincristine (10^{-4} M)	83	15	19
Low temperature (4°C)	88	30	45
Cytocholasin B (4×10^{-5} M)	62	—	1

* fl-anti-Ig = fluorescein-labeled antiimmunoglobulin.
From Edelman et al., 1973.

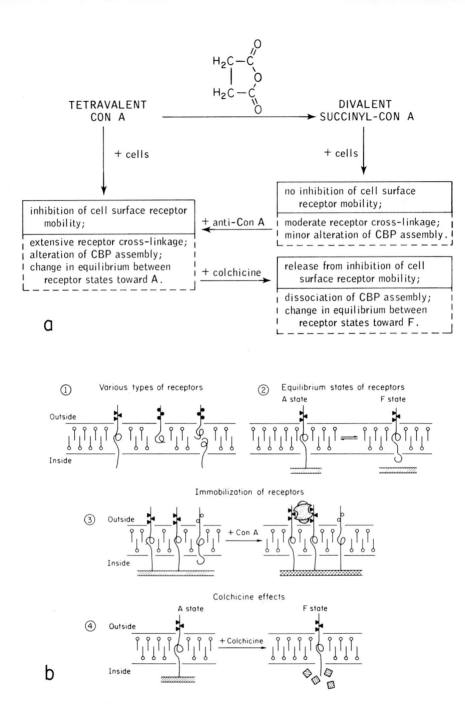

FIG. 17. (a) Summary of the effects of binding Con A or succinyl-Con A on mouse splenic lymphocytes. The experimentally observed effect on restriction of receptor mobility is boxed by solid lines. The hypothesized changes in the colchicine-binding protein assembly (CBP) and the shift in equilibrium of receptor states between A (anchored to the CBP) and F (free from the CBP) are boxed by dashed lines. The addition of anti-Con A to succinyl-Con A bound on cells mimics the effect of Con A alone. Colchicine reverses the

implies that the mobility and distribution of surface receptors can be modulated both by external signals and as the result of changes within the cell itself. The hypothesis is summarized in Fig. 17.

The microtubular proteins of the cell are never observed immediately under the cell membrane in somatic cells, although they are in close proximity to it. This suggests either the existence of an interacting system that cannot be visualized ultrastructurally, or that the microtubules may interact with a microfilament system, which in turn interacts with the receptors. This last is a quite attractive possibility, because it would relate receptor mobility to cell mobility.

Possible Relation to Mitogenesis

(See Cooper, 1971; Greaves and Bauminger, 1972; Edelman et al., 1973).
Lymphocyte mitogenesis is initiated by a perturbation of the resting cell induced by the binding of antigen to its cell surface receptors. It is difficult to analyze the receptor-gene linkage in this system due to the time course of the response. There is a lag period of at least 20 hr before the process becomes irreversible in the entire cellular population, and removal of the mitogen at any time during this period allows the system to return to its original resting state. This does not mean that there are no cellular changes during this period; there are marked but reversible changes in a variety of transport functions and other systems. Thymidine incorporation into new DNA can be detected after approximately 48 hr, and mitotic spindles appear at 72 hr.

The long reversible delay period in mitogenesis following the addition of mitogen is difficult to explain, even assuming a cascade of reactions within each cell. This suggests that there may actually be a sequential interaction of many cells. The delay period might be due to: (1) an asynchronous interaction between many cells; (2) coupled metabolic events, each with a finite time constant; or (3) variability in the population, such that certain cells respond earlier than others. Recent evidence suggests that there is a population distribution within the responding cells, and that the third possibility is correct.

It is tempting to view the induction of mitogenesis as the result of a linkage

---

effects of both Con A and succinyl-Con A plus anti-Con A. From Edelman, et al., 1973. (b) Diagram illustrating some hypothesized interactions between cell surface receptors and colchicine-binding proteins (CBP) and the effects of Con A and colchicine on these interactions. (1) Types of receptor: Some receptors may penetrate the lipid bilayer and interact directly or indirectly with cytoplasmic structures, whereas other receptors may terminate in or on the membrane. (2) Some of the first type of receptor are assumed to interact with CBP in an equilibrium consisting of two states, anchored (A) and free (F). (3) Cross-linkage of Con A receptors by Con A may lead to structural changes in the CBP assembly and affect the equilibria $A \rightleftarrows F$, of other receptors. (4) Colchicine dissociates CBP into subunits and results in a shift in the equilibrium $A \rightleftarrows F$. From Edelman, 1974.

system; that is, a defined protein assembly might be involved in the signalling process, similar to those involved in protein synthesis. This is more attractive than the assumption that mitogenesis occurs simply by changes in the transport of essential metabolites, resulting from alterations in the cell membrane.

There are several suggestive pieces of evidence to support this hypothesis. First, all substances that modulate receptor mobility are mitogenic, while those that do not are nonmitogenic. Second, colchicine and its pharmacological analogues inhibit mitogenesis at a step prior to spindle formation. Considerably more evidence must be amassed, however, before this hypothesis can be excluded or confirmed.

Summary

In summary, three basic problems of immunology have been discussed. First, the selective system consisting of lymphocytes fills its repertoire early in ontogeny, suggesting that germ-line information mainly controls the regulation of gene expression in the system. Later, maturational events in several types of differentiated lymphocytes are required for cellular cooperation to produce an immune response. Second, the selective immune system acts to filter antigenic inputs, deriving its specificity through a series of hierarchical selection events. Third, experiments on the behavior of lymphocyte mitogens suggest the possibility that there are elaborate, structurally defined systems involved in the regulation and modulation of cell surface receptor mobility.

REFERENCES

Cooper, H. L. (1971): Biochemical alterations accompanying initiation of growth in resting cells. In: *The Cell Cycle and Cancer,* edited by R. Baserga. New York: Marcel Dekker.

Cunningham, B. A., Wang, J. L., Gunther, G. R., Reeke, G. N., Jr., and Becker, J. W. (1974): Molecular analysis of the initial events in mitogenesis. In: *Cellular Selection and Regulation in the Immune Response,* edited by G. M. Edelman, pp. 177–197. New York: Raven Press.

Edelman, G. M. (1974): Origins and mechanisms of specificity in clonal selection. In: *Cellular Selection and Regulation in the Immune Response,* pp. 1–38. New York: Raven Press.

Edelman, G. M., Cunningham, B. A., Reeke, G. N., Jr., Becker, J. W., Waxdal, M. J., and Wang, J. L. (1972): The covalent and three-dimensional structure of concanavalin A. *Proc. Nat. Acad. Sci.,* 69:2580–2584.

Edelman, G. M., Rutishauser, U., and Millette, C. F. (1971): Cell fractionation and arrangement on fibers, beads, and surfaces. *Proc. Nat. Acad. Sci.,* 68:2153–2157.

Edelman, G. M., Yahara, I., and Wang, J. L. (1973): Receptor mobility and receptor-cytoplasmic interactions in lymphocytes. *Proc. Nat. Acad. Sci.,* 70:1442–1446.

Fisher, D. B., and Mueller, G. C. (1971): Studies on the mechanism by which phytohemagglutinin rapidly stimulates phospholipid metabolism of human lymphocytes. *Biochim. Biophys. Acta,* 248:434–448.

Frye, L. D., and Edidin, M. (1970): The rapid intermixing of cell surface antigens after formation of mouse-human heterokaryons. *J. Cell Sci.,* 7:319–335.

Gally, J. A., and Edelman, G. M. (1972): Genetic control of immunoglobulin synthesis. *Ann. Rev. Genet.,* 6:1–46.

Greaves, M. F., and Bauminger, S. (1972): Activation of T and B lymphocytes by insoluble phytomitogens. *Nature New Biol.,* 235:67–70.

Gunther, G. R., Wang, J. L., Yahara, I., Cunningham, B. A., and Edelman, G. M. (1973): Concanavalin A derivatives with altered biological activities. *Proc. Nat. Acad. Sci.,* 70:1012–1016.

Haber, E. (1964): Recovery of antigenic specificity after denaturation and complete reduction of disulfides in a papain fragment of antibody. *Proc. Nat. Acad. Sci.,* 52:1099–1106.

Hadden, J. W., Hadden, E. M., Haddox, M. K., and Goldberg, N. D. (1972): Guanosine 3′:5′-cyclic monophosphate: A possible intracellular mediator of mitogenic influences in lymphocytes. *Proc. Nat. Acad. Sci.,* 69:3024–3027.

Novogrodsky, A., and Katchalski, E. (1971): Lymphocyte transformation induced by concanavalin A and its reversion by methyl-α-D-mannopyranoside. *Biochim. Biophys. Acta,* 228:579–583.

Reeke, G. N., Jr., Becker, J. W., Cunningham, B. A., Gunther, G. R., Wang, J. L., and Edelman, G. M. (1974): Relationships between the structure and activities of concanavalin A. *Ann. N.Y. Acad. Sci.,* 234:369–382.

Rutishauser, U., D'Eustachio, P., and Edelman, G. M. (1973): Immunological function of lymphocytes fractionated with antigen-derivatized fibers. *Proc. Nat. Acad. Sci.,* 70:3894–3898.

Rutishauser, U., and Edelman, G. M. (1972): Binding of thymus- and bone marrow-derived lymphoid cells to antigen-derivatized fibers. *Proc. Nat. Acad. Sci.,* 69:3774–3778.

Rutishauser, U., Millette, C. F., and Edelman, G. M. (1972): Specific fractionation of immune cell populations. *Proc. Nat. Acad. Sci.,* 69:1596–1600.

Sharon, N., and Lis, H. (1972): Lectins: Cell-agglutinating and sugar-specific proteins. *Science,* 177:949–959.

Siskind, G. W., and Benacerraf, B. (1969): Cell selection by antigen in the immune response. *Adv. Immunol.,* 10:1–50.

Spear, P. G., Wang, A.-L., Rutishauser, U., and Edelman, G. M. (1973): Characterization of splenic lymphoid cells in fetal and newborn mice. *J. Exp. Med.,* 138:557–573.

Stobo, J. D. (1972): Phytohemagglutinin and concanavalin A: Probes for murine "T" cell activation and differentiation. *Transpl. Rev.,* 11:60–86.

Taylor, R. B., Duffus, W. P. H., Raff, M. C., and de Petris, S. (1971): Redistribution and pinocytosis of lymphocyte surface immunoglobulin molecules induced by antiimmuno-globulin antibody. *Nature New Biol.,* 233:225–229.

Uhr, J. W. (1970): Intracellular events underlying synthesis and secretion of immunoglobulin. *Cell. Immunol.,* 1:228–244.

Unanue, E. R., Perkins, W. D., and Karnovsky, M. J. (1972): Ligand-induced movement of lymphocyte membrane macromolecules. I. Analysis by immunofluorescence and ultra-structural radioautography. *J. Exp. Med.,* 136:885–906.

Yahara, I., and Edelman, G. M. (1972): Restriction of the mobility of lymphocyte immuno-globulin receptors by concanavalin A. *Proc. Nat. Acad. Sci.,* 69:608–612.

Yahara, I., and Edelman, G. M. (1973a): The effects of concanavalin A on the mobility of lymphocyte surface receptors. *Exp. Cell Res.,* 81:143–155.

Yahara, I., and Edelman, G. M. (1973b): Modulation of lymphocyte receptor redistribution by concanavalin A, anti-mitotic agents and alterations of pH. *Nature,* 246:152–154.

Functional Linkage in Biomolecular Systems, edited by
F. O. Schmitt, D. M. Schneider, and D. M. Crothers.
Raven Press, New York © 1975.

Chapter 9

Intermolecular Coupling
in the Receptor-Adenylate Cyclase-Linked
Modulation of Hormone and Transmitter Action

THE ADENYLATE CYCLASE SYSTEM IN EUKARYOTIC CELLS:

Martin Rodbell

The adenylate cyclase system of eukaryotic cells is organized within the matrix of the surface or plasma membrane. It is a complex enzyme system containing at least two components designed for the selective recognition of a hormone and for catalysis of the formation of cyclic AMP from ATP. The hormone recognition component has been variously termed the receptor or discriminator, and is thought to be a protein separate from the catalytic component.

The glucagon-sensitive adenylate cyclase system in rat hepatic plasma membranes has been investigated intensively during the past several years (for recent review see Rodbell, 1972*a,b*). Glucagon binds to the receptor component by a cooperative process having a Hill coefficient of 1.4 to 1.6, suggesting that there may be at least two cooperatively linked subunits within the receptor unit (Rodbell, Lin, and Salomon, 1974). The binding process is selective for glucagon, and is only slowly reversible in the absence of ATP, the substrate of the adenylate cyclase. The intensely hydrophobic carboxy-terminal region of glucagon is required for the binding and action of the hormone. The amino-terminal histidine residue contributes 15 to 30% of the total binding force required for high-affinity binding of the hormone ($K_D = 5$ nM), and its removal markedly reduces the effect of the hormone on adenylate cyclase activity. Thus, the intact molecule, which behaves in solution as if it were randomly coiled, is required for both binding and effectiveness at physiological concentrations.

The receptor component appears to associate initially with the intensely hydrophobic region of glucagon and, possibly in a hierarchial fashion, induces the hormone to fold into an orientation favorable for tight binding, involving the amino-terminal histidine residue. This transaction appears to result in a conformational change of the receptor and, in linked fashion, neighboring receptor molecules; this linkage may account for the apparent positive cooperativity of binding. It is presumed that other changes in the organization and structure of the adenylate cyclase components occur as the result of glucagon binding, but such changes have thus far been recorded only as enhanced adenylate cyclase activity with a concomitant increase in cyclic AMP production.

An important feature of this system, which now appears to apply to a variety of hormone-sensitive adenylate cyclase systems, is a nucleotide requirement in the stimulation of adenylate cyclase activity by glucagon. Increasing the concentration of ATP in the incubation medium produces a selective enhancement of hormone action. However, the addition of GTP in concentrations as low as 10^{-8} M results in a marked enhancement of hormone response even with low concentrations of substrate. Low concentrations of GTP analogues such as $Gpp(CH_2)p$ and $Gpp(NH)p$, which are not hydrolyzed at the terminal phosphate, also enhance hormone action. Since the intact guanine nucleotides are not substrates of adenylate cyclase, do not interact at the catalytic site of the enzyme, and bear no structural resemblance to the hormone, it is likely that they interact with a specific site that has a high affinity for guanine, in contrast to that for adenine nucleotides. This "nucleotide regulatory site" (Rodbell et al., 1974) is present in adenylate cyclase systems activated by such diverse hormones as ACTH, secretin, glucagon, thyrotropin, catecholamines, and prostaglandins. Thus, the nucleotide regulatory site is independent of the nature of the receptor component, suggesting that it is separate from it. Whether this site or process is located on the catalytic component or is a separate molecular entity is presently unknown.

Recent studies of the kinetic characteristics of GTP and glucagon action on the hepatic adenylate cyclase system (Rodbell et al., 1974) have provided evidence that the two ligands activate the enzyme system by a concerted or interdependent process that suggests the reaction scheme:

$$E_1 \xleftrightarrow{\;(H)\;} E_2$$
$$L_1 \updownarrow \qquad \updownarrow L_2$$
$$E_1N \longleftrightarrow E_2N$$

According to this hypothesis, the hormone (H), by a slow transition process, increases the formation of an enzyme state (E_2) that has a higher binding affinity ($L_2 > L_1$) for GTP (N) at the regulatory site, thus inducing the enzyme system to form a high-activity state (E_2N). It was recently discovered (Rodbell, Lin, Salomon, *unpublished observations*) that $Gpp(NH)p$, a nonhydrolyzable analogue of GTP, activates the enzyme system even in the absence of glucagon, whereas GTP activation requires the presence of the hormone. In addition, $Gpp(NH)p$ remains tightly bound to the regulatory site (Salomon, Londos, Rodbell, *unpublished observations*) and activates the enzyme by a slow transition process that requires elevated temperatures ($>30°C$); this process is accelerated in the presence of glucagon. It appears, therefore, that both glucagon and guanine nucleotides induce changes in the state of the enzyme system by allosteric processes that involve the binding of these agents to their respective sites (or components). Similar time- and temperature-dependent activations by Gpp(NH)p have now been observed with all eukaryotic cells examined (mammals, fish, amphibia), irrespective of the nature of the receptor that is coupled to the cyclase, and even in the absence of a functional receptor. The reaction scheme,

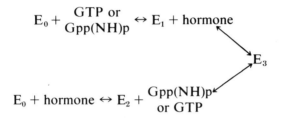

is consistent with the observed kinetic data for hormone and nucleotide activation of the adenylate cyclase system. The predominant form of the enzyme is suggested to be state E_0, an inactive or low-activity state of the enzyme, and the hormone or nucleotides would then induce the formation of intermediate states (E_1 and E_2) that lead to a high-activity state of the enzyme system, E_3.

The nature of the various states of the cyclase systems remains unknown, but they probably represent different coupled forms of the receptor and catalytic subunits. Acidic phospholipids (phosphatidylinositol, phosphatidylserine) are intimately involved in hormone action (Levey, 1971; Rubalcava and Rodbell, 1973), and their removal by specific phospholipases both changes the affinity of glucagon for its receptor in the hepatic adenylate cyclase system and destroys its ability to activate the enzyme (Levey, 1971; Rubalcava and Rodbell, 1973). The acidic phospholipids, which comprise only a fraction of the total membrane phospholipids, may be involved either in the coupling of receptor subunits or of receptor-catalytic subunits.

The nucleotide regulatory process obviously represents a new phase in studies of the regulation of cyclic AMP production by adenylate cyclase systems. Isolation of the component that contains the guanine nucleotide site may help to elucidate the nature of the process that links the hormone reaction occuring at the receptor component with that leading to increased production of cyclic AMP at the catalytic component. The adenylate cyclase system now appears to consist of at least three linked processes, articulated through the flexible domains of protein and lipid to form a highly efficient, dynamic communication system between circulating hormones and neurotransmitters adsorbed at the cell surface and the cyclic AMP response

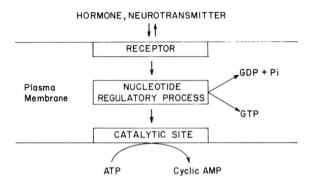

FIG. 1. Suggested linkage arrangement between a circulating hormone or neurotransmitter and the adenylate cyclase system. It is not yet known whether the nucelotide regulatory process takes place on a separate molecular unit or is part of the catalytic unit.

mechanism (protein kinases) within target cells. This linked system is illustrated in Fig. 1.

The differential effectiveness of GTP and Gpp(NH)p as activators of adenylate cyclase systems raises the possibility that the terminal phosphate of GTP is hydrolyzed at the nucleotide regulatory site. If this were the case, and the rate of hydrolysis of GTP were faster than the rate of transition between the various enzyme states postulated above, activation by GTP would require the presence of hormones. In contrast, the hydrolysis-resistant Gpp(NH)p might remain bound to the activation site long enough for the transitions to occur in the absence of hormone.

THE MODULATION OF SKELETAL MUSCLE GLYCOGENOLYSIS AS A MODEL OF CYCLIC AMP ACTION:

Donal A. Walsh

The regulation by cyclic AMP of skeletal muscle glycogenolysis is the mammalian system in which cyclic nucleotide action is at present best understood. This system has therefore served as a model for the investigation of cyclic AMP regulation of other events. The cascade of membrane and cytoplasmic events that lead from the binding of epinephrine to the phosphorylation of the glucose moieties of glycogen (Fig. 2) functions as a highly effective kinetic amplificational mechanism. Cyclic AMP activates protein kinases at a concentration of 10^{-8} to 10^{-7} M, a tenfold amplification occurs when the phosphorylase b kinase reaction is stimulated, and a further 20- to 50-fold amplification is produced by the conversion of phosphorylase b to a.

By analogy to this glycogenolysis cascade, the mechanism of cyclic

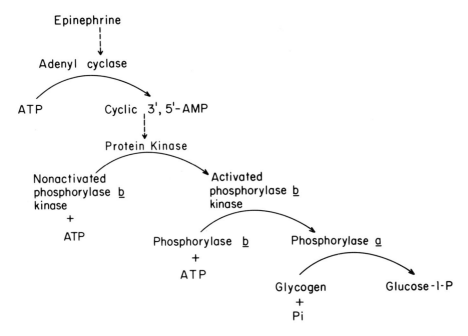

FIG. 2. The cascade of chemical reactions subsequent to the binding of epinephrine by a skeletal muscle cell.

AMP modulation of other physiological events has also been proposed to occur by a system of protein phosphorylation-dephosphorylation (Fig. 3).

Among the substances that can be modified by protein kinases are phosphorylase *b* (activated), glycogen synthetase (inactivated), and lipases (activated). A variety of other proteins, including protamine, histone f_1,

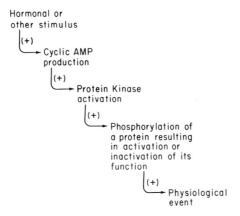

FIG. 3. Proposed model of cyclic AMP action. From Walsh and Ashby, 1973.

ribosomal proteins, and membrane proteins, are phosphorylated *in vivo* in response to a cyclic AMP signal; however, the biological functions of these modifications are unknown. Other proteins that can also be phosphorylated by the cyclic AMP-dependent protein kinases *in vitro* include casein, histones f_{2a}, f_2b, and f_3, troponin, RNA polymerase, and microtubular protein. Many of the effects of cyclic AMP can be explained as a consequence of protein kinase activation, although this effect may not explain all of its actions. For example, there is no good evidence to support its involvement in the phosphorylation of casein, phosvitin, troponin, histones f_{2a}, f_2b, and f_3, or microtubular protein. Numerous methodological problems have been encountered in attempts to determine what substances serve as substrates for cyclic AMP-dependent protein kinases *in vivo*. For example, egg white lysozyme is not normally a substrate for protein kinase, but it can become a substrate if the protein is first denatured (Bylund and Krebs, *unpublished observation*).

The mechanism of protein kinase activation by cyclic AMP is phenomenologically different from the classical ligand-enzyme interactions described in Chapter 2, in that ligand interaction results in physical dissociation of the protein:

$$R_2C_2 + 2cAMP \rightleftharpoons R_2(cAMP)_2 + 2C$$

According to this view, first proposed by Brostrom, Reimann, Walsh, and Krebs (1970), the RC complex of regulatory and catalytic subunits is inactive, while the dissociated C subunit is the active form. The stoichiometry of this reaction was recently determined by Beavo, Bechtel, and Krebs (*unpublished observation*). Table 1 summarizes the evidence supporting a dissociation mechanism for the cyclic activation of protein kinase. However, the available evidence is not sufficient to *prove* that dissociation is a necessary step in the activation process, since a ternary complex could also have catalytic activity.

This proposed dissociation mechanism represents an extreme case of the model proposed by Monod, Wyman, and Changeux (1965, see Chapter 2), in which the subunits actually separate. Since the R and C units must subsequently recombine, this dissociation reaction may not be energetically

TABLE 1. *Evidence for the dissociation mechanism for cyclic AMP activation of protein kinase*

1. "V"-type allosteric kinetics with both substrates (see Chapter 2).
2. Dissociation agents (SDS, urea) yield two dissimilar subunits.
3. Cyclic AMP alone promotes dissociation to yield:
   a. A protein (C) possessing full catalytic activity independent of cyclic AMP;
   b. A cyclic AMP-binding protein (R).
4. Addition of cyclic AMP · R complex inhibits catalytic activity of C.
5. Addition of C to R · cyclic AMP complex promotes release of cyclic AMP.

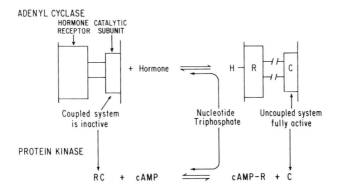

FIG. 4. An activation mechanism for adenylate cyclase as a "V"-type system.

favorable, and the R-cAMP complex might have an independent function.

Our understanding of the mechanism of cyclic AMP activation of protein kinase has been used as a possible model for the hormonal stimulation of adenylate cyclase. Severson, Drummond, and Sulakhe (1972) have shown that the latter activation is also a "V"-type system, in which the maximum velocity rather than the binding curve is altered (see Hammes, Chapter 2). This type of model is shown in Fig. 4, in which the hormone is proposed to induce the dissociation of the R and C subunits. Such a mechanism would be analogous to the activation of the protein kinases, the only difference being that adenylate cyclase is a membrane-bound enzyme while the protein kinases are cytoplasmic. Low levels of ATP increase the rate of release of the C subunit of protein kinase, and the enzyme is activated by the dissociation; a similar increase in liver adenylate cyclase activity is induced by low levels of GTP, and might result from a similar mechanism.

THE ADENYLATE CYCLASE SYSTEM IN BRAIN:

Floyd E. Bloom

Chemical communication between the cells of the nervous system can be analogized to communication in the immune system (see Chapter 7). The nervous system contains a variety of cell types that communicate through specific chemical agents, the neurotransmitters, that bind to receptors on the postsynaptic membrane. The binding of a neurotransmitter to its receptors induces profound alterations in cell membrane properties that can lead to extensive biochemical alterations within the cell.

Any given neuron receives a complex set of inputs from many sources, utilizing a variety of chemical transmitters. Each of these transmitters is presumed not only to have a positive or negative electrical sign (that is, to excite or inhibit the electrical firing of the postsynaptic neuron), but also to possess a biological sign, such that excitation or inhibition by one trans-mitter has a different "meaning" from that of any other.

The reaction of a postsynaptic neuron to the catecholamine neuro-transmitters, norepinephrine (NE) and dopamine (DA), is mediated by an adenylate cyclase system located in the postsynaptic membrane. The bind-ing of DA or NE to their receptors activates this system to produce cyclic 3',5'-AMP from ATP (Fig. 5), and cyclic AMP in turn stimulates a variety of cellular metabolic events. Brain tissue is one of the richest sources of adenylate cyclase in the body. Large regional differences have been found, suggesting that the number of synapses utilizing adenylate cyclase mecha-nisms may vary in these regions.

Table 2 summarizes the actions of NE and DA in three brain regions, the cerebellum, hippocampus, and caudate nucleus. NE and DA inhibit neuronal electrical activity in all three, and this inhibition is mimicked by cyclic AMP. In the cerebellum and hippocampus, the catecholamine inhibition is potentiated by drugs which prevent the degradation of cyclic AMP by inhibiting the enzyme phosphodiesterase. This inhibition is blocked by prostaglandins (PG) of the E series, which in many parts of the peripheral nervous system prevent the cyclic AMP system from responding to a hormone that normally stimulates it. In the caudate nucleus, phospho-diesterase inhibitors do not potentiate dopamine, but prostaglandins of the E series do.

The action of catecholamine transmitters appears to be intimately in-

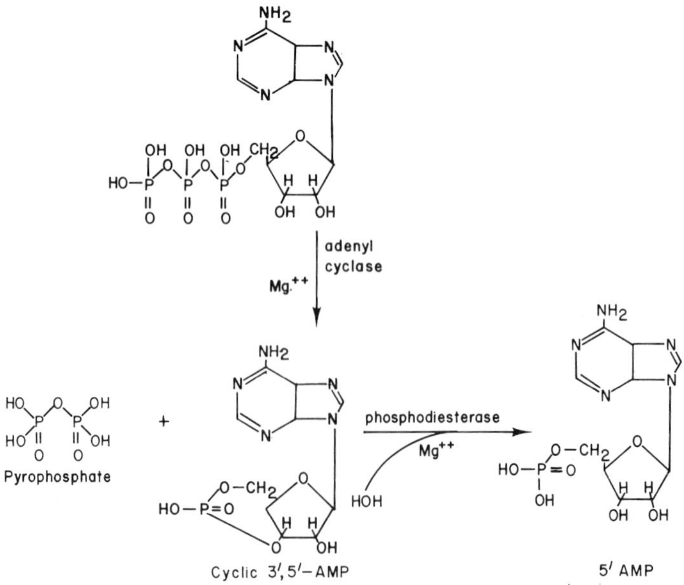

FIG. 5. Formation and hydrolysis of cyclic 3',5'-AMP.

TABLE 2. *Regional comparison of neuronal drug sensitivity in rat brain*

Drugs	Cerebellum (Purkinje)	Hippocampus (pyramidal)	Caudate
Catecholamines	NE and locus coeruleus inhibit	NE and locus coeruleus inhibit	DA inhibits (also apomorp.)
Cyclic AMP	mostly inhibits	inhibits	inhibits
PDE inhibitors	potentiate NE and locus coeruleus	potentiate NE and locus coeruleus	marginal DA potentiation
PGE	blocks NE and locus coeruleus	blocks NE and locus coeruleus	potentiates DA and cyclic AMP
Chlorpromazine	local anesthetic	—	blocks DA
MJ-1999	blocks NE	blocks NE	no effect on DA

volved in many neural systems related to behavior. Many drugs currently used for the treatment of various forms of mental illness interact quite specifically with catecholamine systems. For example, the major pheno-thiazine tranquilizers such as chlorpromazine block the response of caudate nucleus neurons to DA.

Stimulation of the locus coeruleus, which projects inhibitory norepine-phrine-containing fibers to cerebellar Purkinje cells, increases cyclic AMP levels within these postsynaptic neurons, as detected by an immunochemical method (Fig. 6). When this inhibition is removed and electrical activity returns to resting levels, fewer than 10% of the Purkinje cells contain a

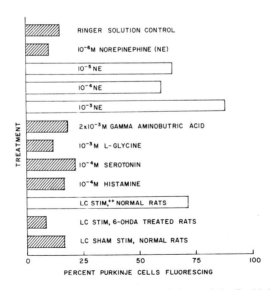

FIG. 6. Specificity of the immunocytochemical stainings of the Purkinje cell cyclic AMP response to NE or LC stimulation. Immunofluorescent staining for cyclic AMP during LC inhibition shows much higher levels than those observed in tissue assayed after the LC inhibition is removed and electrical activity has returned to normal levels.

detectable amount of cyclic AMP. This inhibition is highly selective, occurring only in response to stimulation of the noradrenergic LC pathway or to direct application of NE. Other neurotransmitters that also inhibit the Purkinje cell, including γ-aminobutyric acid, glycine, serotonin, and histamine, have no effect on Purkinje cell cyclic AMP. This further supports the concept that the electrophysiological sign of the transmitter, positive or negative, can be effected through quite different mechanisms.

The activation of adenylate cyclase and the subsequent liberation of cyclic AMP is only the first step in a series of biochemical reactions that markedly alter complex metabolic processes within the postsynaptic cell, as described in the preceding section by Walsh. Many of the effects of catecholaminergic stimulation result from the activation by cyclic AMP of various protein kinases. This system permits a single molecule to induce a wide variety of cellular responses (Figure 7). For this reason, cyclic AMP

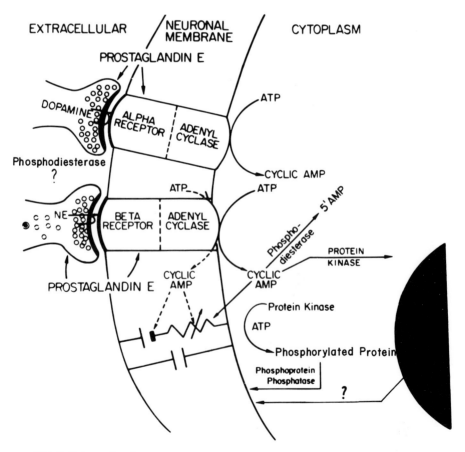

FIG. 7. Schematic of a postsynaptic neuron receiving catecholaminergic inputs.

has been referred to as a "second messenger"; within the cell, it mediates the sequence of biochemical steps that were initiated at the cell surface receptor by the binding of a hormone or neurotransmitter. The fact that the responses of a single cell type to different hormones having different biochemical consequences are all mediated by cyclic AMP formation indicates the existence of genetically predetermined patterns of protein kinases within the cell. These further transduce the chemical message of the hormone bound at the surface receptor.

Adenylate cyclase is part of a linkage system organized to produce a large kinetic amplification of the input signal (see Schwartz, Chapter 1); a small number of transmitter molecules stimulates the formation of a much larger number of cyclic AMP molecules, and these in turn are amplified through their effects on subsequent biochemical steps.

REFERENCES

Brostrom, M. A., Reimann, E. M., Walsh, D. A., and Krebs, E. G. (1970): A cyclic 3',5'-AMP-stimulated protein kinase from cardiac muscle. *Adv. Enzyme Reg.,* 8:191–203.

Levey, G. S. (1971): Restoration of norepinephrine responsiveness of solubilized myocardial adenylate cyclase by phosphatidylinositoi. *J. Biol. Chem.,* 246:7405–7410.

Monod, J., Wyman, J., and Changeux, J.-P. (1965): On the nature of allosteric transitions: A plausible model. *J. Mol. Biol.,* 12:88–118.

Rodbell, M. (1972a): In: *Glucagon,* edited by P. J. Lefebvre and R. H. Unger, pp. 61–75. Oxford: Pergamon Press.

Rodbell, M. (1972b): Cell surface receptor sites. In: *National Institutes of Health Lectures in Biomedical Sciences: Current Topics in Biochemistry,* pp. 187–218. New York: Academic Press.

Rodbell, M., Lin, M. C., and Salomon, Y. (1974): Evidence for interdependent action of glucagon and nucleotides on the hepatic adenylate cyclase system. *J. Biol. Chem.,* 249:59–65.

Rubalcava, B., and Rodbell, M. (1973): The role of acidic phospholipids in glucagon action on rat liver adenylate cyclase. *J. Biol. Chem.,* 248:3831–3837.

Severson, D. L., Drummond, G. I., and Sulakhe, P. V. (1972): Adenylate cyclase in skeletal muscle. Kinetic properties and hormonal stimulation. *J. Biol. Chem.,* 247:2949–2958.

Walsh, D. A., and Ashby, C. D. (1973): Protein kinases: Aspects of their regulation and diversity. *Recent Prog. Horm. Res.,* 29:329–359.

Functional Linkage in Biomolecular Systems, edited by
F. O. Schmitt, D. M. Schneider, and D. M. Crothers.
Raven Press, New York © 1975.

Chapter 10

Transductive Coupling Between Acetylcholine, Its Receptor, and the Postsynaptic Membrane

THE ISOLATION AND CHARACTERIZATION OF THE ACETYLCHOLINE RECEPTOR:

Michael A. Raftery

Studies of the acetylcholine (ACh) system have been greatly facilitated by the universality of this transmitter substance and the existence of several species of electric fish whose electroplaques contain large quantities of receptor that can be isolated and subjected to chemical characterization. The most commonly used sources of receptor material have been *Electrophorus electricus,* an electric eel, and *Torpedo californica* or *Torpedo marmorata,* electric rays.

Although it is now known that the ACh receptor and the acetylcholinesterase enzyme are two distinct protein entities, their relationship within the postsynaptic membrane remains unclear. Their solubilities are markedly different; most of the enzyme is easily extracted into aqueous salt solution, but the receptor is difficult to extract and appears to be deeply embedded

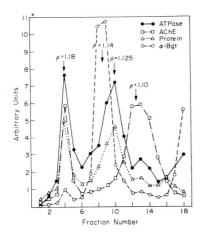
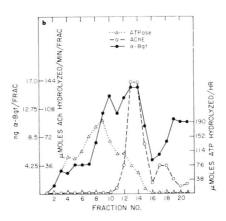

FIG. 1. Sucrose density gradient distribution of electroplax membrane fragments from (a) *Torpedo californica* and (b) *Electrophorus.*

in the membrane. Only the esterase can be removed by treatment with collagenase, also suggesting a more external localization than that of the receptor.

Equilibrium sucrose density gradient centrifugation of electroplax tissue membranes labeled with ^{125}I-α-bungarotoxin (a-Bgt), which binds specifically to the receptor, demonstrates a clear separation of toxin binding and esterase activity (Duguid and Raftery, 1973a,b; Fig. 1). SDS gel electrophoresis patterns of the material obtained from these two fractions are quite distinct. The small amount of toxin associated with the esterase peak in the gradient (Fig. 1b) can be separated by fractionation on a shallower gradient. The two proteins do not appear to be associated with each other or with the same membrane constituents.

Purification of the ACh Receptor

Purification of the ACh receptor is much more difficult than that of the esterase (Leuzinger and Baker, 1967), because no simple assay exists that is comparable to those for catalytic proteins. The one property of the protein that can be used as an assay is the binding of ligand. The availability of the irreversible inhibitor α-bungarotoxin provided a convenient assay method (Schmidt and Raftery, 1973a) that is simpler and more reliable than one using a small, reversibly bound ligand such as ACh.

Membrane fragments or a detergent extract of membranes containing the ACh receptor are slightly acidic, whereas α-bungarotoxin and its iodinated derivative are highly basic, with a pI > 9. This made possible a simple assay procedure in which the receptor-toxin complex, either on membrane fragments or in solution, is retained by DEAE filter paper, while free toxin is not. The amount of radioactive material retained by a DEAE filter is a reliable assay of the amount of receptor material (Schmidt and Raftery, 1973a).

When the α-bungarotoxin binding material from $T.$ $californica$ is solubilized with Triton X-100, it chromatographs as a high-molecular-weight complex (Fig. 2a). This material has a Stokes' radius similar to that of β-galactosidase, whose molecular weight is 450,000. However, centrifugation of the same material yields an S value of 9–10 (Fig. 2b), indicating a much lower molecular weight. This discrepancy is probably the result of comparing a membrane protein that binds a significant amount of detergent with aqueous proteins that do not, and the true value probably lies somewhere between 250 and 400 $\times$ 10^3. The ^{125}I-α-bungarotoxin binding receptor complex has a pI of 4.9 (Fig. 2c).

The receptor protein is further purified by passing the Triton X-100 extract of the electroplax membrane through an agarose affinity column containing a bound ACh analogue (Schmidt and Raftery, 1973b). Most of the protein in the extract passes through the column, while the α-bungaro-

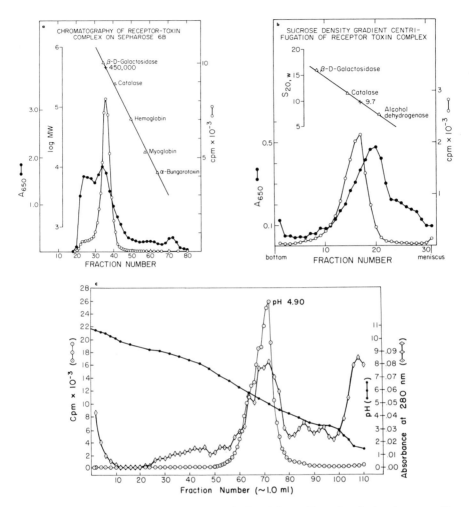

FIG. 2. Characterization of the receptor isolated from *Torpedo* electroplaques with Triton X-100. (a) Chromatography of the receptor-toxin complex on Sepharose 6B. (b) Sucrose density gradient centrifugation of the receptor-toxin complex. (c) Isoelectric focusing of the ^{125}I-α-bungarotoxin binding activity.

toxin binding activity and the esterase are retained. These proteins are then eluted with a gradually increasing concentration of either a specific ligand or NaCl; the esterase binds more tightly than the receptor protein to the ACh analogue column, and the two are easily separated. The purified binding activity can now be obtained with a 63% yield, or 80 to 100 mg/kg tissue (Table 1). The specific activity of this material corresponds to one toxin binding site per 80,000 daltons.

The binding activity eluted from the agarose affinity column contains two major polypeptide fractions when electrophoresed on an SDS gel

TABLE 1. *Purification of AcChR*

	Protein (mg)	Activity (μg of Bgt bound)	Q*	Q'**	Purif. (x)	Recovery (%)
Homogenate	18,600	15,600	0.84	0.105	—	100
Membrane suspension	3,250	15,600	4.8	0.60	5.7	100
Triton extract	1,350	15,600	11.5	1.45	13.7	100
Affinity pool	95	9,800	103	13.0	125.0	63

* $Q \equiv$ μg α-Bgt bound per milligram of protein.
** $Q' \equiv$ nanomoles of α-Bgt bound per milligram of protein.

(Fig. 3); both fractions stain for carbohydrate as well as for protein. It is not yet known whether these represent distinct polypeptide chains or a single protein containing a variable amount of carbohydrate. The toxin binding component contains a total of 5 to 6% carbohydrate, consisting of mannose, galactose, and N-acetylglucosamine. That the binding species is a glycoprotein is also indicated by its complete retention by an affinity column containing concanavalin A.

Further purification of the material eluted from an affinity column can be achieved by sequential chromatography on DEAE, hydroxyapatite, and Sepharose 4B, followed by ammonium sulfate fractionation or by rechromatography on affinity columns. The same polypeptide bands are still present in SDS gels, but the specific activity is increased to one toxin binding site per 65,000 to 70,000 daltons. The material still has a sedimentation value of 9.5S and a pI of about 5. Several groups (Patrick and Lindstrom, 1973; Sugiyama, Benda, Meunier, and Changeux, 1973; Raftery and Schmidt, *unpublished*) have now prepared antibodies to this material, and the close relationship to AChR from electric fish is evident from the ability of such antibodies to affect neuromuscular depolarization in frog muscle (Deutsch and Raftery, *unpublished*).

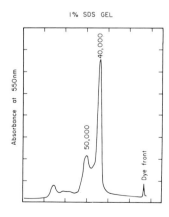

FIG. 3. SDS gel of the binding activity eluted from an affinity column.

The Binding Properties of the ACh Receptor

The association rate constant for ^{125}I-α-bungarotoxin binding to the purified protein is $\sim 10^6$ M^{-1} sec^{-1}. The addition of a cholinergic ligand at low toxin concentrations decreased the rate of toxin-protein association and permitted the calculation of an inhibition constant for ACh of 2 $\times$

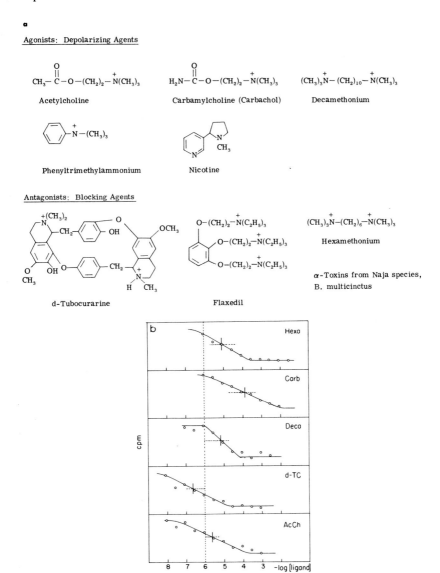

FIG. 4. (a) The cholinergic series of agonists and antagonists used to examine the binding properties of the purified cholinergic receptor. (b) The binding of the series shown in Fig. 4(a) to the cholinergic receptor protein.

TABLE 2. *Binding of cholinergic fluorescent probe**
to the purified cholinergic receptor

Compound	Dissociation constant M
DAP**	1.3 (+0.2) $\times$ 10^{-7}†
AcCh	5 (+1) $\times$ 10^{-6}
D-TC	1.8 (+0.2) $\times$ 10^{-7}
Decamethonium	2.5 (+0.2) $\times$ 10^{-6}
Carbamylcholine	8 (+1.5) $\times$ 10^{-5}

* In 10 mM sodium phosphate, pH 7.4.
** Gift of Dr. D. Sigman.
† α-Bgt prevents binding of DAP.

10^{-6} M. Similar constants were also obtained for a series of cholinergic agonists and antagonists (Fig. 4). The inhibition characteristics of these molecules reflect the nicotinic nature of the isolated receptor (Moody, Schmidt, and Raferty, 1973). The binding properties of the purified protein have also been examined with the fluorescent probe bis-(3-aminopyridinium)-1,10-decane diiodide (DAP), whose structure is similar to decamethonium (Martinez-Carrion and Raftery, 1973). The dissociation constant of the probe can be easily calculated, because its fluorescence is completely quenched when bound to the receptor, and the inhibition of its binding by other compounds can be determined (Table 2).

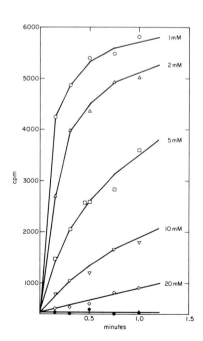

FIG. 5. Toxin binding rate as a function of the millimolar concentration of NaCl.

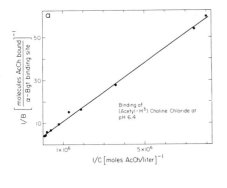
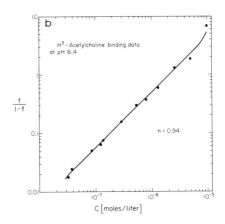

FIG. 6. (a) A reciprocal plot for the binding of ACh, using the number of α-bungarotoxin binding sites as a means of standardization. (b) A Hill plot of this data yields a slope of 1.

The dissociation constant of DAP is dependent on ionic strength, specifically on the cation concentration, and stronger effects are observed for divalent than for monovalent cations. This effect is not restricted to the binding of DAP; as shown in Fig. 5, the rate of toxin binding is also strongly affected by NaCl concentration.

The method of equilibrium dialysis can be used to examine directly the binding of labeled ACh and the relationships between various agonists and antagonists. These studies of ACh binding (Fig. 6) indicate a single class of binding sites, with $K_{dissoc} = 2 \times 10^{-6}$ M. No indications of cooperativity in binding have been observed, and recent data on membrane fragments (R. Vandlen, Y. Chao, and M. A. Raftery, *unpublished*) suggest that this is not due to a loss of cooperative behavior in this solubilized purified system. A comparison of membrane depolarization versus ligand concentration suggests a cooperative interaction, but a series of intermediate steps might separate the process of depolarization from the initial binding of ligand.

At neutral pH, the number of binding sites for ACh, carbamylcholine, tubocurarine, decamethonium, and similar ligands is exactly half the number of toxin binding sites. This suggests that the receptor may resemble glyceraldehyde phosphate dehydrogenase, in which only half of the presumed active sites are catalytically active. This nonequivalence may be preexistent within the receptor and not dependent on ligand-induced changes (J. Bode and M. A. Raftery, *unpublished*).

ACh and carbamylcholine competitively bind to the same sites on the receptor (Fig. 7a), and Na^+ competitively inhibits D-tubocurarine binding (Fig. 7b). However, crossover experiments in which ACh binding is inhibited with Na^+ or tubocurarine do not indicate simple competitive in-

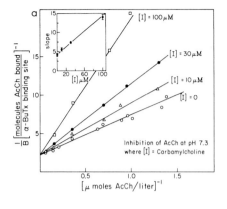

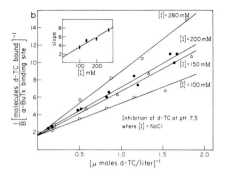

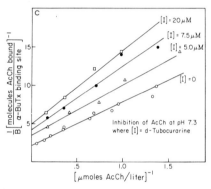

FIG. 7. (a) The inhibition of ACh binding by carbamylcholine. (b) The inhibition of D-tubocurine binding by Na. (c) The inhibition of ACh binding by D-tubocurarine.

hibition for a *single* class of binding sites. The ion binding site is probably not identical with the ACh binding site; however, the strict competition between Ca^{2+} and tubocurarine, toxins, and other antagonists suggests that they bind to the same subsites.

Reconstitution Experiments

The receptor protein purified by successive chromatographic procedures continues to bind large amounts of the Triton X-100 with which it was originally extracted. Most of the detergent can be exchanged for sodium cholate by Sepharose gel filtration in cholate, or by extensive washing on DEAE, first with cholate, then followed by elution with salt.

This purified receptor protein strongly associates with lecithin or other phospholipids; these protein-phospholipid complexes can be demonstrated by density gradient centrifugation and form closed vesicles. The reformed phospholipid-receptor complex binds both α-bungarotoxin and cholinergic ligands. The amount of toxin that can be bound by the complex is identical to that bound by the purified protein before reconstitution; it also remains constant if the phospholipid-receptor association is disrupted by detergent. This observation that toxin association is not altered by the presence of phospholipid is of particular interest in view of discussion regarding the polarity of reconstituted materials (Chapters 3 and 4).

It is not yet known whether the reconstituted system will permit ion flux under appropriate conditions, or whether an ionophore or ion carrier associated with the receptor *in vivo* is still present and can initiate ion flux leading to depolarization in the reconstituted system. However, it is tempting to speculate that the cation binding site may be related to such an ionophore.[1]

APPLICATIONS OF THE ALLOSTERIC MODEL TO THE PHYSIOLOGICAL PROPERTIES OF THE ACETYLCHOLINE RECEPTOR:

Stuart J. Edelstein

An interesting feature of single-cell electroplax preparations from the electric eel, *Electrophorus electricus,* is the cooperative dependence of depolarization on the concentration of ACh analogues. Moreover, the extent of depolarization as a function of ligand concentration varies with different ACh analogues (Changeux and Podleski, 1968), and the extent to which binding can be inhibited by a variety of agents differs significantly (Fig. 8). For example, the affinity label *p*-(trimethylammonium)benzene diazonium difluoroborate (TDF) inhibits the binding of carbamylcholine and decamethonium 20 to 30% and 80%, respectively.

The basic assumption invoked to explain these data was that the critical event for the initiation of a depolarization response is a conformational change in the receptor rather than ligand binding *per se* (Edelstein, 1972). Given an allosteric protein that can exist in two states, T and R (see Chapter 2), the extent of the conformational change in the receptor need not be a linear function of ligand binding. The addition of a ligand, which has a higher affinity for the R state, to a system which is initially in the T state will shift the R ↔ T equilibrium to the R state. However, unless the ligand binds exclusively to the R state, a significant fraction of the receptor population may remain in the T state, even at 100% saturation.

If membrane depolarization is coupled to the fraction of receptor in the R state, the variable effects of cholinergic ligands could result from incomplete shifts of the equilibrium between the two states. This is illustrated in Fig. 9, which compares the effect on the equilibrium between the T and R states for two ligands having different preferences for the R state.

---

[1] The lecture presented by Dr. Raftery is Contribution No. 4901 from the Church Laboratory of Chemical Biology, California Institute of Technology.

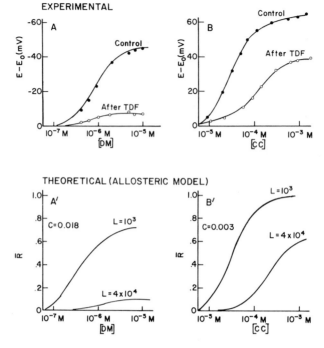

FIG. 8. (*Top*) Membrane depolarization in single-cell preparation from the electric eel in response to increasing concentrations of decamethonium (DM) and carbamylcholine (CM), and the inhibition of these responses by TDF. Data from Changeux, Podleski, and Meunier (1969). (*Bottom*) Theoretical curve derived from the allosteric model (From Edelstein, 1972).

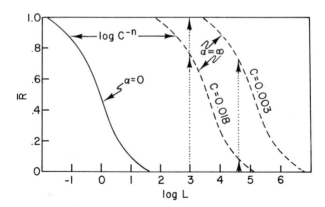

FIG. 9. The fraction of the receptor population in the R state ($\bar{R}$) as a function of the allosteric constant for the equilibrium between the T and R states ($L = T/R$) in the absence of ligand ($\alpha = 0$) and in the presence of two ligands having different preferential affinities for the R state ($c = 0.003$, $c = 0.018$), where c is the ratio of dissociation constants for the T and R states ($c = K_R/K_T$).

In the absence of ligand, the receptor will exist predominantly in the R state if the ratio T/R (L) is small; as L → 100, the protein will be almost completely in the T state, and $\overline{R}$ will approach zero. When the system is saturated with ligand, the extent of conversion to the R state will be dependent on the degree to which the ligand binds preferentially to the R state, given by the coefficient c. The fraction of protein that exists in the R state at saturation will increase as c → 0. A value of $c = 0.018$ represents a 56-fold preference for the R state. In a two-site system having an L of 10^3, a saturation level of ligand with a value of $c = 0.018$ would promote the transition of 75% of the receptor molecules to the R state and depolarization to 75% of the maximum. In contrast, for the ligand with a value of $c = 0.003$, the transition to the R state at saturation is essentially complete. Values of 0.018 and 0.003 for the c coefficients of decamethonium and carbamylcholine, respectively, can be used to replicate the experimental data (Fig. 8). A two-site system was used in these calculations because the Hill coefficient of cooperativity for the system is never greater than 2.

The change in the value of L in the presence of an inhibitor can be calculated from the extent to which the curve is shifted to the right (Edelstein, 1971). A value for L of 4×10^4 has been obtained for TDF, indicating that it increases the stability of the T state. For a given value of c, this increased stability means that the ligand will produce a much smaller shift toward the R state. With the L value that corresponds to TDF, the extent of the transition to the R state in the presence of decamethonium ($c = 0.018$) would be reduced from 75% to 10%, while that for carbamylcholine ($c = 0.003$) would be reduced from 100% to 75%. These changes are indicated in Fig. 9, and the corresponding simulated depolarization curves are shown in Fig. 8.

The close agreement between the theoretically generated and experimental data suggests, although it does not prove, that the model is correct. The model assumes that the proportion of receptor material in the R state is directly related to the voltage change, and that the voltage change is in turn linearly related to conductance change (which is presumably the physiologically significant parameter). Data on the relationship between conductance and voltage are scant (see Rang, 1971), and this point warrants further examination.

In order to relate this model to the properties of the isolated receptor, described in the preceding section by Raftery, it is assumed that the system will relax into the R state if the constraint of the membrane environment is removed, that is, the value of L will decrease to 1 or less. Predictions about the isolated receptor that are based on this assumption agree well with experimental observations.

Table 3 summarizes some of the properties of the ACh receptor within the electroplax membrane and after purification. L values can be related to the apparent dissociation constants for carbamylcholine and deca-

TABLE 3. *Properties of the ACh receptor*

A. In electroplax membrane:
   Carbamylcholine, $K_D = 3 \times 10^{-5}$ M
   Decamethonium, $K_D = 10^{-6}$ M
   Allosteric parameters (n = 2):
       $L = 10^3$; $c = 0.003$ (carb.); $c = 0.018$ (deca.)
B. Isolated receptor:
   Allosteric parameters (n = 2):
       $L = (\alpha_{1/2})^2$; $\alpha^{1/2} = 30$; $K_D = K_{D(\text{electroplax})}/30$

	Predict	Observe (Meunier and Changeux)
Carbamylcholine	$K_D = 10^{-6}$ M	$K_D = 2 \times 10^{-6}$ M
Decamethonium	$K_D = 3 \times 10^{-8}$ M	$K_D = 2 \times 10^{-8}$ M

methonium. Since the magnitude of L is related to the stability of the T state, which has the lower affinity for ligand, large values of L indicate a more stable T state and a relative shift in the corresponding binding curves to the right. In other words, L is related to the extent that the apparent affinity is reduced compared to the affinity of the R state. This relationship can be expressed in terms of $\alpha_{1/2}$, the concentration of ligand at half-saturation divided by the dissociation constant for the R state. Since L is proportional to $\alpha_{1/2}$ raised to a power equal to the number of binding sites (Edelstein, 1971), for a two-site system:

$$L = (\alpha_{1/2})^2$$

Thus, for $L = 1,000$, $\alpha_{1/2} \simeq 30$, and measurements of the binding of the isolated receptor, assumed to be in the R state, should show an apparent affinity 30-fold greater than that estimated from depolarization of the intact cell, that is,

$$K_{D(\text{isol})} = \frac{K_{D(\text{electroplax})}}{30}$$

For carbamylcholine,

$$K_{D(\text{isol})} = \frac{(3 \times 10^{-5})}{30} = 10^{-6} \text{ M}$$

For decamethonium,

$$K_D = \frac{10^{-6}}{30} = 3 \times 10^{-8} \text{ M}$$

These values agree closely with the experimental values of 2×10^{-6} and 2×10^{-8} M obtained by Meunier and Changeux (1973).

The observation that cholinergic antagonists have the same or similar affinities for the intact and isolated receptor is compatable with the allosteric model in terms of nonexclusive binding. These antagonists appear to have a slight (two-three-fold) preference for the T state, which is much lower than the factor of at least 50 for the agonists.

On the basis of this analysis, it appears that a two-state allosteric model can adequately represent electroplax depolarization in terms of an $\overline{R}$ function, and can relate the properties of the isolated receptor to the intact system. It now remains to be determined if the properties of the intact system can be reconstituted using the isolated receptor, lipids, and possibly other factors, along the lines initiated by Raftery and his co-workers, described in the preceding section. In this regard, it would be of interest to know the molecular size of the functional receptor unit in the membrane. While most characterization of the isolated receptor has been carried out in solutions containing Triton X-100, measurements have recently been performed on purified receptor material that is virtually free of Triton (S. J. Edelstein, W. B. Beyer, A. T. Eldefrawi, and M. E. Eldefrawi, *unpublished*). A minimum molecular weight of about 600,000 was established from sedimentation equilibrium studies, and the value was found to decrease to about 320,000 in the presence of Triton X-100. These estimates are in accord with the data of Raftery and co-workers, in which the estimates of molecular weight from exclusion chromatography are higher than those from sucrose gradients, since bound Triton would increase the Stokes' radius but decrease the sedimentation in sucrose gradients as the result of buoyancy effects. Determination of the molecular size within the membrane and the conditions under which that size can be maintained may be an important factor in achieving successful reconstitution.

REFERENCES

Changeux, J.-P., and Podleski, T. R. (1968): On the excitability and cooperativity of the electroplax membrane. *Proc. Nat. Acad. Sci.*, 59:944–950.

Changeux, J.-P., Podleski, T., and Meunier, J.-C. (1969): On some structural analogies between actylcholinesterase and the macromolecular receptor of acetylcholine. *J. Gen. Physiol.*, 54:225s–244s.

Duguid, J. R., and Raftery, M. A. (1973a): Fractionation and partial characterization of membrane particles from *Torpedo californica* electroplax. *Biochemistry*, 12:3593–3597.

Duguid, J. R., and Raftery, M. A. (1973b): The fractionation and partial characterization of membrane fragments derived from the electric organ of *Electrophorus electricus*. *Arch. Biochem. Biophys.*, 159:512–516.

Edelstein, S. J. (1971): Extensions of the allosteric model for haemoglobin. *Nature*, 230:224–227.

Edelstein, S. J. (1972): An allosteric mechanism for the acetylcholine receptor. *Biochem. Biophys. Res. Commun.*, 48:1160–1165.

Leuzinger, W., and Baker, A. L. (1967): Acetylcholinesterase, I. Large-scale purification, homogeneity, and amino acid analysis. *Proc. Nat. Acad. Sci.*, 57:446–451.

Martinez-Carrion, M., and Raftery, M. A. (1973): Use of a fluorescent probe for the study of ligand binding by the isolated cholinergic receptor of *Torpedo californica*. *Biochem. Biophys. Res. Commun.*, 55:1156–1164.

Meunier, J.-C., and Changeux, J.-P. (1973): Comparison between the affinities for reversible cholinergic ligands of a purified and membrane bound state of the acetylcholine-receptor protein from *Electrophorus electricus. FEBS Letters,* 32:143–148.

Moody, T., Schmidt, J., and Raftery, M. A. (1973): Binding of acetylcholine and related compounds to purified acetylcholine receptor from *Torpedo californica* electroplax. *Biochem. Biophys. Res. Commun.,* 53:761–772.

Patrick, J., and Lindstrom, J. (1973): Autoimmune response to acetylcholine receptor. *Science,* 180:871–872.

Rang, H. P. (1971): Drug receptors and their function. *Nature,* 231:91–96.

Schmidt, J., and Raftery, M. A. (1973*a*): A simple assay for the study of solubilized acetylcholine receptors. *Anal. Biochem.,* 52:349–354.

Schmidt, J., and Raftery, M. A. (1973*b*): Purification of acetylcholine receptors from *Torpedo californica* electroplax by affinity chromatography. *Biochemistry,* 12:852–856.

Sugiyama, H., Benda, P., Meunier, J.-C., and Changeux, J.-P. (1973): Immunological characterisation of the cholinergic receptor protein from *Electrophorus electricus. FEBS Letters,* 35:124–128.

Functional Linkage in Biomolecular Systems, edited by
F. O. Schmitt, D. M. Schneider, and D. M. Crothers.
Raven Press, New York © 1975.

TRANSDUCTIVE COUPLING IN SENSORY RECEPTORS

Transductive coupling in sensory receptors is similar to the linked functions discussed in the preceding section, but is unique in the ability of the receptor system to detect extremely small stimulus inputs. For example, the absorption of a single photon is sufficient to alter the synaptic output of a rod photoreceptor, and the adsorption of a single molecule by a taste or olfactory receptor can in some cases elicit an electrical response in that cell. However, the interpretation of sensitivity from such observations must be carefully defined, because the production of a behavioral response usually requires the stimulation of more than one receptor cell.

Such high sensitivity is obviously of great adaptive advantage, because it permits the organism to detect and to act on extremely small environmental alterations. Sense organs exist for the detection in the environment of a wide range of energy modalities, and many receptor systems are capable of detecting and transducing with fidelity a 6 to 10 log unit range of input.

The best-defined sensory system is that which mediates vision. The transduction from absorption of a photon to altered synaptic activity is thought to occur by triggering, through a conformational change in rhodopsin, the release of many Ca^{2+} ions (Chapter 11). It has been proposed that calcium ions may generally serve such a switching function in cellular responses to incoming stimuli. Ca^{2+} release is involved in one fashion or another in many of the biological systems discussed in this volume, the best-characterized example being that of muscle (Chapter 14).

The transduction processes in the nonvisual sensory systems are less well defined. The chemosensory systems (Chapter 12) are particularly interesting because of the large number of compounds to which they can respond, over a wide range of molecular weights. The cells of the receptor systems have differential responses to various stimulus inputs, and the response pattern generated within the system is responsible for identification of the ligand. An exception to this is the pheromone system, which is highly specialized for the reception of molecules generated by other members of the species as a means of communication (Chapter 12).

Bacterial chemotaxis, described in Chapter 13, is a promising system for elucidating the principles of chemosensory transduction. The chemotactic system is utilized by bacteria to detect nutrients and other attractants, so that the organism can move toward them, as well as to repel themselves from harmful substances. Because it is possible to select for a wide range of mutant types, substantial advances have been made in identifying components of the system that link the reception of stimulant molecules at the cell surface to the mechanism that controls flagellar motile activity.

Functional Linkage in Biomolecular Systems, edited by
F. O. Schmitt, D. M. Schneider, and D. M. Crothers.
Raven Press, New York © 1975.

Chapter 11

Transductive Coupling in the Visual System

HISTORICAL INTRODUCTION:

Werner E. Reichardt

One of the first problems investigated in the field of human vision was a
determination of the amount of light both necessary and sufficient to elicit
an elementary photochemical response capable of triggering the sequence of
events leading to the perception of a light flash. The threshold for human
vision was found to be equivalent to a light energy of 2.1 to 5.7×10^{-10}
ergs at the corneal surface (Hecht, Shlaer, and Pirenne, 1942), which corresponds to 58 to 148 quanta of blue-green light. Elimination of such factors
as corneal reflection, absorption by the optic media, and retinal light transmission leads to an upper limit of 5 to 14 quanta actually absorbed by the
retinal rods. Since more than 500 rods were utilized in the experiment, it
precludes any significant two quantum absorptions per rod. In order to
produce a visual effect, one quantum must be absorbed by each of 5 to 14
rods in the retina; that is, a coincidence of 5 to 14 primary events is necessary for the perception of a light flash. This might be due to the fact that
several hundred rods are tied together within the retinal ganglion cells,
which function as a coincidence-detecting network.

That light receptors of the insect eye are also excited by single quanta
has been shown by analyzing the response to a moving contrast stimulus
under the influence of the poissonian fluctuation of the light quanta (Fermi
and Reichardt, 1963). However, in contrast to visual processing in the
human, no coincidence counting occurs in the interneurons of the first
optic ganglion in insect visual systems (Reichardt, 1965; Scholes, 1969;
Kirschfeld and Lutz, 1974).

Intra- and extracellular recordings in the *Limulus* eye confirmed the
earlier inference that a single light quantum can excite a visual receptor
(Yeandle, 1957, 1958; Fuortes and Yeandle, 1964; Scholes, 1964). Under
dim illumination, it was possible to observe small depolarization potentials
whose average occurrence was proportional to the quantum flux and that
showed a first-order poissonian time distribution.

The reception of a light quantum leads to the bleaching of rhodopsin both in solution and *in vivo;* the result is a conversion of rhodopsin into transretinal and opsin (see, for instance, Kropf, 1969):

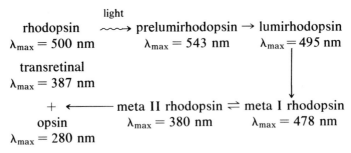

$$\text{rhodopsin} \quad \xrightarrow{\text{light}} \quad \text{prelumirhodopsin} \rightarrow \text{lumirhodopsin}$$
$$\lambda_{max} = 500 \text{ nm} \qquad \lambda_{max} = 543 \text{ nm} \qquad \lambda_{max} = 495 \text{ nm}$$

$$\text{transretinal}$$
$$\lambda_{max} = 387 \text{ nm}$$

$$+ \quad \longleftarrow \quad \text{meta II rhodopsin} \rightleftharpoons \text{meta I rhodopsin}$$
$$\text{opsin} \qquad \lambda_{max} = 380 \text{ nm} \qquad \lambda_{max} = 478 \text{ nm}$$
$$\lambda_{max} = 280 \text{ nm}$$

There is a time lapse of several milliseconds between the absorption of a photon and the production of membrane depolarization. A number of studies have examined the events that occur during this period in order to determine how the conformational transitions involved in the conversion of rhodopsin to retinal and opsin lead to a change in membrane permeability. An electrical response to the absorption of a photon that has no detectable latency was first observed by Brown and Murakami (1964), and was studied in more detail by Cone (1964), Pak and Cone (1964), Brown (1965), and Cone (1967); this response was called the early receptor potential (ERP).

The close relationship between ERP responses and rhodopsin transitions, and the opposite polarities of the different ERP responses (Fig. 1), suggested that they are generated by the net displacement of the charges in or near the rhodopsin molecule as it undergoes changes in conformation. The ERP is neither generated nor affected by ionic membrane events.

The exponential decay of the ERP suggested that the potential generated by charge displacements within the rhodopsin decays passively as the result of charge flow through a resistive capacitive circuit. Such a passive dis-

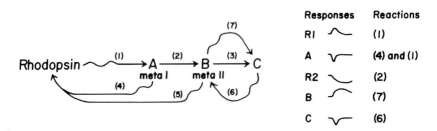

FIG. 1. Photochemical and thermal reactions of rhodopsin, the corresponding ERP, and the photoproduct response. Photochemical reactions are denoted by wavy lines; thermal reactions by straight lines. The five responses are listed along with sketches to show their polarity, waveform, and reactions in which each is involved. (From Cone, 1967.)

charge is to be expected if the rhodopsin molecules are incorporated electrically into the receptor membrane. The density of pigment molecules in this membrane is extremely high, and the charge displacements necessary to produce the ERP are therefore very small. There are approximately 5×10^{12} rhodopsin molecules/cm^2 in the membrane of the rod outer segment. A membrane having a capacitance of 1 μF/cm^2 and displacing one charge per molecule through the membrane would produce a polarization of about 0.4 V. Since the maximum extracellular ERP is about 10 mV, charge displacements in the angstrom range are therefore probably sufficient to produce the ERP. Such small charge displacements are at least three orders of magnitude too small to act as electrical signals for communicating with the synapse. Because the ERPs are generated as the result of conformational transitions in a pigment molecule, they can be used to examine changes in rhodopsin during excitation.

The electrical properties of the extracellular space surrounding the photoreceptors of the squid have been characterized (Hagins, 1965), and the electrical events that follow the absorption of a photon by a squid visual receptor can be summarized as follows:

1. The absorption of a photon has a probability of at least 0.3 of initiating an elementary, quantized chemical response.

2. If a quantized response is produced, it consists of an inward-positive membrane current lasting less than 0.1 sec, and entirely confined to a region within 1 μ of the excited chromophore.

3. The current flows along the cytoplasm of the outer segment, and emerges through the cell membrane over a wide region. The voltage gradient across the retina during this flow comprises the electroretinogram recorded with external electrodes.

4. The average membrane depolarization produced by a quantized response is about 20 μV.

These events indicated that light must initiate an ionic current in squid photoreceptors having three properties: (1) it must flow through the cell membrane in the region of light absorption, (2) the quantum efficiency must be as high or higher than that of vision, and (3) many thousands of electronic charges must flow in a quantized response when a quantum is effectively absorbed.

Theoretical considerations (Baylor and Fuortes, 1970) suggested that rhodopsin may excite the cell by releasing an internal transmitter substance that diffuses to the receptor membrane to modulate ionic conductance. Evidence is now accumulating that this internal transmitter may be Ca^{2+} (Hagins, Penn, and Yoshikama, 1970; Yoshikama and Hagins, 1971; Penn and Hagins, 1972; Hagins and Yoshikami, 1974; Szuts and Cone, 1974; Winkler, 1974), and is described in detail in the next section by Cone.

TRANSDUCTIVE COUPLING IN THE VISUAL SYSTEM:

Richard A. Cone

Structure of the Retinal Rod

Light entering the eye passes through the retina and the inner segment of a visual receptor cell before entering the outer segment where photons are absorbed by the visual pigment (Fig. 2). The pigment molecules are located in a lamellar membrane array derived from invaginations of the plasma membrane, and more than 80% of the protein in these lamellar membrane discs is rhodopsin. As discussed in the preceding section, the absorption of a photon by any one of the 10^8 to 10^9 rhodopsin molecules in an outer segment is capable of altering the electrical activity of the entire rod cell.

The inner segment of the rod cell is packed with mitochondria, which appear to supply the metabolic energy needed to pump Na^+ continuously out of the cell; unlike most plasma membranes, which are highly resistant to Na^+ influx, the plasma membrane surrounding the outer segment of a rod is highly permeable to Na^+. Thus the Na^+ ions pumped out of the cell in the inner segment region rapidly leak back into the cell through the plasma membrane surrounding the outer segment (Hagins, 1972). The effect of light is to reduce transiently the Na permeability of this membrane, thereby reducing the influx of Na ions; the cell therefore hyperpolarizes in response to light. This hyperpolarization in turn probably reduces the rate at which a transmitter substance is released from the synaptic end of the receptor cell (Dowling and Ripps, 1973).

The visual pigment in nearly all photoreceptors is located in the plasma membrane. However, in vertebrate rods (and some cones), the plasma membrane invaginates to form discs that "pinch off" to become intra-cellular vesicles. We are then faced with the problem of how the light absorbed by the pigment in these free-floating discs can affect the Na^+ current flowing into the cell through the plasma membrane.

Structure of Rhodopsin

Rhodopsin molecules are closely packed in the disc membranes; X-ray diffraction and electron microscope evidence suggests that the average center-to-center distance between molecules is only about 70 Å. However, the molecules do not appear to aggregate or to form crystalline structures, but rather to be spaced in a liquid-like array (Blasie and Worthington, 1969).

Data obtained from X-ray studies, electron microscopy, chemical analyses, fluorescent labeling, concanavalin A (con A) binding, and freeze-fracture have led to the tentative structure shown in Fig. 3. Con A binds to a sugar group on rhodopsin located on the outside of the disc; thus at least one part of the rhodopsin molecule must be accessible to the cytoplasmic surface of the disc membrane (Steinemann and Stryer, 1973; Raubach, Nemes, and Dratz, 1974). When this sugar residue was labeled with a chromophore, energy-transfer studies indicated that the sugar residue is located approximately 60 Å away from the site to which retinal (vitamin A aldehyde) binds to opsin (Wu and Stryer, 1972). This analysis is based on the principle that excitation energy can be transferred from one chromophore to another with an efficiency that depends strongly on the distance between the chromophores (Förster, 1965).

Chromophore labeling of other sites (A and B) within the molecule indicated that site A is at least 75 Å from the aldehyde, and that site B is about 60 Å from retinal and 30 Å from site A (Wu and Stryer, 1972). Surface markers that do not penetrate the membrane did not approach retinal closer than 60 Å, suggesting that retinal must reside on the intradiscal face of the membrane, on the opposite face from the sugar group. Additional evidence that rhodopsin spans the disc membrane has been obtained from freeze-fracture studies (Chen and Hubbell, 1973). It is therefore highly likely that rhodopsin spans the membrane, with the sugar residue on the cytoplasmic face and retinal on the intradiscal face, the face which is extracellular prior to the pinching off of the disc. The elongated structure proposed for the rhodopsin molecule is drawn consistent with its molecular weight of about 36,000 (Lewis, Krieg, and Kirk, 1974).

Because rhodopsin is a pigment, it was studied long before the present era of protein chemistry. Over a century ago, Kuhne made the important observation that rhodopsin can be removed from the retina only by treatment with a detergent, and Guidotti (Chapter 4) has recently shown that approximately one-third of the surface area of the rhodopsin molecule binds the detergent Triton X-100. A sizeable portion of the molecular surface thus appears to be hydrophobic, as indicated in Fig. 3. Rhodopsin extracted in aqueous solution retains its color only when gentle detergents are used for the extraction procedure; most detergents denature and bleach the molecule, a fact that stands as a warning for research on other membrane proteins.

The immediate effect of light on the chromophore is to isomerize it, and although the details of this process have yet to be elucidated, it appears that the isomerization produces a dramatic change in the conformation of the chromophore (Fig. 4). The 11-*cis* form of retinal appears to fit with great stereospecificity into a deep hydrophobic groove of the opsin; therefore, any change in the conformation of the chromophore probably forces the conformation of the opsin to change.

Visual excitation is probably triggered by this conformational change. The bleaching process, in which retinal separates from the opsin, takes place minutes to hours after the photon is absorbed, far too late to be in-

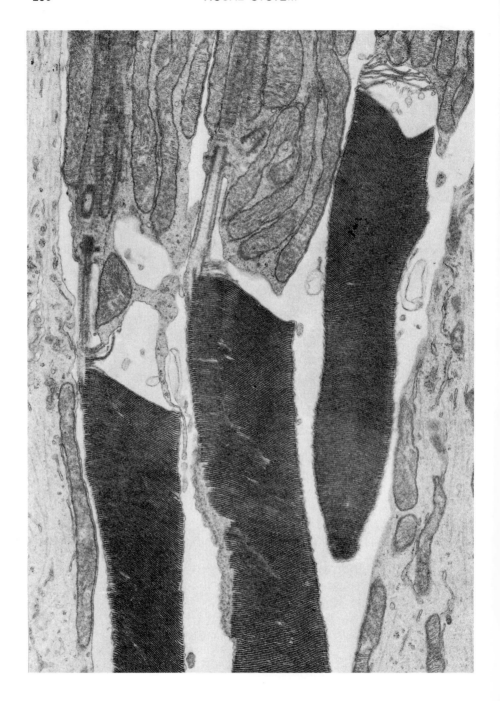

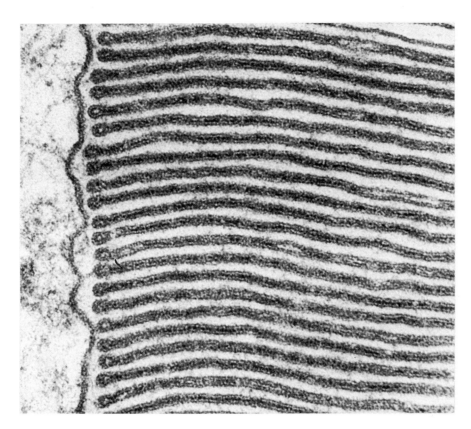

FIG. 2. (Left). Electron micrograph of the inner and outer segments, and the connecting cilium, of guinea pig rod-type visual receptors. (From Clark and Branton, 1968.) (Right). The lamellar disc arrangement of the rod outer segment. (From Dowling, 1967.)

volved in the excitation mechanism. Indeed, many invertebrate rhodopsins do not bleach; photons appear to drive these pigments back and forth between two stable states. Excitation occurs when a photon drives the rhodopsin molecule to a stable "meta" state but not when a photon "photoregenerates" the molecule back to the initial state (Hamdorf, Paulsen, and Schwemer, 1973). This photoregeneration mechanism seems highly efficient; no matter how bright the light there will always be pigment available to excite the cell. In contrast, the slow bleaching and enzymic regeneration process in vertebrates is without apparent purpose; the pigment bleaches in bright light, and the regeneration process limits the rate of dark adaptation.

Following a flash, invertebrate rhodopsins rapidly convert to the stable meta state, and reach this state before the receptor potential decays (Hagins, 1972; Fein and Cone, 1973). Similarly, vertebrate rhodopsins reach the meta II state in a time that is short compared to the receptor potential. But

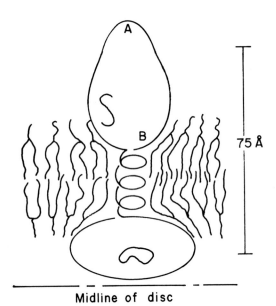

75 Å

Midline of disc

FIG. 3. Tentative structure and disposition of the rhodopsin molecule in the disc membrane. The sugar group, S, and two of the sites labeled with chromophores, A and B, are shown on the cytoplasmic moiety, a helical structure is shown spanning the hydrophobic phase, and 11-*cis* retinal is outlined in the intradiscal moiety. (From Poo and Cone, 1974.)

to date, there is no clear evidence to indicate how the photoinduced conformational change enables the rhodopsin molecule to excite the receptor.

Unlike chlorophyll, rhodopsin molecules are sufficiently widely spaced in the membrane that little, if any, energy transfer occurs between rhodopsin chromophores (Hagins and Jennings, 1959; Brown, 1972). Moreover, rhodopsin does not appear to conserve the energy of the photon for use in some other process. Instead, it appears to use the energy of the photon to "throw a switch," to convert the chromophore into a conformation it virtually never attains by thermal processes. The photoisomerization of the chromophore thus serves as a highly reliable signal that a photon has been absorbed.

Since the chromophore of rhodopsin is intrinsically dichroic, polarized light can be used to observe both the orientation of the chromophore and the motion of rhodopsin in the disc membrane. Rods viewed from the side are dichroic, absorbing light best when the electric vector is parallel to the surface of the disc membranes (Schmidt, 1938). This indicates that the chromophores must lie at least approximately parallel to the plane of the disc membrane. (This is the optimal orientation for absorption of light passing through the receptor.) In contrast, rods are not dichroic when viewed end-on, even after they have been partially bleached with polarized light. This surprising finding (Hagins and Jennings, 1959) remained unexplained until it was found recently that rhodopsin is free to undergo rotational diffusion about an axis perpendicular to the membrane surface

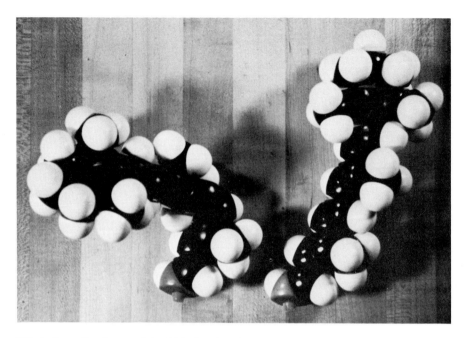

FIG. 4. Corey-Pauling models of 11-*cis*, 12-s-*cis* retinal, and all-*trans* retinal that illustrate the change in shape that may occur when the chromophore is isomerized by the absorption of one photon.

(Brown, 1972; Cone, 1972). As shown in Fig. 5, rods viewed end-on do in fact become dichroic following a polarized bleaching flash, but the dichroism decays very rapidly. Within a few microseconds, the angular orientation of the rhodopsin molecules is randomized by rotational diffusion. For frog rods at 20°C, the rotational diffusion constant, D_{rot}, is about 5×10^4 sec^{-1} (Cone, 1972). Glutaraldehyde fixation prevents this rotational diffusion, apparently by cross-linking rhodopsin molecules (Brown, 1972).

Rhodopsin also undergoes rapid lateral diffusion in the disc membrane (Fig. 6). If one side of a rod is bleached, the remaining pigment rapidly diffuses across each disc and attains a uniform distribution in well under a minute, even in rods more than 13 μ in diameter. For frog and mud puppy rods at 20°C, the diffusion constant, D_{trans}, for lateral (translational) diffusion is about 4×10^{-9} cm^2/sec (Poo and Cone, 1974).

With the aid of the Einstein-Stokes relationships, these two diffusion constants can be used to estimate both the effective radius, r, of rhodopsin, and the viscosity, η, of the membrane:

$$D_{rot} = \frac{kT}{8\pi\eta r^3}$$

$$D_{trans} = \frac{kT}{6\pi\eta r}$$

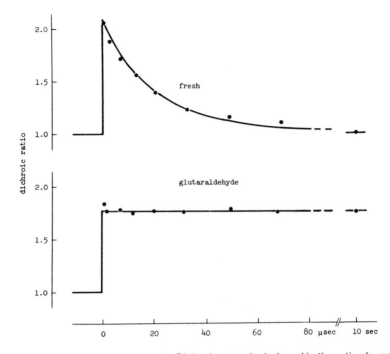

FIG. 5. Rotational diffusion of rhodopsin. Dichroism can be induced in the retina by applying a polarized bleaching flash which selectively activates those rhodopsin molecules
whose chromophores are most closely aligned with the electric vector of the polarized
flash. In a fresh retina, the dichroism rapidly decays as a result of the rotational diffusion
of rhodopsin. If the retina is fixed with glutaraldehyde before the flash is delivered, the
flash-induced dichroism does not decay (note dichroic ratio at 10 sec). (From Cone, 1972.)

If rhodopsin is assumed to be approximately spherical in shape and
mostly submerged in the membrane, the equations indicate that the molecule has an effective radius of approximately 30 Å and experiences a
viscosity in the membrane of about 2 poise. Given the nature of the analysis, these can only be considered as approximate values. However, both
results are reasonable. For example, the molecular weight of rhodopsin,
the spacings observed by X-rays (Blasie and Worthington, 1969), and
freeze-fracture results (Chen and Hubbell, 1973) all suggest that the radius
of rhodopsin is probably about 20 to 30 Å. The effective radius for diffusion
should be somewhat larger, since rhodopsin probably diffuses with a loosely
associated layer of phospholipids, in the same way that solutes in aqueous
solutions diffuse with a loosely associated layer of water molecules. A
membrane viscosity of about 2 poise also appears reasonable, since the
viscosity of the lipid phase in many cell membranes, measured with the aid
of spin-labeled probes, fluorescent probes, and the rate of permeation of
lipid-soluble molecules, has nearly always been found to fall within an order
of magnitude of 1 poise (see Poo and Cone, 1974).

FRESH NECTURUS RODS

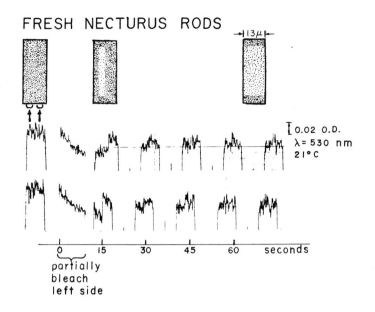

GLUTARALDEHYDE FIXED NECTURUS ROD

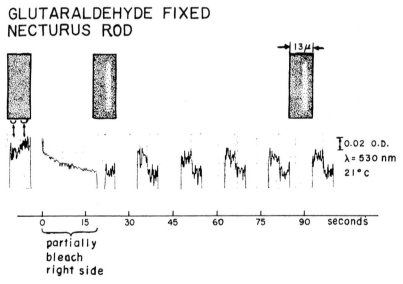

FIG. 6. Lateral diffusion of rhodopsin. In a microspectrophotometer, repeated measurements were made of the absorbance of the left side and then the right side of a rod viewed from the side. The rhodopsin on one side of the rod was then partially bleached (note traces showing rapid decay in absorbance during the bleaching exposure). In fresh rods, as shown by two examples, immediately following the bleach the absorbance on the bleached side was markedly lower whereas the absorbance on the unbleached side was little changed. Within the next few seconds the absorbance on the bleached side rose while that on the unbleached side fell, and in less than a minute the absorbance on both sides became equal. This demonstrates that rhodopsin molecules are free to diffuse across the disc, and reach uniform distribution in a matter of seconds following the bleach. In contrast, if the rods are first fixed in glutaraldehyde, no redistribution of pigment occurs. The diagrams depict the pigment distribution in the rod corresponding in time with the absorbance measurements shown below each diagram. (From Poo and Cone, 1974.)

An argument arose as to the applicability of the simple Einstein equations to the rotational and translational diffusion of rhodopsin. It was argued that a few of the simplifications assumed by Einstein do not hold in the photoreceptor membrane, including the shape of the diffusing molecule, its concentration, and the possible collision of neighboring rhodopsin molecules, particularly in view of the high rhodopsin packing density. However, Cone felt that more finely detailed structural evidence is needed before a major effort should be made to refine the analysis of the diffusion data.

The low viscosity of the membrane and the close spacing of the rhodopsin combine to produce a high collision rate between molecules; calculations indicate that each rhodopsin molecule collides with another about 10^6 times/sec. It is therefore entirely possible that both the excitation and adaptation mechanisms in the receptor may involve rhodopsin-rhodopsin interactions. In addition, the fact that rhodopsin diffuses rapidly even though closely spaced in the membrane indicates that, in general, whenever membrane proteins are found to remain at fixed sites, some type of "anchor" mechanism is probably present. As long as the lipid phase is liquid and not solid, it cannot provide any major retardation of movement, even in membranes with viscosities much greater than rod disc membranes. The most common type of anchor mechanism is probably a direct link between membrane proteins and nonmembrane structures such as microtubules (see Edelman, Chapter 8) or fibrous protein structures such as that formed by spectrin in red blood cells (see Nicolson, Chapter 5). It is also possible that fence-like structures could enclose whole regions of a cell membrane; such a fence-like structure appears to encircle the membrane at the base of some cilia (Gilula and Satir, 1972).

Modulation of Synaptic Activity by Rhodopsin

Many sensory receptors, such as rods and cones, as well as many types of neurons in the retina, olfactory lobe, and other brain regions do not produce self-regenerative action potentials. In such cells, the synaptic activity in most cases appears to be directly modulated by the electrotonic flow of ions. In rods and cones, the light-induced hyperpolarization may decrease the rate at which transmitter is continuously released from the synapse (Dowling and Ripps, 1973).

How might rhodopsin interact with the Na channels to hyperpolarize the cell? As mentioned earlier, Na^+ is continuously pumped out of the receptor in the inner segment region, and continuously leaks back into the cell through Na^+ channels in the plasma membrane surrounding the outer segment. When light is absorbed by either a rod or a cone, some of the Na^+ channels become blocked and the receptor hyperpolarizes. One photon is sufficient to reduce the Na leakage or "dark" current by about 1% at the peak of the receptor potential (Penn and Hagins, 1969). Since Na^+ channels must all be electrically in parallel, a single photoactivated rhodopsin molecule must therefore be capable of contacting at least 1% of the Na^+ channels. Alternatively, rhodopsin might somehow block the pumps in the inner segment, or increase the cytoplasmic resistance in the ciliary connection between the inner and outer segments. Such diverse mechanisms must be considered because the receptor potential develops so slowly that many different mechanisms are possible. The receptor potential has a latency of nearly 0.1 sec at low light levels and is the slowest step in the visual pathway.

To date, it has been difficult to determine with microelectrode techniques the location in the receptor cell where each step of the transduction process takes place. One helpful approach to this problem has been to use osmotic techniques on isolated outer segments (Korenbrot and Cone, 1972). Outer segments break off easily from the rest of the cell at the ciliary connection, and they quickly reseal to become good osmometers. When placed in a hyperosmotic solution they shrink and do not recover in volume unless the solute can permeate the plasma membrane. The rate of volume recovery thus provides a measure of the permeability of the membrane for the solute being tested. A hyperosmotic shock in KCl shrinks the rods and they remain shrunken, indicating that KCl does not permeate the membrane. In contrast, the outer segments recover to their original volume after a hyperosmotic shock in NaCl, indicating that NaCl can permeate the membrane (Fig. 7). However, if the outer segments are exposed to even a small amount of light, the rate at which the original volume is recovered in NaCl is greatly reduced, clearly indicating that light reduces the influx of Na^+ into the outer segment (Fig. 8). In a freshly isolated outer segment, one rhodopsin molecule is capable of transiently blocking 1% of the Na^+ influx, or about 10^7 Na^+ ions, just as in the intact retina. Rhodopsin must therefore hyperpolarize the cell by blocking Na channels rather than by an effect on the pumps in the inner segment or on the resistance in the ciliary connection.

The transduction mechanism has been suggested to involve an internal transmitter (Baylor and Fuortes, 1970), and there is considerable evidence to suggest that this messenger may be Ca^{2+} (Yoshikami and Hagins, 1971). According to this hypothesis, the role of rhodopsin is to release Ca^{2+} from the discs, and the Ca^{2+} ions then diffuse to the plasma membrane where they reversibly block Na^+ channels. An active Ca^{2+} uptake mechanism must then return the Ca^{2+} to the disc lumen.

The Na^+ current is reduced if the extracellular concentration of Ca^{2+} is increased (Yoshikami and Hagins, 1973), but this could be due simply to a rigidifying effect of the membrane of the type described by Träuble (Chapter 3). More convincing evidence in support of the Ca^{2+} hypothesis has been obtained by using Ca^{2+} ionophores, which alter the internal Ca^{2+} concentration by allowing it to pass through the plasma membrane (Hagins and Yoshikami, 1974). In the presence of the Ca^{2+} ionophore X537A, the

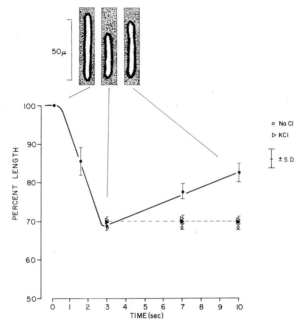

FIG. 7. A comparison of the Na⁺ and K⁺ permeability of isolated rod outer segments in the dark (filled symbols) and in the light (open symbols). The outer segments were hyperosmotically shocked and the rate at which they recover in length following the shock is a measure of the permeability of the plasma membrane to the ions used to produce the shock. Note that no recovery occurred in either light or dark following KCL shocks, but did occur after NaCl shocks if the rods were fully dark-adapted. The rate at which Na⁺ entered the outer segment, about 10^9 ions/sec, is comparable to the rate at which Na⁺ "leaks" into the outer segment in the intact receptor cell. (From Korenbrot and Cone, 1972.)

Na⁺ channels can be blocked by micromolar quantities of extracellular Ca^{2+}. This suggests the cytoplasmic Ca^{2+} activity must be in the range of 10^{-6} to 10^{-5} M. In this case, calculations indicate that a photoactivated rhodopsin molecule need release only 10^2 to 10^3 Ca^{2+} ions to block 1% of the Na channels (Cone, 1973; Hagins and Yoshikami, 1974).

Several tests must be made in order to determine whether or not Ca^{2+} is the transmitter, just as is the case in trying to identify a synaptic transmitter substance. For example, it must be demonstrated that light induces the release of Ca^{2+} from the discs, the time course and quantity of Ca^{2+} released must be appropriate, the Ca^{2+} must be shown to be capable of reaching the Na⁺ channels in the time available, and it must block them reversibly at appropriate concentrations. Finally, an appropriate Ca^{2+} uptake mechanism must also be demonstrated. Szuts and Cone (1974) have recently reported that light does not appear to alter the Na⁺, K⁺, or Mg^{2+} content of the discs significantly, but does cause a marked loss of

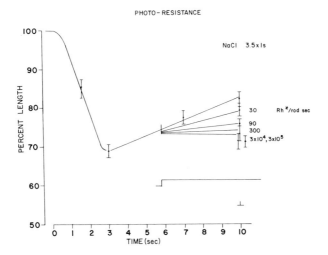

PHOTO-RESISTANCE

FIG. 8. The amount of light required to block the Na$^+$ channels of the isolated outer segment is minute; the rate of recovery in volume following a hyperosmotic NaCl shock is halved, and hence the Na$^+$ permeability is halved, when only 60 to 90 rhodopsin molecules are bleached per second.

Ca^{2+} from the discs. In some experiments, the photoactivation of only 2 to 4 rhodopsin molecules per disc released a major fraction of the Ca^{2+} in the disc, indicating that, under the conditions of the experiment, each photoactivated rhodopsin molecule released in excess of 1,000 Ca^{2+} ions per disc. Although the time course of release is not yet known, it appears likely that sufficient Ca^{2+} is released to block 1% of the Na channels.

Several mechanisms can be postulated for the release of Ca^{2+} by rhodopsin. Assuming that rhodopsin does span the membrane, one relatively simple mechanism would be the formation of a channel through which Ca^{2+} ions could pass. Several such molecular structures are known to exist. Antibiotics such as gramicidin A have been shown to possess a central open core formed by a helical conformation of amino acids. The major glycoprotein of erythrocytes, glycophorin, contains a 23-amino acid hydrophobic region that appears to span the membrane and to form a similar spiral structure suitable for ion passage. Urry (1972) has proposed that such a tube could be formed by what he termed a β-helix, a β-pleated sheet rolled into a tube. The middle of such a helix has an opening about 4 Å in diameter. A similar structure in rhodopsin could use the chromophore as a "plug," that would open out from the channel in response to the absorption of a photon. A second, though less likely possibility is that rhodopsin might be a carrier that migrates within the membrane when activated. Finally, rhodopsin could act by an unknown mechanism on the other molecules or structures which in turn would release Ca^{2+} from the disc.

It is clear that the mechanism of visual excitation is a highly cooperative process in which several different regions of the receptor cell are closely linked: A rhodopsin molecule, once it catches a photon, acts upon a large number of Na^+ channels in the plasma membrane by initiating the release of transmitter particles from the disc (probably 10^2 to 10^3 Ca^{2+} ions); the Na^+ current, which is generated by pumps in the plasma membrane surrounding the inner segment, is thereby reduced and the cell hyperpolarizes; the hyperpolarization in some way affects the components of the ribbon synapse at the other end of the cell to alter the rate of release of transmitter substance, which in turn acts on the next cells in the visual pathway. The overall transductive process is rather slow, requiring about 0.1 sec or more, but it is a highly reliable process, and it enables rods to be faithful, single-photon detectors. At least two steps of amplification occur in this process: each photoactivated rhodopsin molecule must initiate the release of a large number of transmitter particles, and each Na^+ channel blocked by a transmitter particle prevents the entry of a large number of Na^+ ions. The arrival of a single photon is thereby transduced to the blockage of some 10^7 Na^+ ions in a fraction of a second. The signal may be further amplified by the hyperpolarization and its affect on the synaptic apparatus, but at present we know little about the events at the output of the receptor.

TRANSDUCTIVE COUPLING IN THE ROD PHOTORECEPTOR CELL:

Edward A. Dratz

The Structure of the Rod Outer Segment Disc Membrane

An understanding of the structure of the rod outer segment disc membrane and the changes in structure caused by light excitation might be expected to provide clues to the transduction mechanism. Experiments with membrane-impermeable labeling reagents have shown that a substantial fraction of the functional groups of rhodopsin protrude from the surface of the disc membrane (Raubach et al., 1974). Low-angle X-ray diffraction of the rod outer segments has previously had limited usefulness because of the inherent disorder in the spacing of the disc membranes in the rod outer segment. A new method, developed to take account of this disorder, allows a correct structure to be derived from the low-angle X-ray data to 25 Å resolution (Schwartz, Cain, Dratz, and Blasie, 1974). This structure supports the labeling data and shows that a substantial fraction of the mass of rhodopsin protrudes from the outer surface of the disc membrane. Furthermore, the electron density in the center of the disc membrane is sufficiently high that rhodopsin could penetrate deep into the center of the membrane. It is probable that rhodopsin spans the disc membrane, but this has not been directly demonstrated as yet. If rhodopsin does turn out to span the membrane, then a light-activated pore mechanism for release of transmitter by rhodopsin would be favored.

The Interaction of Rhodopsin with Membrane Lipids During Excitation

Some new information, discussed below, seems to indicate a large change in the interaction of rhodopsin with the membrane lipids during excitation. If rhodopsin functions as a light-activated pore, changes in structure brought about by light excitation would not be isolated from the lipids surrounding the protein in the membrane.

As discussed by Reichardt, the excitation of rhodopsin by light is followed by the formation of a series of intermediates in the production of retinal and opsin. Prelumirhodopsin is present within ≤ 6 psec (Busch, Applebury, Lamola, and Rentzepis, 1972), and MII rhodopsin appears after ~ 0.25 msec (Cone, 1967). The subsequent conversions from MII to opsin and retinal are too slow to be involved in the excitation process. The appearance of MII is probably connected to the excitation event.

Rhodopsin strongly interacts with the lipid in the disc membrane, and these interactions are substantially altered during the MI $\rightarrow$ MII transition. This is demonstrated by a large increase (nearly 1,000-fold) in the MI $\rightarrow$ MII rate constant when the disc lipid is displaced by detergent, and the almost complete return to the native value when the detergent is in turn replaced with an egg lecithin (Applebury, Zuckerman, Lamola, and Jovin, 1974). In addition, the MI $\rightleftharpoons$ MII equilibrium can be shifted from MII to MI by the application of pressure, with quantitative reversal to MI at 4,000 lb/in^2. This reversal can be demonstrated only in the rod membrane; it does not occur in an uncoupled system in which the protein has been removed from its lipid milieu by detergent substitution (Lamola, Yamane, and Yip, 1974). This effect of pressure demonstrates that the formation of MII rhodopsin results in an increased volume of lipid within the membrane, suggesting an increase in fluidity (Overath and Träuble, 1973) of some of the lipids in the presence of MII.

The proton NMR spectra of the rod outer segment (ROS) resembles those shown by Metcalfe (Chapter 3) for sarcoplasmic reticulum (SR) membranes. The observed peaks can be assigned to groups such as choline methyls, methylenes between two double bonds, methylenes next to one double bond, methylene next to other methylenes, and terminal methyl groups. An unusual feature of these spectra is their sharpness, which is due to the relatively fluid nature of the ROS. Most membranes are too rigid to exhibit such a sharp ^1H NMR spectrum unless they are first denatured. It is tempting to generalize that excitable membranes (such as ROS disc, SR, or nerve) will be generally found to be much more fluid than nonexcitable ones. The NMR spectra also indicate the presence of at least two domains of lipid within the membrane: (1) rigid areas showing broad NMR resonances, and (2) relatively fluid areas with narrower peaks. The fluid lipids comprise 20 to 30% of the total lipids in most preparations.

There is considerable variation between preparations in the behavior of the NMR spectrum after bright flash illumination. Some preparations show quite marked changes, with a transient sharpening of the spectrum; such a sharpening is indicative of a transient increase in the fluidity of the lipids. This transient fluidity has decayed at the time retinal dissociates from opsin, and in this state the spectrum is very similar to that of dark-adapted membranes.

The increased fluidity of the membranes has not been precisely related to the presence of a rhodopsin-bleaching intermediate. It is probable that the presence of Meta II rhodopsin fluidizes the membrane lipids, which would agree with the high-pressure experiments of Lamola, Yamane, and Yip (1974). Overath and Träuble (1973) have shown that lipids increase their volume upon melting. However, Dratz and others (Millet, Hargrave, and Raftery, 1973) have found that some ROS preparations show little or no effect of light on the NMR spectrum. The reason for this variability is not known, although variable membrane properties are also indicated by other measures such as fragility and light-induced Ca^{2+} release. The rod outer segment disc membranes contain unusually large amounts of poly-unsaturated fatty acids, and at least part of the variability in the properties of the membranes appears to be due to differing degrees of oxidative degradation of the polyunsaturated fatty acids in the membrane preparations.

The NMR spectra of the rod outer segment disc membranes show a reversible transition to a more fluid state as the temperature is raised. This transition is not sharp, but occurs over the range of 10 to 35°C. The lipids alone would be expected to be above their thermal phase transition even at 10°C, and the change observed above this temperature would therefore appear to be due to interactions between lipids and the protein.

In summary, there is a substantial change in the reciprocal interaction between lipids and protein during the MI → MII transition in rhodopsin. Alterations of the lipid environment change the rate of the MI → MII transition, and the changes in the lipid volume that accompany the MI → MII transition shift the rhodopsin equilibrium as a function of pressure. Conversely, the conformational state of the protein affects the properties of the lipid. Changes in the protein initiated by light absorption affect the fluidity of the lipids in favorable preparations.

Since the rod cell is highly specialized and dependent on a membrane organization for its function, it is a useful substrate for the investigation of functional linkage in a membrane system. Information about the interaction between lipids and rhodopsin in the disc membrane is now being accumulated. These interactions seem to be correlated with the *transduction of light into a chemical signal.* The functional linkage between *transduction of the chemical signal to an electrical signal,* which involves the whole rod cell, can be understood in broad outline through the model described in the next section.

A Model for the Transduction of the Chemical to Electrical Signal Within the Rod

The functional linkage between light absorption and electrical excitation in rod photoreceptor cells clearly involves a decrease in sodium permeability of the plasma membrane of the outer segment, as described by Cone. Aspects of the detailed mechanism of this transduction have been inferred from studies of the kinetics of the electrical response of the rod cell as a function of the intensity of the light stimulus. The generalized kinetics of a rod cell photoreceptor in the probable absence of feedback effects from horizontal cells and other photoreceptors is shown in Fig. 9. A detailed analysis of the model based on such data is in preparation (Dratz and Elias, 1974). In summary, the analysis of the kinetics of the photoelectric response of rods can be correlated with the chemical changes occurring in the cell as follows:

1. The voltage (and current) responses show amplitude saturation with

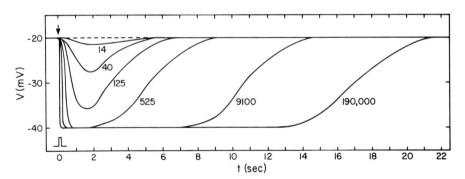

FIG. 9. The generalized voltage measured across a dark-adapted amphibian rod cell after short pulses of light of various intensities (graphs of relative current would have the same shape for small spot stimuli). The number of quanta absorbed/flash, *Q,* is written next to each curve. With moderate shifts in dark-adapted voltage, response amplitude, time scale, or light intensity, these curves are intended to represent the behavior of any rod cell. Mammalian rods show curves of this shape, but they are on a somewhat shorter time scale (Penn and Hagins, 1972). An attempt has been made to remove from these curves complications of feedback from horizontal cells and from other receptors. (For the brighter flashes some cells show a "sag" above the plateau near −40 mV and a small, slow, transient depolarization above approximately −20 mV as the potential returns to the dark-adapted level. The "sag" and the slow transient depolarization have not been accounted for in the model. These effects are probably due to a slight voltage sensitivity of the potassium resistance of the rod cell membrane.) The timing of the light stimulus is shown by the square pulse in the lower left-hand corner of the figure.

a low-light-level flash. The absorption of photons by 100 to 200 rhodopsin molecules results in the release of enough calcium to close essentially all of the plasma membrane sodium channels.

2. Brighter flashes release much more transmitter, and saturating amounts of transmitter reach the plasma membrane much faster. The rise time decreases as 1/quanta absorbed until about 60,000 quanta/rod are absorbed (in the rat) (Penn and Hagins, 1972).

3. The transmitter is returned to the interior of the disk by a metabolically driven pump that restores the cell to the dark-adapted state of low intracellular transmitter concentration. The brighter the flash the longer the pump requires to resequester all the transmitter (Fig. 9).

4. The restorative pump appears to follow first-order kinetics at all light levels. The pump rate constant is independent of light intensity except at light intensities that correspond to the highest concentrations of calcium in the cytoplasm, when it decreases somewhat. This decrease might occur because the diffusion of ATP from the inner segment is not fast enough to supply the pump with sufficient energy to operate at the maximal dark-adapted rate after exposure to the highest cytoplasmic Ca^{2+} concentrations.

5. For a reasonable range of releasable Ca^{2+} concentrations, the data permit the derivation of a range of numbers for the flux of Ca^{2+}/activated rhodopsin (350 to 3,500/sec) and a range of Ca^{2+} dissociation constants from the Na^+ pores ($1/K = 3 \times 10^{-7}$ to 3×10^{-6} M^{-1}).

REFERENCES

Applebury, M., Zuckerman, D., Lamola, A., and Jovin, T. (1974): Rhodopsin. Purification and recombination with phospholipids assayed by the metarhodopsin I → metarhodopsin II transition. *Biochemistry*, 13:3448–3458.

Baylor, D. A., and Fuortes, M. G. F. (1970): Electrical responses of single cones in the retina of the turtle. *J. Physiol.*, 207:77–92.

Blasie, J. K., and Worthington, C. R. (1969): Planar liquid-like arrangement of photopigment molecules in frog retinal receptor disk membranes. *J. Mol. Biol.*, 39:417–439.

Brown, K. T. (1965): An early potential evoked by light from the pigment epithelium-choroid complex of the eye of the toad. *Nature*, 207:1249–1253.

Brown, K. T., and Murakami, M. (1964): A new receptor potential of the monkey retina with no detectable latency. *Nature*, 201:626–628.

Brown, P. K. (1972): Rhodopsin rotates in the visual receptor membrane. *Nature New Biol.*, 236:35–38.

Busch, G. E., Applebury, M. L., Lamola, A. A., and Rentzepis, P. M. (1972): Formation and decay of prelumirhodopsin at room temperatures. *Proc. Nat. Acad. Sci.*, 69:2802–2806.

Chen, Y. S., and Hubbell, W. L. (1973): Temperature- and light-dependent structural changes in rhodopsin-lipid membranes. *Exp. Eye Res.*, 17:517–532.

Clark, A. W., and Branton, D. (1968): Fracture faces in frozen outer segments from the guinea pig retina. *Z. Zellforsch.*, 91:586–603.

Cone, R. A. (1964): Early receptor potential of the vertebrate retina. *Nature*, 204:736–739.

Cone, R. A. (1967): Early receptor potential: Photoreversible charge displacement in rhodopsin. *Science*, 155:1128–1131.

Cone, R. A. (1972): Rotational diffusion of rhodopsin in the visual receptor membrane. *Nature New Biol.*, 236:39–43.

Cone, R. A. (1973): The internal transmitter model for visual excitation: Some quantitative implications. In: *Biochemistry and Physiology of Visual Pigments*, edited by H. Langer, pp. 275–282. Berlin: Springer-Verlag.

Dowling, J. E. (1967): The organization of vertebrate visual receptors. In: *Molecular Organization and Biological Function*, edited by J. M. Allen, pp. 186-210. New York: Harper & Row.

Dowling, J. E., and Ripps, H. (1973): Effect of magnesium on horizontal cell activity in the skate retina. *Nature*, 242:101-103.

Dratz, E. A., and Elias, V. (1974): What can the kinetics of the response of the rod visual receptor tell us about its internal mechanism. *Fed. Proc.*, 33:1576 (Abstr.).

Fein, A., and Cone, R. A. (1973): Limulus rhodopsin: Rapid return of transient intermediates to the thermally stable state. *Science*, 182:495-497.

Fermi, G., and Reichardt, W. (1963): Optomotorische Reaktionen der Fliege *Musca domestica*. Abhängigkeit der Reaktion von der Wellenlänge, der Geschwindigkeit, dem Kontrast und der mittleren Leuchtdichte bewegter periodischer Muster. *Kybernetik*, 2:15-28.

Förster, T. (1965): Light and organic crystals. 1. Delocalized excitation and excitation transfer. In: *Modern Quantum Chemistry, Istanbul Lectures. Part III. Action of Light and Organic Crystals*, edited by O. Sinanoglu, pp. 93-137. New York: Academic Press.

Fuortes, M. G. F., and Yeandle, S. (1964): Probability of occurrence of discrete potential waves in the eye of *Limulus*. *J. Gen. Physiol.*, 47:443-463.

Gilula, N. B., and Satir, P. (1972): The ciliary necklace. A ciliary membrane specialization. *J. Cell Biol.*, 53:494-509.

Hagins, W. A. (1965): Electrical signs of information flow in photoreceptors. *Cold Spring Harbor Symp. Quant. Biol.*, 30:403-418.

Hagins, W. A. (1972): The visual process: Excitatory mechanisms in the primary receptor cells. *Ann. Rev. Biophys. Bioeng.*, 1:131-158.

Hagins, W. A., and Jennings, W. H. (1959): Radiationless migration of electronic excitation in retinal rods. *Trans. Faraday Soc.*, 27:180-190.

Hagins, W. A., Penn, R. D., and Yoshikami, S. (1970): Dark current and photocurrent in retinal rods. *Biophys. J.*, 10:380-412.

Hagins, W. A., and Yoshikami, S. (1974): A role for Ca^{2+} in excitation of retinal rods and cones. *Exp. Eye Res.*, 18:299-305.

Hamdorf, K., Paulsen, R., and Schwemer, J. (1973): Photoregeneration and sensitivity control of photoreceptors of invertebrates. In: *Biochemistry and Physiology of Visual Pigments*, edited by H. Langer, pp. 155-166. Berlin: Springer-Verlag.

Hecht, S., Shlaer, S., and Pirenne, M. H. (1942): Energy, quanta, and vision. *J. Gen. Physiol.*, 25:819-840.

Kirschfeld, K., and Lutz, B. (1974): Lateral inhibition in the compound eye of the fly, Musca. *Z. Naturforsch.* 29c:526-527.

Korenbrot, J. I., and Cone, R. A. (1972): Dark ionic flux and the effects of light in isolated rod outer segments. *J. Gen. Physiol.*, 60:20-45.

Kropf, A. (1969): Photochemistry of visual pigments. *Proceedings of the International School of Physics "Enrico Fermi."* Course XLIII, pp. 28-43.

Lamola, A. A., Yamane, T., and Zipp, A. (1974): The metarhodopsin I → metarhodopsin II equilibrium: Effects of detergents and pressure. *Exp. Eye Res.*, 18:19-27.

Lewis, M. S., Krieg, L. C., and Kirk, W. D. (1974): The molecular weight and detergent binding of bovine rhodopsin. *Exp. Eye Res.*, 18:29-40.

Millett, F., Hargrave, P. A., and Raftery, M. A. (1973): Natural abundance ^{13}C nuclear magnetic resonance spectra of the lipid in intact bovine retinal rod outer segment membranes. *Biochemistry*, 12:3591-3592.

Overath, P., and Träuble, H. (1973): Phase transitions in cells, membrane and lipids of *Escherichia coli*. Detection by fluorescent probes, light scattering and dilatometry. *Biochemistry*, 12:2625-2634.

Pak, W. L., and Cone, R. A. (1964): Isolation and identification of the initial peak of the early receptor potential. *Nature*, 204:836-838.

Penn, R. D., and Hagins, W. A. (1969): Signal transmission along retinal rods and the origin of the electroretinographic *a*-wave. *Nature*, 223:201-205.

Penn, R. D., and Hagins, W. A. (1972): Kinetics of the photocurrent of retinal rods. *Biophys. J.*, 12:1073-1094.

Poo, M.-M., and Cone, R. A. (1974): Lateral diffusion of rhodopsin in the photoreceptor membrane. *Nature*, 247:438-441.

Raubach, R. A., Nemes, P. P., and Dratz, E. A. (1974): Chemical labeling and freeze-fracture studies on the localization of rhodopsin in the rod outer segment disk membrane. *Exp. Eye Res.,* 18:1–12.

Reichardt, W. E. (1965): Quantum sensitivity of light receptors in the compound eye of the fly. *Cold Spring Harbor Symp. Quant. Biol.,* 30:505–515.

Schmidt, W. J. (1938): Polarisationsoptische Analyse eines Eiweiss-Lipoid-Systems, erläutert am Aussenglied der Sehzellen. *Kolloid-Z.,* 85:137–148.

Scholes, J. H. (1964): Discrete subthreshold potentials from the dimly lit insect eye. *Nature,* 202:572–573.

Scholes, J. H. (1969): The electrical responses of the retinal receptors and the lamina in the visual system of the fly Musca. *Kybernetik,* 6:149–162.

Schwartz, S., Cain, J. E., Dratz, E., and Blasie, J. K. (1974): An analysis of lamellar diffraction from disordered membrane multilayers with application to data from retinal rods. *Fed. Proc.,* 33:1575 (Abstr.).

Steinemann, A., and Stryer, L. (1973): Accessibility of the carbohydrate moiety of rhodopsin. *Biochemistry,* 12:1499–1502.

Szuts, E. Z., and Cone, R. A. (1974): Rhodopsin: Light activated release of calcium. *Fed. Proc.,* 33:1471 (Abstr.).

Urry, D. W. (1972): A molecular theory of ion-conducting channels: A field-dependent transition between conducting and nonconducting conformations. *Proc. Nat. Acad. Sci.,* 69:1610–1614.

Winkler, B. S. (1974): Calcium and the fast and slow components of PIII of the electroretinogram of the isolated rat retina. *Vision Res.,* 14:9–15.

Wu, C.-W., and Stryer, L. (1972): Proximity relationships in rhodopsin. *Proc. Nat. Acad. Sci.,* 69:1104–1108.

Yeandle, S. (1957): Ph.D. thesis. Johns Hopkins University, Baltimore.

Yeandle, S. (1958): Symposium on the electrophysiology of the visual system. Comparison of spectral sensitivity at the eye and the optic tectum of the chicken. *Amer. J. Ophthalmol.,* 46:72, 82–87.

Yoshikama, S., and Hagins, W. A. (1971): Light, calcium and the photocurrent of rods and cones. *Biophysical Society Program and Abstracts. Fifteenth Annual Meeting, February 15–18, 1971, New Orleans, La.* 11:47a (Abstr.).

Functional Linkage in Biomolecular Systems, edited by
F. O. Schmitt, D. M. Schneider, and D. M. Crothers.
Raven Press, New York © 1975.

Chapter 12

Transductive Coupling in Chemosensory Systems

THE NATURE OF CHEMOSENSORY SYSTEMS:

Vincent G. Dethier

Chemosensory systems have several unique characteristics. In contrast to the systems described in previous chapters, the stimulant molecules that are bound by membrane receptors originate in the external environment rather than from within the organism, and the number of molecules that can be distinguished by these systems is almost infinite. Most studies in this area have dealt with either mammals or insects, each being suitable for particular kinds of analyses. However, it is frequently difficult to relate data obtained from these disparate organisms.

With the exception of vision, the receptor cells of essentially all insect sensory systems generate action potentials. The insect taste receptor is a spike-generating cell whose membrane is spatially organized for specific functions. Receptors for appropriate chemical stimuli are located in the apical region of the cell. The binding of a stimulus molecule initiates a depolarizing receptor potential that spreads electrotonically to the cell body, where an action potential is generated. The mechanism by which such spatial localization is maintained is unknown (see the discussion by Nicolson in Chapter 5).

The linkage between the binding of a stimulant by the dendritic membrane and the generation of an action potential at the cell body has not yet been determined in chemosensory systems. The taste cell has most often been studied as a "black box," in which appropriate inputs generate a set of outputs that can be observed by electrophysiological or behavioral techniques.

Taste receptor cells are extremely sensitive and highly specific. In the insect taste receptor, the cells are most commonly arranged in clusters of four, with the cells in each cluster having a common origin from a single parent cell. Although these cells are anatomically identical, they are functionally differentiated; one each selectively responds to water and sugar, while two respond to salt.

The water cell responds only to H_2O or D_2O. The sugar cell is preferentially responsive to sugars containing an α-glucoside linkage, although it can also respond to β-glucosides, certain amino acids, and substances such as inositol. The receptor is specific for hexose and pentose sugars, and does not respond to tetroses, heptoses, or octoses. There is some evidence for a competitive inhibition of various sugars. Although mannose does not itself stimulate the sugar cell and has no effect on its response to glucose, it does reduce its response to fructose. A synergistic effect has also been demonstrated for glucose and fructose, such that a mixture of the two produces a greater stimulation than either alone. The high degree of sensitivity of the gustatory system is indicated by the induction of a complete behavioral response by the application of 10^{-8} M sucrose to a population of sugar receptors. One of the salt receptors is responsive to a wide array of salts, as well as to certain amino and organic acids, glycosides, and alkaloids. The adequate stimuli for the second salt cell are not known with certainty.

However, any statement that a given system is or is not highly specific must be made with caution. For several decades, the taste system was examined using only salt, sugar, quinine, and acid; the system was concluded to be specific only because other substances were not examined. It is now known that in the insect taste system there are only preferential specificities; the system actually responds to a variety of compounds, but to different extents.

The insect taste system is frequently preferred to the mammalian as an experimental system because the insect taste receptor is itself a neuron, while the mammalian taste receptor is a modified epithelial cell. In these more complex systems, each nerve fiber receives inputs from more than one receptor, and each receptor is connected to several nerve fibers.

Despite the vast evolutionary distance that separates the mammalian and the insect chemosensory systems, they do have basic functional similarities. The study of each has provided some further understanding of the other. This is particularly true with respect to the nature of transductive coupling and cooperativity. In the section that follows, Beidler examines the interactions between ligand and receptor in the mammalian gustatory system and notes some basic similarities with the insect system. For example, both sugar receptors consist of subunits that exhibit positive cooperativity in ligand binding. Although there has been compelling indirect evidence for the existence of two sites on the sugar receptor of insects (Dethier, Evans, and Rhoades, 1956; Evans, 1963; Morita and Shiraishi, 1968; Omand and Dethier, 1969), direct evidence was obtained only recently (Shimada, Shiraishi, Kijima, and Morita, 1974). Some sugars react with the "fructose site" (furanose site), others with the "glucose site" (pyranose site), while the two sites cooperate in the case of other sugars, notably sucrose and galactose. Other examples of positive cooperativity, as well as evidence for negative cooperativity in the binding of acids to their specific receptor sites, are discussed by Beidler.

Analyses of transductive coupling and cooperativity have not been extensive in the olfactory system. The most progress has been made in studies of the moth pheromone Bombykol, used as a model by Kaissling to discuss the steps leading to the eventual generation of nerve impulses. It is assumed that the binding of the molecule to a specific site in the receptor leads to a change in state or conformation, and that this in turn induces membrane changes that lead to depolarization.

A major limitation to advancement in the field of chemoreception has been the lack of biochemical analysis, primarily due to the small amount of bioreceptor material present within the cell membrane.

TRANSDUCTIVE COUPLING IN THE GUSTATORY SYSTEM:

Lloyd M. Beidler

Receptors of the gustatory system interact with tastants having a wide range of molecular weights, from hydrogen ions to large proteins (Table 1).

TABLE 1. *Molecular-weight range of tastants*

Size (mw)	
Hydrogen ion	1
Glycine	75
Sucrose	342
Quinine sulfate	783
Monellin	10,700
Miraculin	44,000

TABLE 2. *Taste specificity*

α-D-Mannose	sweet
β-D-Mannose	bitter
D-Asparagine	sweet
L-Asparagine	bitter

Large proteins such as miraculin[1] have a lag period of approximately 30 sec between application of the tastant and production of a nerve impulse, while the lag period for a substance of small molecular weight such as NaCl is only 20 to 50 msec. This difference is due at least in part to diffusion (Beidler, 1961). The gustatory system also shows great specificity, and can discriminate even closely related molecules (Table 2).

The sensitivity of the taste system varies extensively (Table 3), ranging

---

[1] Miraculin is an unusual molecule which makes all sour tastants taste sweet.

TABLE 3. *Sensitivity of the gustatory system to specific tastants*

Urea	10^{-1} M
Sucrose	10^{-2} M
HCl	10^{-3} M
Na saccharin	10^{-5} M
Strychnine	10^{-7} M
Miraculin	10^{-7} M

from thresholds of 0.1 M for urea to 10^{-7} M for substances such as miraculin. Catfish are capable of responding to 10^{-10} M of some amino acids. As techniques for measuring gustatory responses are refined further, their sensitivity will probably be demonstrated to be at least two log units greater than current values.

A typical taste papilla on the front of the tongue (Fig. 1*a*) is 0.5 to 1 mm in diameter. There are 3 to 5 taste buds on these papillae in the human, whereas the rat has only one. The taste bud itself is ~ 50 μ in diameter and contains approximately 30 to 50 cells (Fig. 1). The microvilli of the apical end of taste cells extend into a central pore that communicates with the saliva-covered surface of the tongue. The remainder of the taste bud is well protected from the external environment, as is true of most sensory receptors. The adsorption of tastant molecules is believed to take place on the protruding microvilli of the receptor cell (Fig. 2). This event is communicated to another portion of the membrane, probably via a conformational change in membrane components, and an electrical depolarization is initiated that elicits nerve impulses in the innervating fibers.

There are large species differences in the responsiveness of taste cell membranes to given chemicals. For example, taste cells in rodents are far more sensitive to Na^+ than K^+, whereas the opposite is observed in carnivores; and hamsters respond to cyclamate as a sweet substance, while rats do not.

Marked differences can be observed for the cells of a single taste bud and for single nerve fibers in response to the application of a given tastant (Fig. 3), indicating that the membranes of the microvilli differ significantly in their properties. Not all differential response profiles appear to be under direct genetic control, although the genetic basis for the bitter taste of phenylthiourea is well known.

The almost infinite number of compounds that can be detected by the gustatory and olfactory systems suggests a similarity to the immune system (see Chapter 7). It was suggested by Lehninger and Nossal that the diversity found in chemosensory systems might have a similar genetic basis. The binding energy of a tastant-receptor interaction is usually rather low; for example, the binding strength for the binding of NaCl to its receptors is approximately 2 kcal. This suggests that binding is strongly dependent on

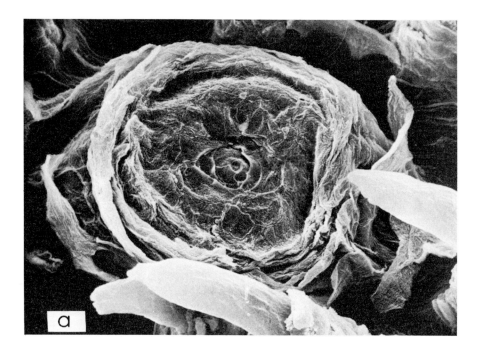

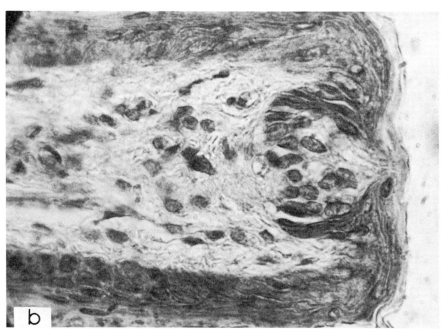

FIG. 1. (a) A surface view of a taste fungiform papilla from rat tongue. (b) A cross section of a taste bud of a rat fungiform papilla. 115×.

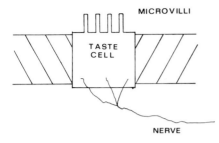

FIG. 2. Model of a taste receptor.

tertiary structural effects. It was originally assumed that, for example, all receptor sites bind sugars with the same selectivity. This is not the case, and a wide variety of differential responses to quite similar substances can be demonstrated in various taste nerve fibers (Table 4).

This heterogeneity of receptor cell responsiveness has made it virtually impossible to relate molecular structure to taste response, since such studies require homogeneous populations of receptors. In the gustatory system, the receptor population remains constant in its response to chemicals, but the responses of the individual members of that population vary widely.

Taste buds are constantly subjected to a variety of adverse conditions (heat, cold, acid, etc.). Fortunately, the taste cells have a half-life of only ~10 days (Beidler and Smallman, 1965). They are continually replaced by cells outside the taste bud, which undergo mitotic division, penetrate the

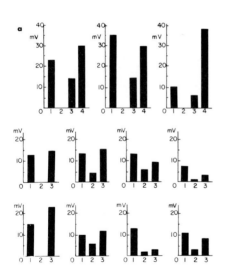

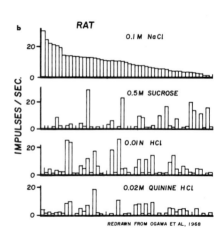

FIG. 3. (a) Differential responsiveness of taste cells to the application of (1) 0.1 M NaCl, (2) 0.5 M sucrose, (3) 0.02 M quinine hydrochloride, and (4) 0.05 M HCl. Depolarizations in response to various stimuli were measured following the insertion of microelectrodes into single taste cells. (b) Differential responsiveness of single taste nerves to specific tastants (redrawn from Ogawa, Sato, and Yamashita, 1968).

TABLE 4. *Differential responsiveness of single taste nerves to closely related tastants*

Part A

1.0 M	Impulses/10 sec			
	A	B	C	D
Sucrose	199	46	36	30
Xylose	62	27	34	25
Glucose	28	18	38	12

Courtesy of C. Mistretta.

Part B

0.5 M	Impulses/10 sec					
	A	B	C	D	E	F
DL Alanine	112	33	18	12	14	13
Glycine	102	44	21	24	51	52
DL Threonine	54	16	18	20	35	65

Courtesy of C. Mistretta.

bud, differentiate and become innervated. X-ray studies also suggest that damaged microvilli can be repaired over a 1- to 2-day period. The entire taste bud disappears if the nerve itself is cut, then redevelops when the nerve regenerates. A similar rapid turnover rate may also occur in the olfactory system, where the receptor cells are similarly exposed to the external environment. In contrast, the receptors of more protected sensory systems, such as the auditory system, are probably not replaced during the lifetime of the organism.

Interactions Between Ligand and Receptor

The response of a taste cell population to an increasing concentration of simple tastants, such as a pure salt or sugar, is hyperbolic (Fig. 4*a*), and a sigmoid relationship between these parameters can be demonstrated using a semilog plot (Fig. 4*b*). More complex curves are obtained for mixtures of tastants.

For both insect and mammalian data, this sigmoid relationship between cellular response and log C can be adequately described by an equation for ligand binding to independent sites:

$$R = \frac{CKR_s}{1 + CK}$$

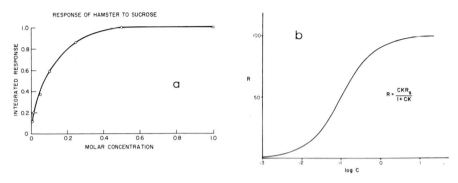

FIG. 4. (a) The integrated response from a population of neurons as a function of sucrose concentration. (b) A similar semilog plot of the same data shows a sigmoid relationship.

where R_S is the maximum response of the system and K is the association constant. Substances such as potassium chloride, which have more than one taste and bind to more than one set of receptors, can be accurately described by combining several such equations.

A fairly complex concentration-response relationship is observed for a series of acids compared on the basis of concentration required to produce equivalent responses (Table 5). The wide variation is due partly to the

TABLE 5. Concentrations of various acidic substances required to produce a response equivalent to that to 5 mM HCl

Acid	mM
Sulfuric	2.2
Hydrochloric	5.0
Nitric	5.9
Dichloroacetic	9.0
Formic	11.6
Lactic	15.6
Butyric	150.0

response actually being a function of pH rather than acid concentration, but in addition, acids are not equally sour at equal pH. The binding of acids to proteins can be described by

$$\log \frac{R_S - R}{R} = \text{pH} + \text{p}K_i + 0.86Z\omega$$

where R_S is the maximum bound, Z is a function of the charge on the molecule at a given pH, and ω is an electrostatic function (Tanford, 1961). A similar expression satisfactorily describes the response of taste cells to acid. This equation shows an apparent negative cooperativity for the binding of acid to the taste receptors; this is probably not negative cooperativity in the allosteric sense (see Chapter 2), but rather a charge effect. Unless an anion is bound simultaneously, the binding of a positively charged hydrogen ion by the receptor will increase its net positive charge and cause it to repulse additional hydrogen ions.

Several instances of positive allosteric cooperativity have been suggested for the gustatory system. In the rat, the amino acid receptor site may contain four subunits, all of which must bind ligand in order to activate the receptor. Insect and mammalian sugar receptors also appear to consist of subunits which show positive cooperativity, and an allosteric model has been proposed to explain these types of data (Morita and Shiraishi, 1968).

It is sometimes difficult in a biological system to obtain data sufficiently quantitative to distinguish between alternative hypotheses. For example, the theoretical curve for a two-subunit sugar receptor showing positive cooperativity is similar to that for two independent sites with two different binding constants. In this particular case, a series of mixture experiments were required to demonstrate positive cooperativity convincingly.

Mechanism of Transduction

The initial event in gustatory transduction is generally assumed to be the induction of a conformational change in the receptor molecule by ligand binding. This event then induces an alteration of membrane potential that results in the activation of the innervating fibers, a process that requires only 25 to 50 msec. This communication is believed to occur via a membrane process rather than one that involves the cytoplasm, since conditions which adversely affect the cytoplasm have little or no effect on the transmission process.

Several attempts have been made to alter the receptor response to ligands by disrupting membrane structure. The application of trypsin or detergent to the tongue has little effect. A significant decrease in response to tastants can be obtained by the application of agents that bind sulfhydryl groups, such as parachloromercurobenzine sulfate (PCMBS) or N-ethylmaleimide. In erythrocytes, the relative effectiveness in binding membrane SH groups depends upon the ease with which the reagent penetrates into the interior of the membrane over a 3-hr period.

The application of low concentrations of PCMBS or ethylmaleimide to sugar receptors markedly decreases their ability to respond to ligand (Fig. 5). The response slowly returns if water is applied to remove the SH reagents, and, in the case of PCMBS, returns more rapidly in the presence of cysteine. This treatment is specific for sugars and other sweetening agents, and has no effect at these concentrations on the response of the same cell population to NaCl, acid or bitter molecules.

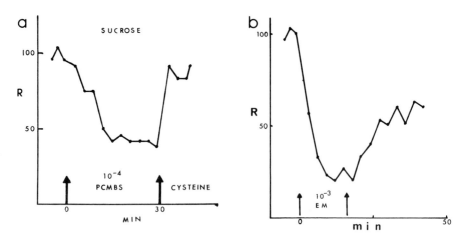

FIG. 5. The effect of PCMBS (*a*) and ethylmaleimide (*b*) on taste fibers responding to 0.5 M sucrose.

Although these SH reagents initiate an electrical response within 20 to 50 msec, the block subsequently responds only after prolonged application. This suggests that these agents rapidly move to the receptor sites and react with them to initiate the usual nerve impulses, but then slowly penetrate the membrane and react with SH groups that are involved with the conformational changes required for the total transduction process. The responses of salt receptors are decreased after prolonged exposure to higher concentrations of SH reagents, suggesting that they are less accessible to the interior of the microvilli plasma membranes than they are to the sugar receptors. Mercuric chloride, which penetrates rapidly and binds to virtually all membrane SH groups, obliterates all receptor responses almost immediately. This effect is also reversible.

In summary, as in all sensory systems, the gustatory receptor is extremely sensitive, in some cases responding to only a few tastant molecules. The reaction between the tastant ligand and the receptor, which presumably causes a conformational change in the latter that results in physiological excitation, can manifest either positive or negative cooperativity. Thus, gustatory sensation is mediated by a functionally linked transductive process.

TRANSDUCTION IN THE OLFACTORY SYSTEM:

Karl-Ernst Kaissling

Individuals within a given species communicate via pheromones, chemical stimulants for which a specialized olfactory receptor mechanism is highly developed in many species. In certain moths, the male can detect a female several miles away by reception of the pheromone that she secretes. (For references on insect olfaction see Kaissling, 1971, on insect pheromones see Jacobson, 1972; Priesner, 1973.) The olfactory receptors of insects are located on their antennae. These are covered with olfactory hairs, each of which contains dendritic processes of the receptor cells, surrounded by an external wall (Fig. 6). Stimulant molecules must diffuse through small channels in the external wall of the hair to reach the dendritic receptors. This mechanism is capable of concentrating the odorant by a factor of at least 10^5 over the concentration in the surrounding air.

The sensitivity and specificity of receptor cells of the silkmoth *Bombyx mori* have been examined using extracellular recording techniques (Fig. 7). Studies with tritium-labeled Bombykol of high specific activity (Kasang, 1968) demonstrated that the adsorption of a single pheromone molecule per sense cell is sufficient to elicit a nerve impulse (Kaissling and Priesner, 1970), although a behavioral response (wing movement) can be obtained only when a minimum of several hundred molecules are bound. The receptor cells have a spontaneous firing rate of ~1 spike/10 sec, and ~300 molecules per antenna (with some 30,000 receptor cells) must be bound in order to produce a firing rate significantly above background. If the binding of a single Bombykol molecule were to open one ion gate having a conductance of ~10^{-10} mho, it would produce a sufficient depolarization for the generation of a nerve impulse (Kaissling, 1971, 1974). As shown in Fig. 7, the application of a square wave stimulus of odor concentration in an airstream produces a constant receptor potential for the duration of the stimulus application, and the potential slowly returns to its original value when the stimulation ceases. The receptor potential in the dendritic region is associated with the generation of a series of nerve impulses in the region of the cell soma. The receptor potential appears with a minimum latency of 10 to 20 msec, and has a decay half-life of approximately 1 sec. The frequency of generated nerve impulses does not merely reflect the degree of depolarization, indicating that a transductive process occurs between the two processes. The transduction of the odor stimulus to the receptor potential must involve at least six steps:

$$(1) \quad S_{gas} \rightarrow S_{adsorbed} \quad \text{adsorption}$$
$$(2) \quad S_{adsorbed} \rightleftharpoons S_{at\ receptor} \quad \text{diffusion}$$
$$(3) \quad A + S_{at\ receptor} \rightleftharpoons AS \quad \text{binding}$$
$$(4) \quad AS \rightleftharpoons A'S \quad \text{activation}$$
$$(5) \quad A'S \text{ induces } \Delta G_{membrane} \quad \text{increased conductance}$$

$$(6) \quad \left.\begin{array}{c} S_{adsorbed} \\ \\ S_{at\ receptor} \end{array}\right\} \rightleftharpoons S_{inactivated} \quad \text{early inactivation}$$

In (1), the stimulus molecule is adsorbed from the air onto the outer surface of the hair wall. The molecule then diffuses through the channels of the

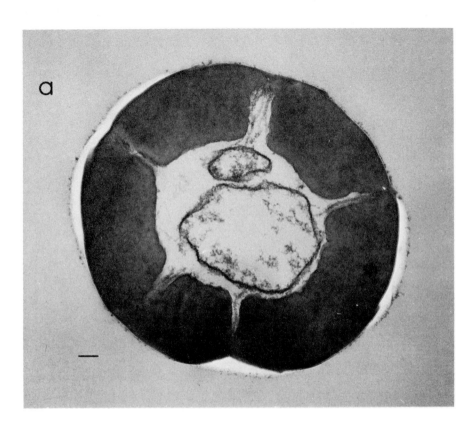

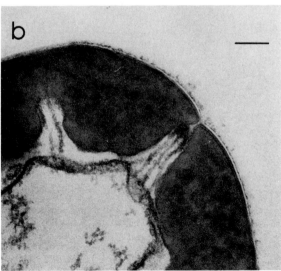

FIG. 6. (a) Cross section through an olfactory hair of a *Bombyx mori* antenna. Each hair contains the dendrites of two receptor cells. (b) Odorant molecules diffuse through pores in the protective external wall to reach the dendritic membrane of the receptor cell via many small tubules. (Electron micrographs from Steinbrecht and Müller, 1971.) Scale 0.1 μ.

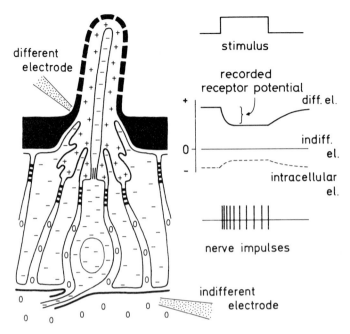

FIG. 7. Extracellular recording technique for an insect olfactory hair. The different electrode can be inserted into the base of the hair, as shown in the diagram (Kaissling, 1971).
Alternatively, the capillary electrode can be slipped over the hair after its tip is cut off to
provide electrical contact to the receptor cell within the hair. This proceuure does not
alter the cellular response for several hours.

hair wall (2) and combines with a hypothetical receptor molecule (A) on
the cell membrane (3). It is assumed that this binding leads to a change
in the state or conformation of the receptor, designated by A' (4), and that
this altered conformation or "activation" induces the membrane alteration(s)
that leads to an increased membrane conductance ΔG (5) and to depolarization. The constant amplitude and the decay of the receptor potential while
Bombykol molecules accumulate and remain on the hair indicate a fairly
rapid ("early") inactivation process (6). This might result from a chemical
modification of the odor molecule (not highly probable), physical dilution
into the extracellular space, transport into the cell, or another mechanism.
After transduction, the inactivated odorant (probably still Bombykol)
diffuses slowly from the hairs toward the antennal epithelium and is finally
decomposed by enzyme-catalyzed reactions that occur over a period of
several minutes. Experimental evidence is available regarding the initial
adsorption and diffusion processes, as well as for the "late" metabolic
degradation of the pheromone (Kasang, 1971; Kasang and Kaissling, 1972;
Steinbrecht and Kasang, 1972). Although the intervening steps remain
hypothetical at this time, they are based on data obtained in similar systems.

Figure 8 illustrates the variable responses of the Bombykol receptor to a series of similar long-chain molecules. The response curves differ significantly, and do not all reach the same saturation maximum. All compounds seem to be equally well adsorbed to the antennal surface (Kasang and Kaissling, 1972) and may have similar diffusion coefficients. The differential kinetic effects of these Bombykol analogues could be explained as differences in their affinity for the hypothetical receptor molecules (step 3), in their ability to form an active-receptor-stimulant complex $A'S$ (step 4),

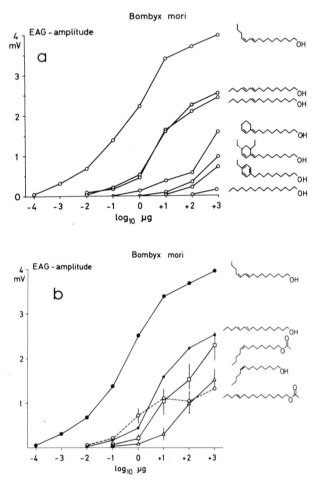

FIG. 8. (*a,b*) Dose-response curves of the *Bombyx mori* pheromone receptor a series of Bombykol analogues. The cyclic compounds (called cyclobombykols) were prepared by Dr. P. Schudel and his colleagues at Givaudan-Esrolko at Zurich, Switzerland. Dr. E. Priesner kindly provided the three additional compounds in *b*. In *a* and *b*, the top curve is the response to Bombykol. Ordinate: Steady amplitude of summated receptor potentials (EAG = electroantennogram). Abscissa: Stimulus intensity as load of the odor source.

in the increase of membrane conductance per activated complex $g_{A'S}$ (step 5), or possibly in the velocity of early inactivation (step 6). The total increase of membrane conductance $\Delta G_{\text{membrane}}$ might follow the equation

$$\Delta G_{\text{membrane}} = g_{A'S} \cdot A'S \tag{1}$$

with $g_{A'S}$ being compound-specific but independent of stimulus intensity. $g_{A'S}$ could also vary with stimulus intensity, as in the case of cooperation between receptor molecules. Finally, the receptor potentials of some compounds show shorter or longer decay times, suggesting that also the early inactivation mechanism (step 6) may be specific (Roelofs and Comeau, 1971b; Kaissling, 1974). Therefore, steps 3 to 6 could be compound-specific.

A simple alteration of the normal 10-*trans*, 12-*cis* double bond arrangement of Bombykol to the all-*trans* form reduces its effectiveness by 100-fold; a 10^6-fold decrease in effectiveness is observed for the saturated alcohol (Fig. 8a). There are also quite effective compounds whose chemical structures are markedly different from that of Bombykol, such as the cyclobombykols (Fig. 8a) or some acetates (Fig. 8b). Alterations in chain length and double bond position of monounsaturated acetates (Fig. 9) produce relatively smaller changes in effectiveness in Noctuid moths, and indicate that the distance from the double bond to the nonpolar end of the molecule is more critical for the EAG response than the distance to the polar portion (Priesner, 1973). Similar data from another species have been used to generate a quantitative model for the binding of the odorant to the receptor. The model assumes a three-point attachment by weak, noncovalent interactions (Neuwirth, 1973; Kafka, *pers. comm., in press*). Other investigators have proposed a four-point attachment for the red-banded leaf roller pheromone, *cis*-11-tetradecenyl acetate (Roelofs and Comeau, 1971a). A striking example that suggests binding only at certain regions of the odor molecule is the alarm-pheromone undecane, which is about 10^3 times as active as decane or dodecane on the olfactory cells of the ant *Lasius fuliginosus* (Dumpert, 1972; Kafka, *in press*).

The development of quantitative binding models is difficult because it is not yet known why a given compound is less effective than the key compound of a receptor cell. There are at least four possible explanations for the lesser effectiveness of a given compound. First, a smaller affinity of the stimulant to the receptor molecules which might shift the dose-response curve to higher stimulus concentrations, according to the mass action law. Second, the weaker ability to form active complexes $A'S$ which could be responsible for a smaller maximum response; this can be seen in Fig. 8 (Kaissling, 1974). Third, the early inactivation could have high velocities, as suggested by shorter decay times of the receptor potential, and therefore alter the steady-state response. Fourth, a smaller $g_{A'S}$ would also change the dose-response curve, as seen in equation (1). The reason for assuming a

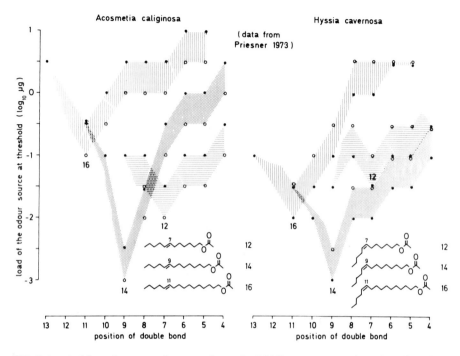

FIG. 9. Load of the odor source for a small standard EAG response as a function of double-bond position for a 12, 14, and 16 carbon chain. The compounds are *cis*- (filled circles) and trans- (open circles) isomers of monounsaturated acetates. From EAG measurements in two species of moths. (Data from Priesner, Jacobson, and Bestmann, cited in Priesner, 1973.)

compound-dependent $g_{A'S}$ will be discussed below. When interpreting receptor potentials, the nonlinear relationship between conductance and voltage that may be expected in such systems must also be considered (Morita, 1969; Kaissling, 1971).

Recent experiments suggest that a compound can, indeed, be less effective due to a smaller conductance per active receptor $g_{A'S}$. Weak stimuli (10^{-2} μg) of Bombykol show a very irregular time course of the receptor potential and correspondingly irregular impulse firing (Fig. 10). These fluctuations may be due to "elementary" receptor potentials induced by single molecules. The same cell shows a small but very smooth receptor potential and regular spike firing with a 1000-fold concentrated stimulus (10 μg) of *cis*-10-tetradecenol. In this case, the receptor potential could be composed of a large number of very small elementary receptor potentials. The large number of potentials could be due to numerous active complexes resulting from a high affinity of the compound for the receptor. The small size could be due to a very small effect of the compound on the membrane conductance per activated receptor. Other compounds, such as one of the cyclobom-

Bombyx mori ♂

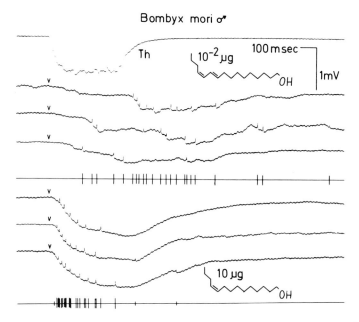

FIG. 10. Single cell recording of receptor potentials and nerve impulses. Upper line (Th): Airstream velocity of the stimulus (0.5 sec duration) recorded by a thermistor. The three upper traces are produced by three stimuli with 10^{-2} μg bombykol on the odor source and show fluctuating receptor potentials and irregular impulse firing. The three lower traces from the same cell stimulated with a 1,000-times stronger stimulus of cis-10-tetradecenol show a smooth time course and more regular spike distances. The impulses of each group of three traces are added on a separate line. The fluctuating potential might be composed of a few large elementary receptor potentials from a small number of activated receptor molecules. The smooth type could be explained by many small superimposing elementary potentials induced by the "wrong" compound. The upper three traces also show the long latencies of the receptor potentials found with weak bombykol stimuli. This delay might be due to the diffusion of the molecules to the receptors. (cf. Kaissling, 1974.)

bykols (Fig. 8a), show weak effectiveness, but a fluctuating response indicative of a low affinity but a "normal" $g_{A's}$. These results correspond to the statistical analysis of postsynaptic potentials of Katz and Miledi (1972, 1973), who showed that the lifetimes of single ion channels differ for various transmitter analogues.

Studies with a large number of related compounds might enable us to distinguish between those molecular properties of the stimulant that are necessary for binding and those that induce the right kind of activation or conformational change in the receptor molecule.

These studies indicate that the transduction of sensory information can be extended beyond the demonstration that the binding of stimulant molecules by their receptors produces action waves in sensory nerve fibers; the transductive process basic to chemoreception can be dissected into a series of distinct steps. Information about the functional linkage in this biomolecular cascade can be deduced from the relationship between the molecular structures of the stimulant ligand and excitatory parameters within the system, such as receptor potentials.

REFERENCES

Beidler, L. M. (1961): Taste receptor stimulation. In: *Progress in Biophysics and Biophysical Chemistry*, Vol. 12, pp. 109–137. London: Pergamon Press.
Beidler, L. M., and Smallman, R. (1965): Renewal of cells within taste buds. *J. Cell Biol.*, 27:263–272.
Dethier, V. G., Evans, D. R., and Rhoades, M. V. (1956): Some factors controlling the ingestion of carbohydrates by the blowfly. *Biol. Bull.*, 111:204–222.
Dumpert, K. (1972): Alarmstoffrezeptoren auf der Antenne von *Lasius fuliginosus* (Latr.) (Hymenoptera, Formicidae). *Z. vergl. Physiol.*, 76:403–425.
Evans, D. R. (1963): Chemical structure and stimulation by carbohydrates. In: *Olfaction and Taste*, Vol. I, edited by Y. Zotterman, pp. 165–176. New York: Pergamon Press.
Jacobson, M. (1972): *Insect Sex Pheromones*. New York: Academic Press.
Kafka, W. A. (1974): Physicochemical aspects of odor reception in insects. *Ann. N.Y. Acad. Sci.* (*in press*).
Kaissling, K. E. (1971): Insect olfaction. In: *Handbook of Sensory Physiology. Volume IV. Chemical Senses-Part I*, edited by L. M. Beidler, pp. 351–431. Berlin: Springer-Verlag.
Kaissling, K. E. (1974): Sensory transduction in insect olfactory receptors. In: *Biochemistry of Sensory Functions. Volume 25. Colloquium Gesellsch. Biolog. Chemie*, edited by L. Jaenicke. Heidelberg: Springer-Verlag (*in press*).
Kaissling, K. E., and Priesner, E. (1970): Die Riechschwelle des Seidenspinners. *Naturwiss.*, 57:23–28.
Kasang, G. (1968): Tritium-Markierung des Sexuallockstoffes Bombykol. *Z. Naturforsch.*, 23b:1331–1335.
Kasang, G. (1971): Bombykol reception and metabolism on the antennae of the silkmoth Bombyx mori. In: *Gustation and Olfaction*, edited by G. Ohloff and A. F. Thomas, pp. 245–250. New York: Academic Press.
Kasang, G., and Kaissling, K. E. (1972): Specificity of primary and secondary olfactory processes in Bombyx antennae. In: *International Symposium on Olfaction and Taste IV*, edited by D. Schneider, pp. 200–206. Stuttgart: Wiss. Verlagsgesellsch.
Katz, B., and Miledi, R. (1972): The statistical nature of the acetylcholine potential and its molecular components. *J. Physiol.*, 224:665–699.
Katz, B., and Miledi, R. (1973): The characteristics of "end-plate noise" produced by different depolarizing drugs. *J. Physiol.*, 230:707–717.
Morita, H. (1969): Electrical signs of taste receptor activity. *International Symposium on Olfaction and Taste III*, edited by C. Pfaffman, pp. 370–381. New York: Rockefeller University Press.
Morita, H., and Shiraishi, A. (1968): Stimulation of the labellar sugar receptor of the fleshfly by mono- and disaccharides. *J. Gen. Physiol.*, 52:559–583.
Neuwirth, J. (1973): Multiple-Site Wechselwirkung zwischen Duftmolekülen und Akzeptoren. Diplomarbeit an der Technischen Universität München, Physik-Departement, E 10, 60p.
Ogawa, H., Sato, M., and Yamashita, S. (1968): Multiple sensitivity of chorda tympany fibers of the rat and hamster to gustatory and thermal stimuli. *J. Physiol.*, 199:223–240.
Omand, E., and Dethier, V. G. (1969): An electrophysiological analysis of the action of carbohydrates on the sugar receptor of the blowfly. *Proc. Nat. Acad. Sci.*, 62:136–143.
Priesner, E. (1973): Artspezifität und Funktion einiger Insektenpheromone. *Fortschr. Zoologie*, 22:49–135.
Roelofs, W. L., and Comeau, A. (1971a): Sex pheromone perception: Synergists and inhibitors for the red-banded leaf roller attractant. *J. Insect Physiol.*, 17:435–448.
Roelofs, W. L., and Comeau, A. (1971b): Sex pheromone perception: Electroantennogram response of the red-banded leaf roller moth. *J. Insect. Physiol.*, 17:1969–1982.
Shimada, I., Shiraishi, A., Kijima, H., and Morita, H. (1974): Separation of two receptor

sites in a single labellar sugar receptor of the flesh-fly by treatment with p-chloromercuri-benzoate. *J. Insect Physiol.,* 20:605–621.

Steinbrecht, R. A., and Kasang, G. (1972): Capture and conveyance of odour molecules in an insect olfactory receptor. In: *International Symposium on Olfaction and Taste IV,* edited by D. Schneider, pp. 193–199. Stuttgart: Wiss. Verlagsgesellsch.

Steinbrecht, R. A., and Müller, B. (1971): On the stimulus conducting structures in insect olfactory receptors. *Z. Zellforsch.,* 117:570–575.

Tanford, C. (1961): *Physical Chemistry of Macromolecules.* New York: John Wiley & Sons.

Functional Linkage in Biomolecular Systems, edited by
F. O. Schmitt, D. M. Schneider, and D. M. Crothers.
Raven Press, New York © 1975.

Chapter 13

Transductive Coupling in Chemotactic Processes: Chemoreceptor-Flagellar Coupling in Bacteria

INTRODUCTION:

Daniel E. Koshland, Jr.

The study of what we usually regard as neural systems involves complex organisms having more than one cell type. However, the history of biochemistry contains numerous instances in which a particular biochemical mechanism has been found to be common to organisms ranging from the smallest to the largest. Although the phenomenon of chemotaxis is widespread in living systems, bacterial chemotaxis has been of particular interest since it is a sensing system and is present in a very simple organism. Hopefully, then, this primitive sensing system will follow historical precedent and provide biochemical clues to the more complex sensory systems of higher organisms. In this discussion and those of Drs. Adler and Berg that follow, components of this sensory system will be shown to comprise the elements shown in Fig. 1; these elements are not dissimilar to those of higher sensory systems.

The mechanism by which bacteria respond to their environment has been of interest since the nineteenth century, when Pfeffer (1888) and Engelmann (1902) found that bacteria could be trapped in a spot of light, apparently as the result of migration to the light source. They also demonstrated chemotaxis, by observing that bacteria would congregate in a capillary containing an attractant such as a sugar or amino acid (Fig. 2). This assay is still in use, although a much more elegant and quantitative modification has been developed (Adler, 1969). This selectivity was demonstrated by Adler (1969) to be based on specific receptor molecules. This same selectivity of response to sensory input is seen in higher systems, as indicated by the high specificity for pheromone reception (see Kaissling, Chapter 12).

The movements of bacteria such as *E. coli* and *Salmonella typhimurium* follow a random walk pattern of approximately straight lines, with periodic turns at varying angles (Fig. 3). The straight portions are commonly referred to as "runs" and the turns as "tumbles" or "twiddles." Random changes in direction are also observed in a gradient of an attractant, but there is a net migration in the direction of the attractant. Sensory input leads to a be-

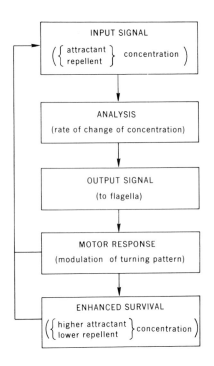

FIG. 1. Components of the chemical sensing system of bacteria.

havioral response that manifests itself as a net movement. The available data suggest that this net migration of bacteria results from modulation of the length of the runs between tumbles (Berg and Brown, 1972; Macnab and Koshland, 1972). Quantitative analyses of these bacterial movements indicate that suppression of tumbling in a favorable direction is more responsible for migration than enhancement of tumbling in an unfavorable direction.

One of the most important questions concerning the sensory control of movement involves the mechanism by which the bacteria detect a gradient, a formidable task for an organism only 2 μm in length. Spatial sensing and

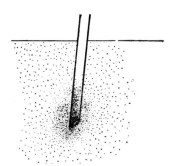

FIG. 2. Capillary containing attractant immersed in solution without attractant causes gradient which leads bacteria to swim into capillary.

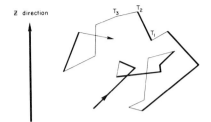

FIG. 3. Idealized picture of bacterial motion. Trajectories consist of roughly straight-line runs interrupted by "twiddles" or "tumbles" in which abrupt changes in direction occur. (From Macnab and Koshland, 1974.)

temporal sensing devices both have ample precedent. By adapting the stopped-flow apparatus of chemical kinetics to the problems of chemotaxis, it was possible (Macnab and Koshland, 1972) to alter the environment of the bacteria from one uniform concentration to another, in order to examine the chemotactic mechanism. As shown in Fig. 4, bacteria were forced through a mixing chamber and then delivered to a microscope stage, where their pattern of movement was analyzed after mixing was complete.

It was first determined that the bacteria swim normally at any uniform concentration of attractant; that is, the path length between tumbles is the same at the initial concentration before mixing (c_i) and the final concentration after mixing (c_f). This information was necessary to establish that the swimming pattern was not dependent on the absolute concentration of an attractant when the attractant was uniformly distributed in space. Since this was the case, the apparatus in Fig. 4 could be used to distinguish between

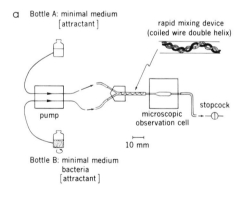

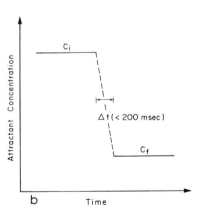

FIG. 4. Temporal gradient apparatus. (a) Attractant concentrations are (i) bottle B, C_i (≥ 0); (ii) bottle A, C_i' ($>$, $=$, or $<C_i$); (iii) observation cell (as a result of stream mixing), C_f ($>$, $=$, or $<C_i$). Bacteria experience $C_i \rightarrow C_f$, and thus can be subjected to positive, zero, or negative temporal gradients as desired. Gradient is given by $\Delta C/\Delta t$, where $\Delta C = C_f - C_i$ and Δt is mixing time. (From Macnab and Koshland, 1972.) (b) Principle of apparatus—Bacteria are initially at uniform concentration C_i and are plunged suddenly into uniform concentration C_f. They are observed in a no-gradient situation in which they would swim normally if they have no memory and utilize instantaneous sensing by receptors at head and tail. (From Macnab and Koshland, 1972.)

instantaneous spatial sensing and temporal sensing. Instantaneous spatial sensing refers to a mechanism in which receptors at the head and tail of the bacteria make an instantaneous comparison of the concentrations of attractant at their head and tail and determine whether the bacterium is moving up or down the gradient. In contrast, temporal sensing would involve a comparison of attractant concentration over a time interval — for example, the concentration in present time is compared with the concentration of attractant in past time as a means of determining whether the bacterium is swimming up or down the gradient.

If the former were the correct mechanism, the bacteria should swim normally after mixing, since they would see an instantaneous uniform distribution of attractant. If the latter were correct, they should behave abnormally, since they would be comparing the final concentration with a different previous concentration.

The latter alternative was found to be correct; the rapid mixing experiments indicated that the bacteria utilize a temporal mechanism (Fig. 5). When the concentration of attractant was the same in both chambers prior to mixing, bacterial movement consisted of the normal pattern of mod-

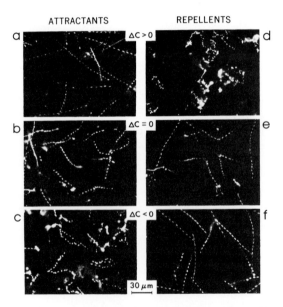

ATTRACTANTS   REPELLENTS

FIG. 5. Motility tracks of *Salmonella* in the interval 2 to 7 sec after subjection to temporal gradients of attractants and repellents. Photographs taken in dark field with stroboscopic illumination operating at 5 pulses/sec. (a, b, and c) Attractants. (a) Serine increase from 0 to 7.5×10^{-4} M; (b) no concentration change (control); (c) serine decrease from 10^{-3} to 2.4×10^{-4} M. (d, e, and f) Repellents. (d) Phenol increase from zero to 7.5×10^{-4} M; (e) no concentration change (control); (f) phenol decrease from 3×10^{-4} to 7.5×10^{-5} M. The smooth motility response to "favorable" gradients (a and f) and the tumbling response to "unfavorable" gradients (c and d) eventually give way to the normal motility pattern (b and e). (From Tsang et al., 1973.)

erately long runs interspersed with tumbling. When the bacteria were subjected to a decrease in concentration, their movements initially consisted of shorter runs with frequent tumbling; this was followed by a gradual relaxation back to the original pattern. A rapid increase in concentration produced the opposite response, that is, long runs with infrequent tumbling that again gradually relaxed back to the normal pattern. The abnormal migration in a uniform concentration of attractant demonstrated that some time-dependent process is involved; the bacteria compare their past and present environment over an interval of time rather than the difference in concentration between their head and tail. Hence a rudimentary memory is involved. The gradual relaxation back to a normal pattern further indicates that a memory device is involved. The relaxation time is a function of the gradient and its direction; the response is longer for positive than negative gradients, and longer for steep gradients than shallow ones. A precisely inverse relationship occurs when repellents are used (Fig. 5).

One major advantage of a temporal mechanism is that the flagella need not be localized in one position, since the directional property is generated by the movement of the bacterium in space. A mechanism that involved an instantaneous spatial comparison would require localization of receptors at the head and tail regions.

One of several possible mechanisms for this rudimentary memory device is shown in Fig. 6. An attractant or repellent may induce conformational changes in two enzymes which jointly control the pool level of an unknown compound X, which in turn controls flagellar movement. If enzyme 1 responds rapidly to the increasing concentration of attractant and enzyme 2 only slowly, the level of compound X will change, and will either increase or suppress tumbling. It is not yet clear whether compound X might be analogous to the neurotransmitters of higher species, or might be as simple as the level of a proton gradient, or is some compound special to bacteria. Regardless of whether the specific compounds are the same for bacteria and higher species, the receptor-effector mechanisms may be quite similar.

We are faced with the problem of whether the use of the term "memory" is justified for this mechanism. Is it simply a semantic device with no real

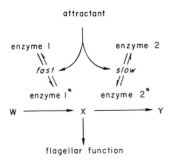

FIG. 6. Schematic illustration of one possible time-dependent mechanism. Attractant alters conformation of enzymes 1 and 2 to catalytically more active forms, enzyme 1 rapidly and enzyme 2 slowly. The compound X, which controls flagellar function, therefore tends to increase in positive gradients, decrease in negative gradients, and remain unchanged in zero gradients. (From Macnab and Koshland, 1972.)

(1) Lower limit-short memory, little

extension of body length

(2) Upper limit — long memory span,

information communicated too late

FIG. 7. Useful memory concept applied to bacterial motion.

similarity to the memory process of higher organisms? This problem has been examined from the point of view of the usefulness of this memory to the biological organism. If the term memory is not simply semantic, there should be some limits on its usefulness. Bacteria have been shown to operate by a random walk process in the elegant tracking experiments of Berg and Brown (1972). Figure 7 illustrates the potential upper and lower limits of a bacterium operating by this process. If the memory span were extremely short, the distance moved before the memory fades would be little more than could be achieved by a mechanism utilizing receptors at either end of the cell. Such a mechanism would therefore have no real advantage over a spatial one, and it would be difficult to justify its use in the biological system. The other extreme, that of a very long memory, would provide no useful information, since the signal to tumble would come too late to control the direction appropriately. A useful memory should therefore have a duration intermediate between these extremes.

Studies (Macnab and Koshland, 1974) have indicated that this memory length is of the order of 1 to 10 sec when the bacterium is responding to an actual gradient. This represents 10 to 100 body lengths, and is considerably more effective than would be provided by a spatial sensing mechanism.

The mechanism emphasizes that the memory of higher species is not designed to record all input signals completely. It is an advantage to remember some events, but our minds would be extremely cluttered if we were to remember everything. The phenomena of long- and short-term memory are undoubtedly based on the principle that permanent memories are not generally formed unless the input signal is reinforced by repeated stimuli, by the intensity of the experience, or by prior information that indicates its significance. This prevents us from remembering too much, just as the bacterium is prevented from remembering too long.

Returning to the schematic outline of Fig. 1, we now see that the chemical sensory system of a tiny *Salmonella* or *E. coli* cell is already complex. An input signal of an attractant or repellent stimulates the cell, probably by inducing a conformational change in a protein receptor molecule. This is then transformed into a rate of change of concentration, since the bacteria detect a gradient during their swimming through a temporal sensing device which integrates over time. A gradient in space is therefore detected by the velocity of movement of the bacterium through space, which, it is suggested, then produces a conformational change over time within the signaling system. This signaling system apparently involves the level of some molecule or process, which might be as simple as a proton or as complicated as a membrane depolarization. The signal alters the turning pattern of the bacterium in such a way as to suppress tumbling when it is moving up a positive gradient of attractant and to diminish tumbling or leave it unchanged when the organism is moving down such a gradient. The final result is an enhanced survival pattern that allows the bacterium to swim toward nutrients and away from toxic materials.

The following sections by Adler and Berg elaborate further on the properties of this sensory system. Since nature is parsimonious with its mechanisms and tends to use repeatedly the same basic mechanisms, some of the principles revealed in these simple bacterial systems may be applicable to higher, more complex organisms.

BACTERIAL CHEMORECEPTION:

Julius Adler

The movement of bacteria into a capillary tube containing an attractant (Fig. 8) can be used as an assay method for chemotaxis. Above the recognition threshold (10^{-7} M for L-aspartate in Fig. 8a), the number of bacteria accumulating within the capillary increases to a maximum, then declines. This apparent inhibition at high concentrations results from rapid diffusion of the attractant; bacteria congregate outside the mouth of the tube but do not enter, since they are unable to detect a concentration gradient above that at which their receptors become saturated. Curves similar to that in Fig. 8a are observed with a wide variety of attractants, including sugars and amino acids.

Chemotaxis can be considered as as series of events: (1) the detection of an attractant or repellant, (2) analysis of this information and transmission to the flagella, (3) a flagellar response altering the manner of swimming, and (4) the swimming process itself.

Until recently (Adler, 1969), it was not known whether or not the attract-

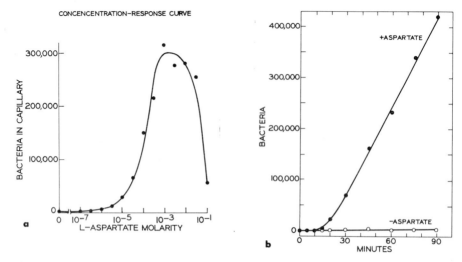

FIG. 8. (a) The number of *E. coli* entering a capillary tube containing the attractant L-asparatate in 1 hr as a function of attractant concentration. (b) The number of bacteria in capillary tube containing L-aspartate (10^{-3} M) as a function of time. The usual assay time is 1 hr.

ant itself is detected. The chemoreceptor hypothesis proposes that bacteria detect the actual attractant molecule, while the metabolism hypothesis suggests that the bacterium detects a metabolic product, or ATP produced from metabolism of the attractant, rather than the chemotactic agent itself. The evidence favors the chemoreceptor hypothesis.

One major line of evidence against the metabolism hypothesis is the lack of any correlation between the ability of a bacterium to metabolize a chemical and its ability to attract (Adler, 1969). For example, both glucose and glycerol can be metabolized for energy production, yet only glucose serves as an attractant (Fig. 9a). Many amino acids, sugars, citric acid cycle intermediates, and so on, which can be metabolized and yield ATP, fail to serve as attractants.

Conversely, a number of chemicals which cannot be metabolized act as attractants. For example, D-fucose, a D-galactose analogue that cannot be metabolized, is an attractant (Fig. 9b). However, D-galactose is detected at a lower concentration.

If the metabolism hypothesis were correct, mutants incapable of metabolizing galactose should also be incapable of responding to a galactose gradient. This is not the case; mutants missing both the enzymes for galactose metabolism and all four of the known transport systems for galactose are attracted to this substance as well as wild-type bacteria (Fig. 9c). The mutant bacteria have a much lower apparent threshold for the sugar than

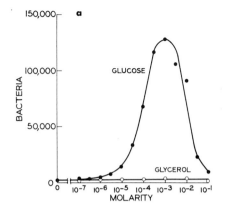

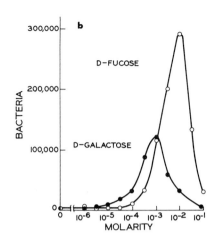

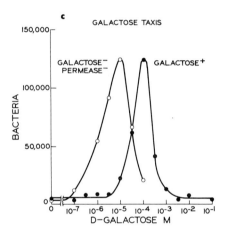

FIG. 9. (a) Both glucose and glycerol are capable of being metabolized by *E. coli*, yet glucose is an attractant and glycerol is not (Adler, 1969). (b) Conversely, D-fucose is not metabolized, yet it is an attractant. (Adler, 1969). (c) Galactose taxis in wild-type bacteria (filled circles) and in a mutant lacking galactose metabolism and galactose permease (open circles) (Adler, 1969).

the wild type, because metabolism of the attractant and consequent destruction of the gradient does not occur.

These observations indicated that bacteria possess what were called "chemoreceptors" (Adler, 1969) for the detection of attractants: devices, presumably located on the cell surface, that are not dependent upon either the transport or metabolism of the attractant. Three basic approaches have been utilized to determine the number of different receptors present in bacteria such as *E. coli*: (1) competition experiments; (2) the use of mutants that specifically lack one chemotactic response; and (3) the induction of a specific chemotactic response by having the attractant present in the growth medium.

In contrast to the usual chemotaxis experiment, in which only the capillary contains attractant, in a competition experiment (Fig. 10) both the capillary

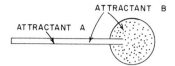

FIG. 10. The design of a competition experiment to determine if two attractants are detected by the same or different receptors.

and solution contain a second attractant, B, at a concentration sufficient to saturate the bacterial chemoreceptor. If the chemotactic response to A remains at its usual level in the presence of a saturating concentration of B, the two must be detected by different receptors. However, the response to A will be inhibited if the two are detected by the same receptor. Competition experiments using most of the known attractants have indicated that *E. coli* possesses a large number of different chemoreceptors.

Perhaps the most definitive way to determine the number of distinct chemoreceptors is to isolate mutants lacking a particular receptor, using the technique shown in Fig. 11. Bacteria are deposited at the center of a Petri dish containing a low concentration of agar (so that the bacteria can swim) and an attractant. The bacteria will swim out from the center as the local supply of attractant is metabolized, at any given time forming a ring at the location of the gradient that they have produced. Any mutants that cannot respond to the attractant will remain near the origin. These are isolated after the procedure is repeated several times to remove all wild-type bacteria. There are many possible mutations that might result in an inability to respond to an attractant, and the mutant population is not homogeneous. Mutant cells must be cloned to obtain pure populations; those missing only the desired chemoreceptor, called "specifically nonchemotactic," are used for the purpose presently under discussion. Other types are "generally nonchemotactic," that is, fully motile but incapable of responding to any chemotactic agents. Of course, there are other mutants that are not motile.

Having obtained, for example, a mutant having a nonfunctional or absent

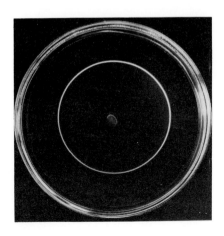

FIG. 11. The isolation of mutants lacking a specific type of chemoreceptor. A ring of wild-type bacteria forms as the supply of attractant is depleted from the center, leaving at the origin those mutants lacking positive chemotaxis for the attractant. (From Adler, 1969).

galactose chemoreceptor, it is possible to determine what other chemicals also fail to attract the mutant, and are therefore probably detected by the galactose receptor.

The list of chemoreceptors for positive taxis in *E. coli,* found by these three criteria, is shown in Table 1. The specificity of each chemoreceptor is indicated (Mesibov and Adler, 1972; Adler, Hazelbauer, and Dahl, 1973).

TABLE 1. *Chemoreceptors in E. coli*

Attractant	Threshold molarity
N-Acetyl-glucosamine receptor	
N-Acetyl-D-glucosamine	1×10^{-5}
Fructose receptor	
D-Fructose	1×10^{-5}
Galactose receptor	
D-Galactose	4×10^{-7}
D-Glucose	4×10^{-7}
D-Fucose	3×10^{-5}
Glucose receptor	
D-Glucose	1×10^{-5}
D-Mannose	1×10^{-5}
Maltose Receptor	
Maltose	2×10^{-6}
Mannitol receptor	
D-Mannitol	7×10^{-6}
Ribose receptor	
D-Ribose	3×10^{-6}
Sorbitol receptor	
D-Sorbitol	1×10^{-5}
Trehalose receptor	
Trehalose	6×10^{-6}
Aspartate receptor	
L-Aspartate	6×10^{-8}
L-Glutamate	2×10^{-6}
Serine receptor	
L-Serine	4×10^{-7}
L-Cysteine	6×10^{-6}
L-Alanine	7×10^{-5}
Glycine	2×10^{-5}

Also attractive: O_2, various inorganic ions (From Mesibov and Adler, 1972; Adler, Hazelbauer, and Dahl, 1973.)

Negative chemotaxis can be studied with similar techniques (Tso and Adler, 1974*a*). Repellent is put into the bacterial suspension but not into the capillary; bacteria then "escape" into the capillary for "refuge" and are counted (Fig. 12*a*). Soft agar plates containing plugs of repellent can also be used (Fig. 12*b*). Many repellent substances have been found (Table 2 contains a partial list). Competition experiments have been done, and mutants have been isolated that specifically lack the ability to be repelled by acid, indole, a group of five hydrophobic amino acids, and salicylate. On

a   NEGATIVE   CHEMOTAXIS   **b**

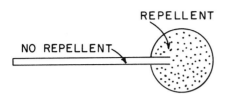

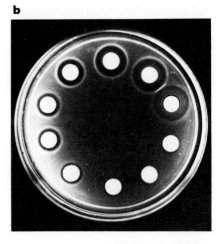

FIG. 12. Assay methods for negative chemotaxis. (*a*) Repellent is added to the medium containing the bacteria, and bacteria are forced to migrate into the capillary tube which lacks repellent. The number of bacteria within the tube is then determined. (*b*) Plugs of hard agar containing material to be tested as a repellent, each containing a different concentration of the repellent acetate (starting with none at 1 o'clock and increasing clockwise from 3×10^{-4} to 3 M) are placed into soft agar containing the bacteria. Within 1 hr, the area of the plug containing a repellent will be vacated. This method can also be used for the isolation of mutants, which would not flee the area (Tso and Adler, 1974*a*.)

this basis, and on the basis of chemical structures, the repellents can be divided into chemoreceptor classes (Table 2). Very likely there is a chemo-receptor for each class.

Most substances that act as repellents are harmful to the organism. One exception is that of leucine, probably a repellent as a result of its similarity to the toxic amino acid valine. However, the ability of a substance to harm

TABLE 2. *Partial List of Repellents*

Short-chain fatty acid class
   Acetate, propionate, *n*-butyrate, *iso*-butyrate, etc.
Aliphatic alcohol class
   Methanol, ethanol, *n*-propanol, *iso*-propanol, etc.
Hydrophobic amino acid class
   L-Leucine, L-isoleucine, L-valine, L-tryptophan, L-phenylalanine,
     L-glutamine, L-histidine
Indole class
   Indole, skatole, etc.
Aromatic class
   Benzoate, salicylate, etc.
Inorganic ion class
   Co^{2+}, Ni^{2+}
Acid (H^+) and base (OH^-)

From Tso and Adler, 1974*a*.

the organism is unrelated to the mechanism of chemotaxis. Phenol is just as toxic to *E. coli* as to *Salmonella,* yet it is not a repellent for *E. coli,* and mutants that do not run away from a toxic substance such as indole are equally susceptible to its toxic effects as the wild type. Chemoreceptors permit the detection of a repellent at a sufficiently low concentration to prevent its harmful effects.

Each chemoreceptor is presumed to utilize a protein – the "recognition component" – to bind specifically the chemicals it can detect. This protein is believed to be in or associated with the cytoplasmic membrane (the physiologically active inner cell membrane, in contrast with the relatively inert outer envelope surrounding a bacterium) and to be part of a transport system. It thus serves a dual function, to sense the attractant and to bring about its transport (Fig. 13).

A large number of mutants which lack galactose taxis have been isolated (Hazelbauer and Adler, 1971; Ordal and Adler, 1974). These are of three basic types (Fig. 13). Some either lack the galactose-binding protein completely or have point mutations that result in a defective conformation that is incapable of binding the sugar. As a result, galactose taxis is missing and galactose transport is also defective (type A mutants). Type B mutants show normal galactose taxis, but are deficient in or lack the ability to transport galactose. Still a third type of mutant (type C) specifically lacks galactose taxis, but has a normal transport mechanism for glucose and apparently contains a normal galactose binding protein. The gene involved in this type C mutation is presumed to affect a process or to produce a substance responsible for sensing the occupancy of the binding protein by galactose and then signaling this information to the chemotactic mechanism that ultimately affects the flagella.

Mutants lacking the binding protein are not attracted by galactose (Hazelbauer and Adler, 1971; Kalckar, 1971), and both the chemotactic response and the ability to bind galactose are recovered (M. Goy, *unpublished*) following reversion of a point mutation in the structural gene for the galactose binding protein (Boos, 1972). Other evidence for a link between chemotaxis and binding protein is the observation that, for a series of galactose analogues, the extent to which the analogue acts as an attractant

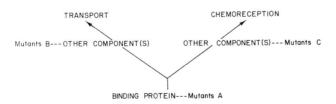

FIG. 13. Role of binding protein in chemoreception, and the relationship between chemoreception and transport (From Hazelbauer and Adler, 1971.)

is directly correlated to its binding (Hazelbauer and Adler, 1971). A third line of evidence is that osmotically shocked bacteria lacking the binding protein are not attracted to galactose.

The galactose-binding protein has been purified and shown to have a molecular weight of 35,000 (Anraku, 1968). Each bacterium contains 6,000 to 10,000 molecules (W. Boos, *unpublished*). Its dissociation constant for galactose was originally reported to be 10^{-6} M (Anraku, 1968), but later work showed that the protein actually has two dissociation constants for galactose, 10^{-7} M and 10^{-5} M (Boos, Gordon, Hall, and Price, 1972), indicative of two binding sites per molecule. The protein has no known enzymatic activity, but it is known to be involved in galactose transport (Anraku, 1968; Boos, 1972, Boos et al., 1972, Boos and Gordon, 1971).

The degree of association between chemoreceptor binding proteins and the cytoplasmic membrane varies; some are tightly associated while others are only loosely bound, if at all. This was demonstrated using an osmotic shock technique for removing the *E. coli* periplasmic proteins, that is, proteins located in the region between the cytoplasmic membrane and cell wall. Binding proteins for galactose, maltose, and ribose were found in the osmotic shock fluid (Hazelbauer and Adler, 1971), while others were not. The binding protein for maltose has been purified from *E. coli* by Schwartz et al. (O. Kellerman, *unpublished thesis*), and that for ribose has been purified from *Salmonella typhimurium,* characterized, and shown to serve the ribose chemoreceptor (Aksamit and Koshland, 1972; Aksamit and Koshland, 1974).

The tightly bound (not osmotically shockable) receptors involved in sugar chemotaxes utilize a component of the phosphotransferase system that is also involved in transport processes (Kundig, Kundig, Anderson, and Roseman, 1966; Simoni, Levinthal, Kundig, Kundig, Anderson, Hartman, and Roseman, 1967). The reaction sequence catalyzed by this system is

(1) phosphoenolpyruvate + HPr protein $\xrightarrow{\text{enzyme I}}$

P − HPr protein + pyruvate

(2) P − HPr protein + sugar $\xrightarrow[\text{additional protein}]{\text{enzyme II}}$

sugar − P + HPr protein

The enzymes II for this reaction are tightly bound to the cytoplasmic membrane and are sugar-specific, with different enzymes for fructose, mannitol, sorbitol, and so on, and two having different specificities for glucose. Mutants missing a particular enzyme II show no taxis toward chemicals handled by that enzyme II. Glucose taxis is absent only in mutants lacking both enzymes II for glucose and the galactose receptor, which also binds glucose. The enzymes II are thus the binding proteins for certain chemoreceptors (Adler and Epstein, 1974).

Enzyme I and the HPr protein are also required for the chemotactic response; this may be explained by (1) a requirement for transport in this case, or (2) the enzymes II may not bind substrates well when enzyme I and HPr are missing (Adler and Epstein, 1974).

The enzymes II are not required here for metabolism of the sugar molecules: Sugar phosphates do not serve as attractants even when they can be transported into the cell, and a mutant unable to metabolize glucose-6-phosphate further is still attracted to it (Adler, 1969). The fact that phosphorylated sugars are transported but are not attractants eliminates the idea that the phosphotransferase system is required simply to transport and phosphorylate the sugars so that they will be available to an *internal* receptor.

Although some of the properties of chemoreceptors have been elucidated, it is not yet understood how the chemoreceptor molecule is linked to subsequent processes. A conformational change is known to occur when galactose binds to its receptor protein (Boos and Gordon, 1971; Boos, 1972; Boos et al., 1972; Rotman and Ellis, 1972), and presumably such changes are sensed by the next component in the system, but little is known about this linkage. The available evidence suggests that the parameter of importance for a chemotactic response is the fraction of the binding protein that changes occupancy with time (Mesibov, Ordal, and Adler, 1973; Ordal and Adler, 1974; Brown and Berg, 1974).

A crucial point for determining the nature of the linkage between chemoreceptor and flagella is the location of the chemoreceptors. Although the osmotically shockable binding proteins and enzymes II are probably distributed randomly over the cell membrane, it is theoretically possible that only those located at the base of the flagellum are involved in chemotaxis. Such a system would involve a simpler linkage than one in which all binding proteins and enzymes II are chemotactically active. Assuming the latter to be correct, there are several possible ways in which the receptor could be linked to the flagella: (1) release of a diffusible substance following chemoreceptor binding (Macnab and Koshland, 1972); (2) induction of a change in membrane potential, which would spread from the chemoreceptors to the flagella; or (3) alteration of the membrane configuration, which would propagate to the flagella.

This problem is being examined using generally nonchemotactic mutants, whose mutations are believed to affect the final common pathway for the transfer of information to the flagella (Fig. 14) (Armstrong, Adler, and Dahl, 1967; Adler, 1969). Such mutants are of two types, those that never tumble and those that almost always tumble. As a result, they are unable to alter their basic swimming pattern sufficiently to respond to either attractants or repellents. Mutations that produce general nonchemotaxis have been localized to a group of four genes, suggesting that there are four components in this final common pathway (Armstrong and Adler, 1969; J. S. Parkinson and R. W. Reader, *unpublished*).

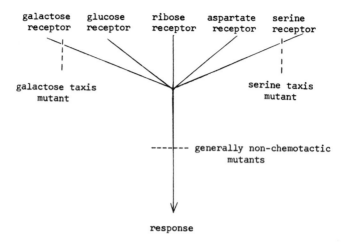

FIG. 14. Information from each of the many chemoreceptors is believed to be funnelled through a final common pathway. (From Adler, 1969.)

One observation that may yield information about the mechanism of information transduction to the flagella is its requirement for methionine (Adler and Dahl, 1967; Adler, 1973). Mutants that cannot synthesize methionine are unable to tumble, and are therefore incapable of responding to either attractants or repellents unless methionine is added to the medium. Although the precise role of the amino acid in this system is not known, it is presumed to be involved in regulating the tumbling frequency (Aswad and Koshland, 1974; Ordal, Reader, Kort, Tso, Larsen, and Adler, 1974).

An *E. coli* bacterium usually has about six flagella, which may originate anywhere on the cell surface and can function as a bundle (Fig. 2*a*). The long filament region of the flagellum had been well characterized, but little was known about the basal portion of the *E. coli* flagellum until "intact" flagella were isolated (DePamphilis and Adler, 1971). The filament is attached to a hooked region, which in turn attaches to a rod portion on which are mounted four rings; these are embedded in specific layers of the cell envelope (Fig. 15).

Flagella are now known to rotate (Berg and Anderson, 1973; Berg, 1974; Silverman and Simon, 1974), and can do so in both clockwise and counter-clockwise directions (Silverman and Simon, 1974). It was recently shown that attractants make them rotate counterclockwise, while repellents make them rotate clockwise (Larsen, Reader, Kort, Tso, and Adler, 1974*b*). Mutants that swim but never tumble always rotate their flagella counter-clockwise, while those that almost always tumble almost always rotate their flagella clockwise (Larsen et al., 1974*b*). Thus, "runs" of smooth, straight swimming result from the counterclockwise rotation of flagella and the presence of an effective bundle, while "twiddling," or tumbling

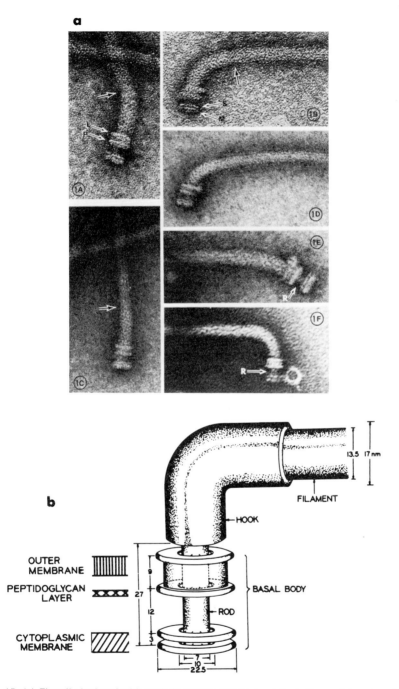

FIG. 15. (a) Flagella isolated with both filaments and bases intact. R = rod, L = top ring, P = next to topmost ring, M = bottom ring, S = next to bottom ring. Unlabeled arrows indicate junction between hook and filament. (b) A model of the flagellar base. (From DePamphilis and Adler, 1971.)

FIG. 16. Summary scheme.

results from clockwise rotation and occurs because the bundle comes apart (Larsen et al., 1974*b*). This agrees well with the observed changes in tumbling frequency produced by changes in concentration of attractant (Berg and Brown, 1972; Macnab and Koshland, 1972; Brown and Berg, 1974) or repellent (Tsang, Macnab, and Koshland, 1973). Similar results have been reported for monotrichously flagellated bacteria (Taylor and Koshland, 1974).

The energy source for the rotation of flagella (both the clockwise and the counterclockwise rotation) is not ATP directly, but rather the intermediate of oxidative phosphorylation — unlike the case for muscle, eukaryotic flagella, cilia, or sperm (Larsen et al., 1974*a*). Studies by Macnab and Koshland (1974) have led them to suggest that light-induced tumbling of *Salmonella* involves excitation of a flavin.

In summary (see Fig. 16), bacteria have receptors (chemoreceptor proteins) and effectors (rotating flagella), connected by a yet unknown transmission system that might be considered as the "brain" of *E. coli;* this system "decides" whether to act on an input message, how to act on it, and what to do if there are competing messages such as the simultaneous presence of attractants and repellants (Tsang et al., 1973; Tso and Adler, 1974*b*). The nature of the message sent by the chemoreceptors to the flagella is still unknown.

FLAGELLAR CONTROL OF BACTERIAL MOTION:

Howard C. Berg

On the basis of hydrodynamic considerations, it is rather remarkable that a bacterium can swim at all (Taylor, 1952). When a person swims, his limbs generate thrust by accelerating water backwards. This thrust is opposed by the drag due to the forward acceleration of water produced by the motion of the body. It is the inertia rather than the viscosity of the surrounding fluid that is important. The relative importance of inertial and viscous forces is expressed by a ratio called the Reynold's number,

$$R = \frac{\rho v l}{\eta}$$

where ρ is the density of the fluid, v is the velocity of flow, l is a length roughly equal to the diameter of the moving object, and η is the viscosity of the fluid. The Reynold's number for the human is about 10^5; for *E. coli* it is only about 10^{-5}. Human motion is dominated by inertial forces, that of *E. coli* by viscous forces. When a person stops moving his limbs, he coasts several body lengths; when an *E. coli* stops moving its flagella, it coasts only about a millionth of its body length. A bacterium is locked into the fluid much as a person would be if he were to swim in a medium as viscous as asphalt! The power required for a microorganism to maintain a velocity v is of order $\eta v^2 l$; for *E. coli*, this represents only a small fraction of the basic metabolic rate.

E. coli swims by moving long, thin helical filaments (Fig. 17) that function together in a bundle. This bundle appears to rotate as a screw at about 50 revolutions/sec. The way in which the filaments use viscous forces to generate thrust (and torque) is well understood (Taylor, 1952; Chwang and Wu, 1971; Coakley and Holwill, 1972), but the mechanics of bundle formation are not.

The flagellar filament contains a single protein, *flagellin,* having a molecular weight of about 40,000 and no known enzymatic activity. A number of major structural changes in the filament, including a fourfold increase in mass caused by binding of univalent antibodies (Greenbury and Moore, 1966), have no effect on its function. If the filaments are linked to one another, however, the cell ceases to move (Greenbury and Moore, 1966; DiPierro and Doetsch, 1968). This also occurs when a flagellotropic phage binds to a filament (Raimondo, Lundh, and Martinez, 1968). These and other hitherto unexplained observations provide compelling evidence in support of the idea, first considered seriously by Doetsch (1966), that each flagellar filament rotates relative to the cell body as a rigid or semirigid helix (Berg and Anderson, 1973). These arguments lead to the conclusion that

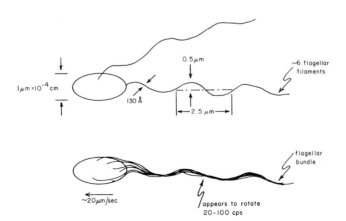

FIG. 17. The morphology of an *E. coli* bacterium. The flagellar filaments are about 130 Å in diameter and about 5 to 10 μm in length. In the wild type they are helical with a wavelength of 2.5 μm and an amplitude of 0.5 μm.

a flagellum is driven at its base by a rotary motor, implying the existence of biological equivalents to a rotor, a stator, and rotary bearings.

A bacterium is so small that it is unable to swim in a straight line. Changes in direction are produced by Brownian motion (diffusion); in water at 32°C, diffusion causes an *E. coli* (approximated as a sphere 1 μm in radius) to change its direction in time t by an angle

$$\theta_t = 53\sqrt{t}$$

where θ_t is in degrees and t is in seconds. The cell will thus drift on the average 90° in less than 4 sec, at which time it will have "forgotten" the direction in which it was originally moving. This drift imposes a fundamental limit on the time over which the bacterium may usefully integrate its sensory inputs.

How, then, does *E. coli* swim in a purposeful manner? Experimental approaches to this question have been difficult because of the great speed of the organisms relative to their size; they swim 10 to 30 diameters per second. At magnifications high enough for close observation, they rapidly move out of the plane of focus. This problem was overcome by the development of a tracking microscope that automatically follows individual bacteria in three dimensions (Berg, 1971). This instrument was made fully automatic, because events of interest occur on a time scale on the order of 0.1 sec. The system operates as follows: The bacteria are suspended (ca. 10^7 per milliliter) in a small windowed chamber on an electromechanical transducer that can be driven rapidly in the x, y, and z directions. Since, as noted above, the bacteria are locked into the medium by viscous forces, the motion of the chamber does not perturb their swimming. One bacterium is followed at a time. A detector senses the error in the position of its image relative to a point fixed in the reference frame of the laboratory, and the transducer moves the chamber to reduce this error to zero. The bacterium thus remains in focus in the center of the field, and the motion of the transducer provides a measure of the motion of the bacterium relative to the medium in which it is suspended. The data, position x, y, z as a function of time, are analyzed in real time by analogue techniques and off line by digital methods. Although the tracking chamber is small, it is large enough for the insertion of a capillary containing an attractant. The concentration of the attractant at the position of the bacterium can be computed from the equations for diffusion, given the time at which the capillary was inserted and the distance of the bacterium from its mouth (Futrelle and Berg, 1972).

A wild-type *E. coli* moves along a relatively straight path (runs), jiggles or jumps about in place (twiddles), and then runs in a new direction (Berg and Brown, 1972). Twiddles occur at random; the run lengths follow a Poisson interval distribution with a mean of about one sec. The twiddle lengths also follow a Poisson interval distribution with a mean of about 0.1

sec. The speed during a run is relatively constant, and varies little from run to run; the speed during a twiddle is lower. The change in direction that occurs during a twiddle is much too large to be explained by diffusion; the bacterium actively picks a new direction. The flagella move during a twiddle, but apparently no longer work together in a bundle. If these changes in direction were entirely random, the distribution of changes in angle would be a sine function with a maximum at 90°. Instead, the curve is skewed toward smaller angles, with a maximum at about 60°. Shorter twiddles lead to smaller changes in direction. This is what one would expect if a twiddle occurs when the flagellar bundle becomes unstable. If the disorganization is slight, the recovery is more rapid and the change in the orientation of the bundle relative to the body of the cell is smaller. A twiddle is a rare random event; the molecular details of the twiddle generation process (the structure of the "twiddle generator") remain to be determined.

In the absence of a gradient, the addition of aspartate has no effect on bacterial movement. The addition of serine suppresses twiddling slightly, but not enough to explain the directed motion within a gradient. When the bacteria move in a spatial gradient of either amino acid, twiddles are suppressed when they move up the gradient but not when they move down it (Berg and Brown, 1972). Twiddles still occur when the bacteria move up the gradient, but the probability of their occurrence is lower. There is no correlation between the change in direction generated by a twiddle and the direction of motion of the bacterium relative to the gradient, nor does the gradient alter the speed at which the bacterium runs.

What function of the attractant concentration does the bacterium measure? It is known that tactic responses in bacteria occur when the intensity of a spatially uniform stimulus changes with time. Engelmann (1883) showed this for light with *Bacterium photometricum* (a species of *Chromatium*) by suddenly decreasing the intensity of illumination; every bacterium backed up, stopped, and then resumed its normal motion. The same response occurred when the preparation was suddenly exposed to CO_2. Metzner (1920) demonstrated the same thing for heat. When a culture of *Spirillum volutans* was uniformly cooled, the bacteria responded by shuttling back and forth. Macnab and Koshland (1972) have demonstrated the temporal nature of chemotaxis in *Salmonella* by suddenly adding or diluting out attractants. They have used this technique to show that repellents and attractants have the opposite effects (Tsang et al., 1973), for example, that twiddles can be suppressed by suddenly adding an attractant or by diluting out a repellent.

It is possible to study chemotaxis in the absence of spatial inhomogeneities in the concentration of an attractant by generating or destroying the attractant enzymatically (Brown and Berg, 1974). For example, the concentration of glutamate can be varied via the reaction

$$\text{alanine} + \text{2-ketoglutarate} \underset{}{\overset{\text{transaminase}}{\rightleftharpoons}} \text{pyruvate} + \text{glutamate}$$

Once the enzyme has been added (before a significant amount of glutamate has been generated), the solution is homogeneous and isotropic; therefore, any change in the motion of the bacteria must be due to a temporal inhomogeneity. When glutamate is generated, the bacteria twiddle less; when it is destroyed, there is no effect. The response is asymmetric, just as it is in the experiments with spatial gradients. (Macnab and Koshland observe a short-lived increase in twiddling rate when an attractant is suddenly diluted out or when a repellent is suddenly added, but the sizes of these stimuli are much larger than those used in the tracking experiments.) Perhaps a twiddle occurs when the concentration of some intermediate or the potential across a membrane reaches a threshold, just as a nerve fires when sufficiently depolarized. If so, a positive temporal gradient (of an attractant) moves the cell away from this threshold; a negative temporal gradient has little effect. The molecular details of this process are not known; however, the data obtained from the enzyme experiments can be fit by a model, suggested by the work of Mesibov et al. (1973), in which the bacterium responds to the time rate of change of the fractional amount of receptor occupied (Brown and Berg, 1974).

Our present understanding of the transductive coupling that occurs in bacterial chemotaxis is summarized in Fig. 18. Specific receptors (both for attractants and for repellents) are located at or near the surface of the cell. The status of these receptors is monitored by an integrator, which controls the firing rate of the twiddle generator. If more attractant (or less repellent) is bound, the twiddle generator is suppressed. When the generator fires, it perturbs the flagellar bundle and the bacterium changes its direction. Since the flagella do work, a power source is required; however, the power needs of the integrator and the twiddle generator are not known. Some of the most intriguing unanswered questions have to do with the nature of the linkage between the integrator and the twiddle generator and between the twiddle generator and the motor.

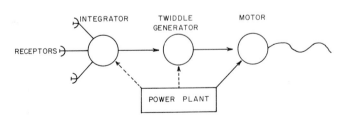

FIG. 18. Functional linkage in bacterial chemotaxis.

REFERENCES

Adler, J. (1969): Chemoreceptors in bacteria. *Science*, 166:1588–1597.

Adler, J. (1973): A method for measuring chemotaxis and use of the method to determine optimum conditions for chemotaxis by *Escherichia coli*. *J. Gen. Microbiol.*, 74:77–91.

Adler, J., and Dahl, M. M. (1967): A method for measuring the motility of bacteria and comparing random and non-random motility *J. Gen. Microbiol.*, 46:161–173.

Adler, J., and Epstein, W. (1974): Phosphotransferase-system enzymes as chemoreceptors for certain sugars in *Escherichia coli* chemotaxis. *Proc. Nat. Acad. Sci.*, 71:2895–2899.

Adler, J., Hazelbauer, G. L., and Dahl, M. M. (1973): Chemotaxis toward sugars in *Escherichia coli*. *J. Bacteriol.*, 115:824–847.

Aksamit, R., and Koshland, D. E., Jr. (1972): A ribose binding protein of *Salmonella typhimurium*. *Biochem. Biophys. Res. Commun.*, 48:1348–1353.

Aksamit, R., and Koshland, D. E., Jr. (1974): Identification of the ribose binding protein as the receptor for ribose chemotaxis in *Salmonella typhimurium*. *Biochemistry (in press)*.

Anraku, Y. (1968): Transport of sugars and amino acids in bacteria. I. Purification and specificity of the galactose- and leucine-binding proteins. *J. Biol. Chem.*, 243:3116–3122.

Armstrong, J. B., and Adler, J. (1969): Complementation of nonchemotactic mutants of *Escherichia coli*. *Genetics*, 61:61–66.

Armstrong, J. B., Adler, J., and Dahl, M. M. (1967): Nonchemotactic mutants of *Escherichia coli*. *J. Bacteriol.*, 93:390–398.

Aswad, D., and Koshland, D. E., Jr. (1974): Role of methionine in chemotaxis. *J. Bacteriol.*, 118:640–645.

Berg, H. C. (1971): How to track bacteria. *Rev. Sci. Instrum.*, 42:868–871.

Berg, H. C. (1974): Dynamic properties of bacterial flagella motors. *Nature*, 249:77–79.

Berg, H. C., and Anderson, R. A. (1973): Bacteria swim by rotating their flagellar filaments. *Nature*, 245:380–382.

Berg, H. C., and Brown, D. A. (1972): Chemotaxis in *Escherichia coli* analysed by three-dimensional tracking. *Nature*, 239:500–504.

Boos, W. (1972): Structurally defective galactose-binding protein isolated from a mutant negative in the β-methylgalactoside transport system of *Escherichia coli*. *J. Biol. Chem.*, 247:5414–5424.

Boos, W., and Gordon, A. S. (1971): Transport properties of the galactose-binding protein of *Escherichia coli*. Occurrence of two conformational states. *J. Biol. Chem.*, 246:621–628.

Boos, W., Gordon, A. S., Hall, R. E., and Price, H. D. (1972): Transport properties of the galactose-binding protein of *Escherichia coli*. Substrate-induced conformational change. *J. Biol. Chem.*, 247:917–924.

Brown, D. A., and Berg, H. C. (1974): Temporal stimulation of chemotaxis in *Escherichia coli*. *Proc. Nat. Acad. Sci.*, 71:1388–1392.

Chwang, A. T., and Wu, T. Y. (1971): A note on the helical movement of micro-organisms. *Proc. Roy. Soc. B*, 178:327–346.

Coakley, C. J., and Holwill, M. E. J. (1972): Propulsion of micro-organisms by three-dimensional flagellar waves. *J. Theor. Biol.*, 35:525–542.

DePamphilis, M. L., and Adler, J. (1971): Attachment of flagellar basal bodies to the cell envelope: Specific attachment to the outer, lipopolysaccharide membrane and the cytoplasmic membrane. *J. Bacteriol.*, 105:396–407.

DiPierro, J. M., and Doetsch, R. N. (1968): Enzymatic reversibility of flagellar immobilization. *Can. J. Microbiol.*, 14:487–489.

Doetsch, R. N. (1966): Some speculations accounting for the movement of bacterial flagella. *J. Theor. Biol.*, 11:411–417.

Engelmann, T. W. (1883): *Bacterium photometricum*. Ein Beitrag zur vergleichenden Physiologie des Licht-und Farbensinnes. *Pflüg. Arch. ges. Physiol.*, 30:95–124.

Engelmann, T. W. (1902): Die Erscheinungsweise der Sauerstoffausscheidung chromophyllhaltiger Zellen im Licht bei Anwendung der Bakterienmethode. *Pflüg. Arch. ges. Physiol.*, 57:375–390.

Futrelle, R. P., and Berg, H. C. (1972): Specification of gradients used for studies of chemotaxis. *Nature*, 239:517–518.

Greenbury, C. L., and Moore, D. H. (1966): The mechanism of bacterial immobilization by anti-flagellar IgG antibody. *Immunology*, 11:617–625.

Hazelbauer, G. L., and Adler, J. (1971): Role of the galactose binding protein in chemotaxis of *Escherichia coli* toward galactose. *Nature New Biol.,* 30:101–104.

Kálckar, H. M. (1971): The periplasmic galactose binding protein of *Escherichia coli. Science,* 174:557–565.

Kundig, W., Kundig, F. D., Anderson, B., and Roseman, S. (1966): Restoration of active transport of glycosides in *Escherichia coli* by a component of a phosphotransferase system. *J. Biol. Chem.,* 241:3243–3246.

Larsen, S. H., Adler, J. Gargus, J. J., and Hogg, R. W. (1974*a*): Chemomechanical coupling without ATP: The source of energy for motility and chemotaxis in bacteria. *Proc. Natl. Acad. Sci.,* 71:1239–1243.

Larsen, S. H., Reader, R. W., Kort, E. N., Tso, W.-W., and Adler, J. (1974*b*): Change in direction of flagellar rotation is the basis of the chemotactic response in *Escherichia coli. Nature,* 249:74–77.

Macnab, R. M., and Koshland, D. E., Jr. (1972): The gradient-sensing mechanism in bacterial chemotaxis. *Proc. Nat. Acad. Sci.,* 69:2509–2512.

Macnab, R., and Koshland, D. E., Jr. (1974): Bacterial motility and chemotaxis: Light-induced tumbling response and visualization of individual flagella. *J. Mol. Biol.,* 84:399–400.

Mesibov, R., and Adler, J. (1972): Chemotaxis toward amino acids in *Escherichia coli. J. Bacteriol.,* 112:315–326.

Mesibov, R., Ordal, G. W., and Adler, J. (1973): The range of attractant concentrations for bacterial chemotaxis and the threshold and size of response over this range. *J. Gen. Physiol.,* 62:203–223.

Metzner, P. (1920): Die Bewegung und Reizbeantwortung der bipolar begeisselten Spirillen. *Jahrb. wiss. Bot.,* 59:325–412.

Ordal, G. W., and Adler, J. (1974): Properties of mutants in galactose taxis and transport. *J. Bacteriol.,* 117:517–526.

Ordal, G. W., Reader, R. W., Kort, E. N., Tso, W.-W., Larsen, S. H., and Adler, J. (1974): Chemotaxis: The role of L-methionine in tumbling mutants. (*In press*).

Pfeffer, W. (1888): Über chemotaktische Bewegungen von Bakterien, Flagellaten und Volvocineen. *Untersuch Botan. Inst. Tübingen,* 2:582–661.

Raimondo, L. M., Lundh, N. P., and Martinez, R. J. (1968): Primary adsorption site of phage PBS1: The flagellum of *Bacillus subtilis. J. Virol.,* 2:256–264.

Rotman, B., and Ellis, J. H., Jr. (1972): Antibody-mediated modification of the binding properties of a protein related to galactose transport. *J. Bacteriol.,* 111:791–796.

Silverman, M. R., and Simon, M. I. (1974): Flagellar rotation and the mechanism of bacterial motility. *Nature,* 249:73–74.

Simoni, R. D., Levinthal, M., Kundig, F. D., Kundig, W., Anderson, B., Hartman, P. E., and Roseman, S. (1967): Genetic evidence for the role of a bacterial phosphotransferase system in sugar transport. *Proc. Natl. Acad. Sci.,* 58:1963–1970.

Taylor, G. (1952): The action of waving cylindrical tails in propelling microscopic organisms. *Proc. Roy. Soc. A,* 211:225–239.

Taylor, B. L., and Koshland, D. E., Jr. (1974): Reversal of flagellar rotation in monotrichous and peritrichous bacteria: Generation of changes in direction. *J. Bacteriol.,* 119:640–642.

Tsang, N., Macnab, R., and Koshland, D. E., Jr. (1973): Common mechanism for repellents and attractants in bacterial chemotaxis. *Science,* 181:60–63.

Tso, W.-W., and Adler, J. (1974*a*): Negative chemotaxis in *Escherichia coli. J. Bacteriol.,* 118:560–576.

Tso, W.-W., and Adler, J. (1974*b*): "Decision"-making in bacteria: Chemotactic response of *Escherichia coli* to conflicting stimuli. *Science,* 184:1292–1294.

Functional Linkage in Biomolecular Systems, edited by
F. O. Schmitt, D. M. Schneider, and D. M. Crothers.
Raven Press, New York ©1975.

FUNCTIONAL LINKAGE IN CONTRACTILE TISSUE

Physiologists have long believed that the most effective system in which to examine a general physiological process is that in which the function is most highly differentiated. For this reason, striated muscle has proven a valuable tissue in which to investigate the general phenomenon of contractility through chemomechanical transduction. Classes of proteins identified as components in the contractile mechanism of striated muscle (actin, troponin, tropomyosin, myosin) have also been demonstrated in other tissues, including the central nervous system (particularly in nerve terminals), and in various kinds of free cells. It seems likely that the interprotein interaction that produces tension and/or shortening in muscle and that involves functional linkage at several vital points is basically similar in all systems. The existence of chemomechanical transductions similar to those in muscle are now being considered by neuroscientists interested in the exocytotic release of transmitters at synapses, in the possible role of fibrous proteins in axoplasmic flow, and in the fast transport of materials down or up the axon or dendrite.

The phenomena dealt with in preceding chapters have been ones in which the stimulus reception and its membrane-borne transduction were at least partially understood, as were the ultimate physiological or behavioral events, but in which the intervening events—the linkage between receptor binding and cellular effect—have not been elucidated. For example, we do not know how information concerning the binding of an antigen is transduced into a stimulus for cell division in the immune system, what the pattern of protein phosphorylations induced by cyclic AMP means to a stimulated cell, or how calcium binding by a mitochondrion switches the organelle into a metabolically active state.

Functional linkage is involved at each step in the contractile mechanism, from the release of Ca^{2+} ions from the excitable sarcoplasmic membrane and their combination with the subunits of troponin, through allosteric interactions of the juxtaposed subunits or subunit polymers of the proteins, troponin, tropomyosin, and actin in the thin filaments, and light and heavy meromyosin in the heavy filaments. The interaction of one molecule of tropomyosin with seven subunits of actin is a striking example of cooperativity. Finally, the transduction from chemical to mechanical energy in the cross-link interaction that produces the sliding of the thin over thick filaments is an excellent example of transductive coupling.

Throughout the conference, the critical role of Ca^{2+} in the coupling between membrane-borne receptors and cellular or tissue effectors has been established as an empirical fact; the process *is* calcium-dependent. However, in muscle, the membrane-released calcium ions can be traced to their combination with troponin subunits; this in turn initiates the train of coupled events that results in shortening and/or tension production.

Functional Linkage in Biomolecular Systems, edited by
F. O. Schmitt, D. M. Schneider, and D. M. Crothers.
Raven Press, New York © 1975.

Chapter 14

Cooperative Interactions in Contractile Processes

THE MOLECULAR BASIS OF MUSCLE CONTRACTION:

Hugh E. Huxley

The characteristic striated appearance of muscle tissue arises from the presence of overlapping arrays of thick filaments containing myosin and thin actin filaments (Fig. 1; Hanson and Huxley, 1953). It is now generally agreed that contraction occurs as the result of a process in which these overlapping arrays slide past each other, so that the thin filaments move toward the center of the A band. This movement shortens the sarcomere, although the actual length of the individual filaments remains unchanged (Huxley and Hanson, 1954; Huxley and Niedergerke, 1954).

The sliding force between the filaments is believed to be generated by cross-bridges that project from the myosin filaments (Fig. 1b). These cross-bridges are the biochemically active portions of the myosin molecule, and their interaction with actin generates the longitudinal force that produces contraction.

The myosin molecule consists of a two-chain α-helical tail structure approximately 1,300 to 1,400 Å in length, attached to two separate head units each containing an ATPase site and an actin-binding site. The two main chains (plus some auxiliary smaller polypeptide chains) have a total molecular weight of about 470,000. The backbone of the thick filament consists of interacting myosin tails (Fig. 2a), which form a regular helical pattern having (probably) three molecules in register at each level, a separation between levels of 143 Å, and a pitch of approximately 430 Å.

The available physicochemical evidence suggests that a portion of the linear region of the myosin molecule, the S_2 region, does not bind strongly to the backbone of the thick filament, and may act as a "hinge" to permit movement of the head region from the backbone toward the actin filament. The head region appears to be able to tilt at different angles with respect to the actin filament (Fig. 2b), a long polymer of globular actin molecules (G actin) about 55 Å in diameter, two strands per filament, in double helical array and having a helical repeat distance of about 360 to 370 Å.

In a resting muscle, the interaction between the heads of the myosin molecules and actin appears to be blocked. In this state, the cross-bridges are not attached, and passive stretching of the muscle is readily produced;

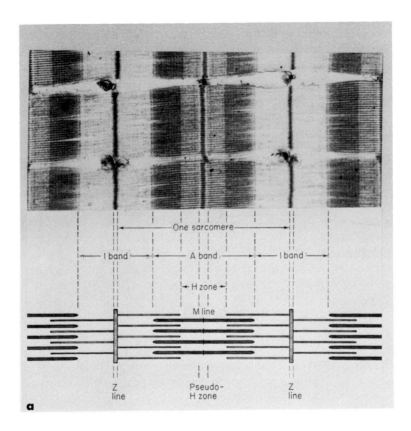

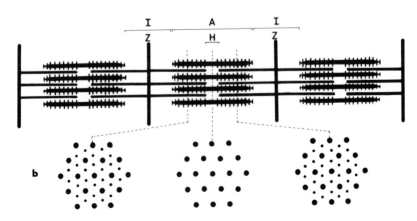

FIG. 1. (*a*) The structure of striated muscle. (*b*) Expanded view of the muscle filaments, showing myosin cross-bridges and cross-sectional views through two areas of the A band.

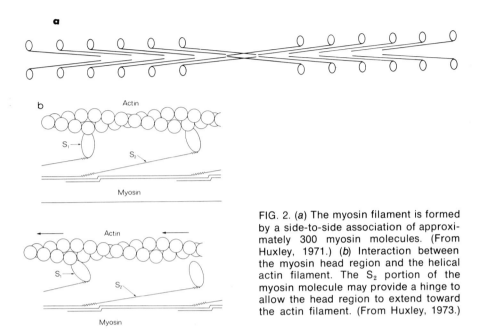

FIG. 2. (a) The myosin filament is formed by a side-to-side association of approximately 300 myosin molecules. (From Huxley, 1971.) (b) Interaction between the myosin head region and the helical actin filament. The S_2 portion of the myosin molecule may provide a hinge to allow the head region to extend toward the actin filament. (From Huxley, 1973.)

little force is necessary to cause the two sets of filaments to slide past each other. It is believed that the ATP molecule has already been cleaved to ADP and P_i in the resting state, but that these reaction products remain tightly bound to the head of the myosin molecule to prevent new ATP binding and cleavage.

The initiation of muscle contraction results in an interaction between the myosin head and actin filament. This is believed to involve attachment in a perpendicular configuration, followed by a structural transition in which the myosin tilts over forcibly with respect to the actin filament, thus drawing the actin filament toward the center of the A band (Fig. 2b). The available evidence suggests that each such interaction produces a movement of about 80 Å. ADP and P_i are released from the cross-bridges at an as yet undetermined point in this cycle. Another ATP molecule then attaches and dissociates the cross-bridge so that it can begin another cycle, now reattached to a site further along on the actin filament. The energetics of the process can be explained by the splitting of one or two ATP molecules per cycle. These cycles occur approximately 5 to 10 times/sec (in frog sartorius muscle at 0°C), depending on the characteristic shortening velocity of the muscle. The interaction between the two filaments does not occur by a synchronous reaction of all cross-bridges simultaneously, which would produce contraction in spurts; rather, an overall steady force and movement results from a summation of nonsynchronous interactions. (For general review articles, see Huxley, 1969, 1971, 1972, 1973.)

The regular helical arrangement of myosin cross-bridges in resting muscle gives rise to a characteristic low-angle X-ray diffraction pattern. Parts of this pattern become markedly attenuated during contraction, indicating that the regular helical arrangement is disturbed and that the cross-bridges are actually in motion. The actin filament also has a characteristic X-ray pattern; however, this pattern remains almost unchanged during contraction, indicating that the positioning of the actin monomers within the thin filaments is relatively unaltered.

However, several important changes do occur in the internal structure of the thin filaments of vertebrate striated muscle during contraction as a consequence of the on-off switching process. In addition to actin, the thin filament contains the regulatory proteins tropomyosin and troponin. (For a general review, see Ebashi and Endo, 1968). Tropomyosin is a two-chain α-helical molecule slightly more than 400 Å in length. Tropomyosin molecules have a high affinity for actin, and appear to lie in each of the two long-pitch helical grooves of the two-chain actin helix. Isolated tropomyosin molecules self-associate in an end-to-end manner to form linear polymers having a repeat length slightly less than 400 Å. They probably bond to actin with a repeat of seven actin monomers, or 385 Å, which coincides with the approximate natural repeat of a tropomyosin polymer. The third protein of the thin filament, troponin, is a complex of three subunits having a total molecular weight of 80,000 to 90,000. Troponin complexes bind to the actin-tropomyosin filament at 385-Å intervals; one complex is associated with one tropomyosin molecule and seven actin monomers. A simple model of the thin filament is shown in Fig. 3.

On-off switching of the actin filament has now been shown to be a function of Ca^{2+} binding to one of the three troponin subunits. Muscle contains a complex system for the storage of Ca^{2+} in the sarcoplasmic reticulum in the resting state and its release following nervous stimulation. Below 10^{-7} M, little Ca^{2+} is bound by troponin, and the attachment of myosin-ATP to actin is blocked; ATP splitting cannot occur under these conditions and the muscle remains relaxed. When the free Ca^{2+} concentration increases

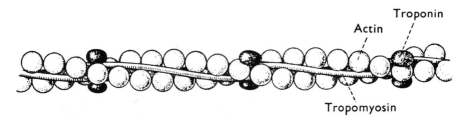

FIG. 3. Model of the thin filament. The actin monomers form a two-chain α-helical structure, with the tropomyosin two-chain structure lying in the major groove and troponin complexes at seven-monomer intervals. (From Ebashi and Endo, 1968.)

after stimulation, Ca^{2+} is bound by the troponin and the resulting conformational change in the actin-troponin complex permits the attachment of
the myosin heads, after which the contractile process and ATP hydrolysis
can occur.

The available evidence thus indicates that the binding of myosin to the
actin filament is sterically blocked by tropomyosin in the resting state,
and that binding in the activated state occurs when a conformational
change in troponin induced by the binding of Ca^{2+} allows the tropomyosin
to move away from the myosin binding site within the actin groove.

The structural changes that occur during the on-off transition have been
examined by comparing the structural density distributions of thin filaments
under different conditions. The end-on view of a pure actin filament has
only two major regions of density, corresponding to the two actin chains. A
similar projection of a filament containing either tropomyosin alone or
tropomyosin plus troponin has two additional regions of density in the
grooves of the actin structure. These are positioned asymmetrically, and
indicate that each tropomyosin strand is more closely associated with one
of the chains of polymerized actin monomers than with the other. This
suggests that each tropomyosin molecule is involved in the regulation of
one chain of actin monomers in the two-chain actin structure (Spudich,
Huxley, and Finch, 1972).

One particular region of the X-ray diagram of intact muscle is extremely
sensitive to the exact position of the tropomyosin strand within the actin
filament. There is a characteristic change in this region in a contracting
muscle that indicates a sideways movement of the tropomyosin. As shown
in Fig. 4a, the tropomyosin of a resting muscle is located some distance from
the middle of the helical groove. The X-ray data indicates that the tropomyosin moves 10 to 20 Å toward the center of the groove when the muscle
is activated. Further evidence for this displacement has been obtained by

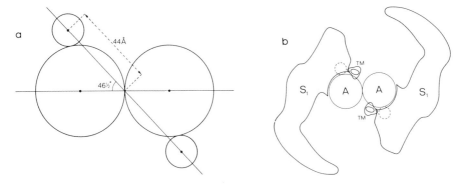

FIG. 4. (a) The relative positions of actin and tropomyosin in the resting state. (b) An
end-on projection of the actin-S_1 structure. (From Huxley, 1972.)

three-dimensional reconstructions of electron micrographs to compare the position of tropomyosin in the presence and absence of the inhibitory component of troponin, which switches off the filament (T. Wakabayashi, H. E. Huxley, J. T. Finch, and A. Klug, *in preparation*).

Prior to these studies, Moore, Huxley, and DeRosier (1970) had obtained evidence from three-dimensional reconstructions that myosin S_1 subunits attach to actin in the absence of ATP by projecting deeply into the actin groove (Fig. 4*b*), with attachment occurring in a configuration involving a 45° tilt and an approximately 45° skewing. Tropomyosin could control this attachment by a steric blocking mechanism.

Preceding chapters have dealt with the level of the cell membrane, in many cases involving Ca^{2+}-related events. In the case of muscle, we are dealing with the cellular response to the membrane change induced by neural stimulation, the release of Ca^{2+} from the sarcoplasmic reticulum. This is one of the few instances in which the cellular response to a membrane event has been elucidated.

MOLECULAR MOTIONS IN THE MUSCLE FILAMENTS:

Carolyn Cohen

Although X-ray diffraction diagrams from muscle are not detailed and are often difficult to interpret, considerable evidence indicates that both the actin and myosin filaments undergo conformational changes as a function of physiological state. As also discussed by Huxley, the thin filament contains actin, tropomyosin, and the troponin complex; and actin is "switched on" by a specific movement of tropomyosin induced by a conformational change in troponin. The interaction of myosin filaments with actin to produce ATP hydrolysis involves conformational changes in both the rod and globular portions of the myosin molecule. There are cooperative features in both these assemblies; the state of several actin monomers is affected by the position of one tropomyosin molecule, and the state of one myosin molecule may influence that of its neighbor. The protein assemblies in muscle thus display functional linkages analogous to those of the simpler globular proteins (see Chapter 2), but at levels of organization that may extend to the entire cell.

The Actin Filament

Tropomyosin: Tropomyosin is a fully α-helical coiled coil about 400 Å in length (Fig. 5) that is frequently described as the archetype of the α-proteins. In the coiled-coil conformation, the two α-helical subunits wind around each other to produce a long-pitch helix or supercoil (Crick, 1953; Cohen and Holmes, 1963). The important aspect of the structure is not the bending of

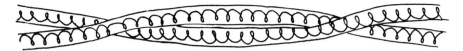

FIG. 5. Schematic diagram of the two-chain α-helical coiled-coil structure of tropomyosin.

each α-helix to form the supercoil, but the fact that this bending produces a regular pattern of side-chain interactions; Crick (1953) has described this as a "knobs-into-holes" packing. This regular packing or interlocking of side chains stabilizes the highly charged tropomyosin molecule. The coiled-coil conformation places the nonpolar groups along the contact line between helices, with charged groups interacting with solvent (Sodek, Hodges, Smillie, and Jurasek, 1972). The molecule can thus be viewed as a sturdy two-stranded elastic cable.

The molecular movement of tropomyosin can be illustrated by first considering a crystal, the paradigm of a static system. Tropomyosin is the only native fibrous protein that forms large crystals. These crystals are remarkably high in solvent content, with about 95% of the lattice volume occupied by water. The bonding of the molecules within the crystals is not adventitious as in crystals of globular proteins; rather, the interactions are related to those that occur within muscle. Moreover, the crystal lattice displays certain dynamic features of the tropomyosin molecule.

Electron micrographs of tropomyosin crystals show a very open kite shaped mesh of cross-connected strands (Fig. 6a), with a 400-Å periodicity along the strands. The strands are wavy, and appear to be doubled in some places on the micrographs, indicating that they consist of two filaments. A consideration of both electron micrographs and X-ray diffraction diagrams of the tropomyosin crystal indicates that the filaments are polymers of polar tropomyosin molecules, about 400 Å in length, bonded end to end (Fig. 6b) (Caspar, Cohen, and Longley, 1969). Although the two molecular filaments appear to be parallel in projection, they are actually directed along opposite body diagonals in the unit cell (Fig. 6b). Periodic pertubations of the molecules resulting from the cross-connections of the filaments within the lattice cause the coiled-coil molecules to form a still larger coil.

Troponin is the regulatory complex of the thin filaments in vertebrate striated muscle. The entire troponin complex can be bound within the very open mesh of the tropomyosin crystal, and in negatively stained preparations it appears as a light-staining node on the long arms of the mesh. Preliminary results from X-ray diffraction diagrams obtained from crystals prepared with and without troponin indicate that the presence of a small amount of troponin in the lattice causes changes in unit cell dimensions as well as in intensities (Cohen, Caspar, Parry, and Lucas, 1971; Cohen, Caspar, Johnson, Nauss, Margossian, and Parry, 1972). In the a axis proa

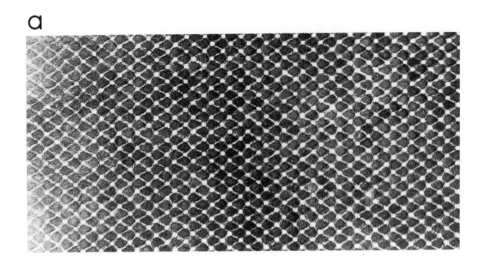

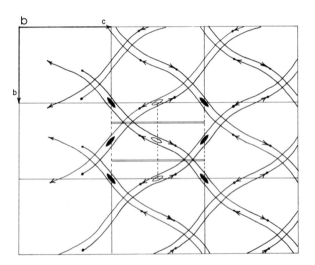

FIG. 6. (a) Electron micrograph of negatively stained tropomyosin crystal. (b) Molecular configuration and symmetry elements in corresponding projection of the tropomyosin crystal lattice. A comparison of X-ray diffraction patterns and electron micrographs indicates a crystal structure made of filaments which are 400-Å-long polar molecules bonded end-to-end. The positions of the ends of the molecules have not yet been determined. The arrowheads have been marked to indicate the orientation and axial period of the molecules in the filaments. The pairs of molecules making up the strands which appear parallel in projection actually run along opposite body diagonals of the unit cell. The molecules have a coiled-coil structure, which in turn forms a supercoil due to interactions in the lattice. (From Caspar et al., 1969.)

jection (Fig. 6b), the rectangular cell with bound troponin is less elongated than in the lattice without troponin.

A remarkable feature of this effect is that whatever the unit cell parameters, the length of the body diagonal remains constant. This can be understood by examination of a model of the tropomyosin crystal lattice that shows how the filament are cross-connected (Cohen et al., 1971). If the end-to-end connections between molecules are made invariant, but the molecules can pivot and slip at crossover points, the length of the body diagonal will remain constant. Thus the molecules are bent differently in lattices of different cell dimensions, but only certain of the linkages vary.

How can we relate these results on crystals to the structure and movements of tropomyosin in muscle? An illustration of the thin filament (Fig. 3) shows that the array of actin monomers is in fact polar, and that the polar tropomyosin filaments are wound in each of the two grooves of the actin helix. The form that the filament assumes is therefore a supercoil, or coiled-coiled coil, and the bending of the tropomyosin filaments in the grooves of the actin helix is comparable to that of tropomyosin in the crystal lattice. The period of the troponin complexes along the actin filament is determined by the projected length of the tropomyosin molecule as it winds in the grooves of the actin helix. X-ray diffraction of whole muscle shows a meridional reflection at 385 Å that corresponds to the axial repeat of the troponin complexes. Tropomyosin molecules 410 Å in length, when bent into a regular supercoil with a radius of about 30 Å, give an axial repeat of 395 Å. If additional kinking in the tropomyosin also occurred, it could shorten the period to that observed. The important point is that the specific attachment of troponin to the supercoiled tropomyosin filament occurs at one point on each tropomyosin molecule, and the resulting axial separation is almost exactly equal to the length of seven actin monomers.

There is now convincing X-ray diffraction evidence for the movement of tropomyosin in the grooves of the actin helix (see Huxley, above). This is induced either by the "switching on" of troponin or by the formation of rigor links between nucleotide-free myosin and actin, both of which are described in more detail by Weber in the next section. The tropomyosin filament appears to roll from a position near the outer surface of the groove to one about 20° further toward its center. The 385-Å X-ray reflection shows that the axial spacing of the troponin remains constant. We can distinguish two kinds of linkages here, just as there were two kinds of linkages in the tropomyosin crystal lattice. The end-to-end bonding of tropomyosin would be invariant and forms an essential connection, whereas the short-range side-chain links to actin would vary depending on the state of troponin; they are thus analogous to the crossover linkages between tropomyosin molecules in the crystal lattice. The molecular movement of tropomyosin on the thin filament is a reversible sideways rolling without axial displacement.

Troponin: Troponin has three subunits: one (TnT) binds to tropomyosin; a regulatory unit (TnC) binds Ca^{2+} to control the conformation of the complex and thus the position of the tropomyosin; and a third (TnI) is the steric inhibitor of tropomyosin. Although a crystal structure is not yet available for the troponin complex, the way in which the complex may function can be inferred from some of the properties of these subunits. Coprecipitation of the TnT subunit with tropomyosin produces a crystal in which the axial period is again 400 Å, but with cross-connections at 100 Å and 300 Å. Symmetry considerations indicate that the tropomyosin filaments facing each other cross-link with the TnT components. This net-like structure can collapse into a paracrystalline fibrous aggregate that is identical to the aggregate formed when tropomyosin and TnT are precipitated in the presence of divalent cations (Cohen et al., 1972; Margossian and Cohen, 1973).

The structure formed by tropomyosin and TnT in the presence of the TnC component depends on the concentration of Ca^{2+} in the medium. Little TnC is bound at 10^{-8} M Ca^{2+}, and the same crystal structure is formed as in the absence of Ca^{2+}. The paracrystalline structure is markedly altered when Ca^{2+} is increased to physiological levels, indicating a Ca^{2+}-dependent linkage between TnT and TnC.

Although solubility problems make it difficult to do this type of experiment with the TnI subunit, it is possible to demonstrate binding between TnC and TnI. Hitchcock, Huxley, and Szent-Györgyi (1973) have shown that the binding of the TnC-TnI complex to actin-tropomyosin is Ca^{2+}-dependent; increasing the Ca^{2+} level decreases the interaction between this complex and actin. These studies of the interrelationship between the troponin complex and tropomyosin lead to the heuristic model shown in Fig. 7 (Margossian and Cohen, 1973).

A Ca^{2+} switch controls the interactions between the subunits of the troponin complex. These interactions are relatively loose at low Ca^{2+} levels, and the binding of the inhibitory component to actin blocks the movement of tropomyosin towards the inner portion of the groove. Above a

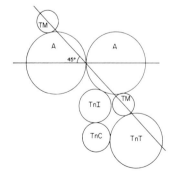

FIG. 7. Heuristic model for thin filament in resting state showing cross section at the level of the troponin complex (see also Fig. 4).

critical level of Ca^{2+}, the linkages within the troponin complex are tight-
ened and that between TnI and actin weakens. This altered structure no
longer sterically blocks the movement of tropomyosin toward the center
of the actin groove, and the myosin-binding sites on the actin are exposed.
There are again two kinds of linkage within this system, the specific and
conserved linkage between TnT and tropomyosin and the variable linkages
that depend upon the Ca^{2+} level in other parts of the complex.

The Myosin Filament

The myosin molecule has an unusual shape and a distinctive mode of
assembly (Fig. 8). The molecule is polar and displays two kinds of specific
interactions; molecules that point in opposite directions are bonded together at the center of the thick filament, while growth proceeds by the
addition of molecules pointing in the same direction (Huxley, 1963). The
constraints placed on packing have been derived from X-ray diagrams of
muscle and studies with *in vitro* myosin aggregates. X-ray diffraction studies
(Huxley and Brown, 1967) have revealed that the cross-bridges in relaxed
muscle are helically arranged at axial intervals of 145 Å. The rotational
symmetry was not clearly established, but was thought to be twofold.
Specific interactions between myosin molecules that relate to the center of
the filament can be demonstrated by precipitating either the whole molecule
or the rod portion with divalent cations (Cohen, Lowey, Harrison, Kendrick-Jones, and Szent-Györgyi, 1970; Harrison, Lowey, and Cohen, 1971).
These aggregates were used to demonstrate that the molecules are about
1450 Å long and that they display antiparallel overlaps of either 900 or
1300 Å, depending upon the reaction conditions (Fig. 9a). Just as the
end-to-end linkage of tropomyosin is conserved in a variety of its poly-
morphic forms, so one might expect that the specific interactions displayed
by the *in vitro* aggregates will be related to the native filament. The helical

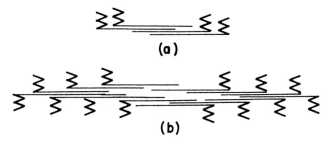

FIG. 8. Possible mode of assembly of myosin molecules to form filament. (a) Growth is
initiated by interactions of the rod portions of polar molecules oriented in opposite
directions. (b) Growth proceeds by the addition of molecules pointing in the same direction. (From Huxley, 1963.)

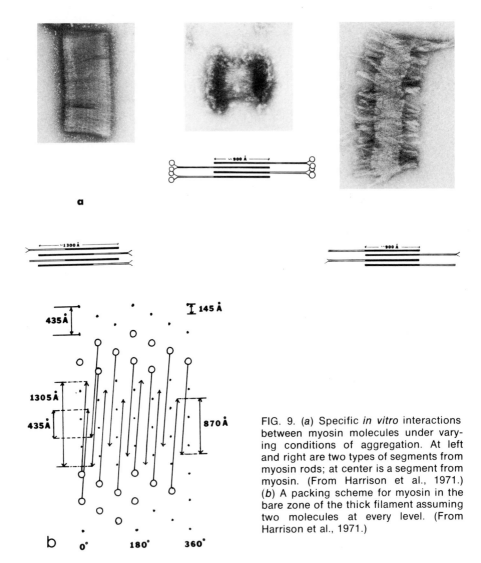

FIG. 9. (a) Specific *in vitro* interactions between myosin molecules under varying conditions of aggregation. At left and right are two types of segments from myosin rods; at center is a segment from myosin. (From Harrison et al., 1971.) (b) A packing scheme for myosin in the bare zone of the thick filament assuming two molecules at every level. (From Harrison et al., 1971.)

symmetry deduced from X-ray studies and the interactions indicated by the *in vitro* aggregates led to the construction of a two-dimensional packing scheme for the central portion of the filament that accounted for a number of features of the assembly (Fig. 9b).

A convincing solution for the packing of myosin in the entire thick filament was recently advanced by Squire (1973), who suggested a general model for myosin filaments in which the essential feature is that only one molecule is present at each point of the surface lattice. (Previous models required more than one.) This led him to recognize that the rotational symmetry of the myosin filament in vertebrate striated muscle is more likely to be threefold than twofold; that is, there are three molecules at every 145-Å level. (In Fig. 9b, therefore, one would need to add a molecule at each level.) This led to the development of a detailed molecular model for the packing in the myosin filament (Squire, 1973). In this model, the packing in the polar portion of the filament is generated by two specific polar molecular overlaps, of 720 Å and 430 Å. A plausible solution for the basic pattern of connections in the resting filament has therefore now been defined.

X-ray studies (Huxley and Brown, 1967) have indicated that striking structural transitions occur in the thick filament during contraction, and that there is extensive radial and circumferential movement of the bridges but little longitudinal movement. More disorder appears to occur, however, than can be accounted for simply by the number of cross-bridges attaching to actin, suggesting that a cooperative effect might occur within the thick filament during contraction. The existence of such a cooperative interaction between myosin molecules is also suggested by the experiments in which highly stretched muscle is switched on. Under these conditions, the actin filaments are essentially removed from the myosin filaments, yet there is considerable disordering of cross-bridges (Haselgrove, 1970; Huxley, 1972).

The helical ordering of bridges within the thick filament is maintained by a delicate ionic balance. For example, a cooperative order-disorder transition can be reversibly induced in *Limulus* muscle simply by increasing the ionic strength from 0.12 to 0.17 (Wray, Vibert, and Cohen, 1974). The bridges thus appear to be highly labile; however, the essential connections between the rod portions of the molecules are maintained in the backbone of the filament during such movements, as they are during contraction.

There may be a relation between cooperative transitions in the thick filament and the activation process. The actin filaments are located some distance away from the thick filament, and the myosin molecules must extend toward the actin in order for any interaction to occur (Fig. 2). Although vertebrate thin filaments contain troponin for the regulation of actin-myosin interaction, some invertebrates, such as molluscs, lack troponin. In these muscles, the Ca^{2+} switch is localized on the thick filament, and the myosin molecules are directly sensitive to calcium ions (Szent-Györgyi, Szenkirályi, and Kendrick-Jones, 1973). Most invertebrates (including insects) seem to have both systems (Lehman, Kendrick-Jones, and Szent-Györgyi, 1972). In insect flight muscle, the addition of Ca^{2+} causes the myosin bridges to move toward the actin, although no attachment can occur until the muscle is stretched (Miller and Tregear, 1971). In *Limulus* muscle, the cooperative disordering of the cross-bridges as a function of ionic strength suggests an analogy to ionic effects during activation. The transition may be part of the response by the myosin-linked system to activation. The myosin of the vertebrate thick filament might possibly retain a vestigial Ca^{2+} switch that causes the myosin heads to project upon activation (see also Haselgrove, 1970; Lowy, 1972). Such a mechanism could explain the apparent cooperative effects in the vertebrate thick filament.

This discussion has dealt with cooperative aspects of myosin interactions during activation; there is no evidence in vertebrate muscle for a cooperative turnover of myosin cross-bridges during contraction, and it is generally accepted that the region of overlap contains independent force generators. More complex interactions involving cooperative effects between cross-bridges may, however, occur in thick filaments of insect flight muscle, in which stretch is required for full activity, and in the molluscan "catch" muscle, in which actin-myosin cross-links are stable for long periods of time.

In summary, the striking molecular motions in the actin and myosin filaments of muscle illustrate the importance of conserved and variable linkages in the functioning of protein assemblies.

REGULATION OF MUSCLE CONTRACTION THROUGH COOPERATIVE INTERACTIONS IN THE ACTIN FILAMENT:

Annemarie Weber

The actin filament is "turned on," that is, becomes capable of reacting with myosin, by the binding of four Ca^{2+} ions to troponin (Ebashi, Kodoma,

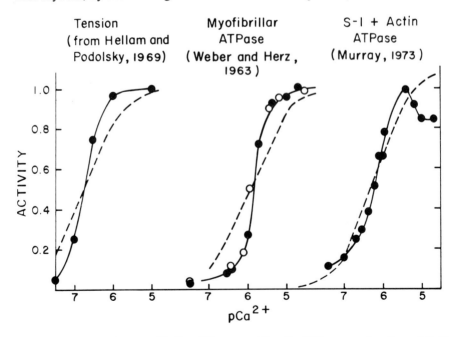

FIG. 10. Muscle tension, myofibrillar ATPase, and S-actin ATPase as a function of Ca^{2+} concentration. The dashed curve shows how activity would change if it were a function of Ca^{2+} binding to a single site.

and Ebashi, 1968; Bremel and Weber, 1972). That this is a switch mechanism based on cooperative interactions can be demonstrated when muscle tension or ATPase activity is determined as a function of Ca^{2+} (Fig. 10).

The actual binding of Ca^{2+} to troponin is not cooperative; that is, it does not show the type of ligand binding observed for hemoglobin and oxygen — rather, each site binds Ca^{2+} independently (Bremel and Weber, 1972). This situation is similar to that for the acetylcholine receptor (see Chapter 9), in which a steep function for depolarization was not reflected in a sigmoidal binding curve. A Scatchard plot of calcium binding to troponin (bound to isolated regulated actin filaments) indicates that there may actually be negative cooperativity for Ca^{2+} binding (Weber and Bremel, 1971; Weber and Murray, 1973). Since the actin filament is not turned on (actin-activated ATPase activity) until the fourth calcium ion is bound (Weber and Bremel, 1971), the cooperativity may be attributed to a requirement for the simultaneous presence of all four calcium ions. This might be considered as an allosteric interaction of the type described in Chapter 2, in which the system assumes its alternative conformation in response to the addition or removal of the fourth Ca^{2+} ion:

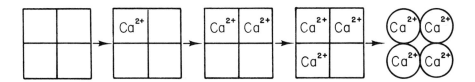

However, one must consider that all calcium ions bind to the same subunit of the troponin molecule (Potter, Seidel, Leavif, Lehrer, and Gergely, 1974), and that the binding of the first ion may not be entirely without effect on the conformation of that subunit (Head and Perry, 1974). Nevertheless, the final conformational change of the troponin molecule that turns on the actin filament can occur only when all four calcium sites are occupied.

When actin is turned on by the calcium-induced response of troponin, the active sites of the actin molecule become accessible for interaction with ATP-activated myosin. While actin and myosin are dissociated in the resting state, in the "on" state actin interacts with ATP-activated myosin to permit the development of force and shortening. This is accompanied by ATP hydrolysis if myosin is assembled into filaments.

Transmission of the calcium response from troponin to actin requires tropomyosin. As discussed by Huxley, during the resting state and in the absence of calcium, tropomyosin seems to block sterically the area of the actin active site for myosin. Tropomyosin no longer occupies the myosin domain after saturation of troponin with calcium, but has moved toward the groove between the two actin strands (Huxley, 1972). The change of tropomyosin position therefore appears to be responsible for the trans-

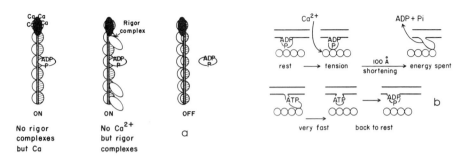

FIG. 11. (a) Actin binds to myosin-ATP when four Ca^{2+} are bound to troponin, and forms rigor complexes with nucleotide-free myosin in the absence of Ca^{2+}. (b) Simplified current concept of the series of steps occurring during muscle contraction.

mission of information between troponin and actin and, in addition, for the switching on of its seven associated actin monomers. This view becomes still more convincing when one examines another way in which the actin filament can be turned on, one that does not involve calcium. Actin filaments can be turned on in the absence of calcium as a result of the formation of rigor complexes (Bremel and Weber, 1972). These complexes are formed as the result of a high affinity (about 9000 cals; Lowey, 1971) between nucleotide-free myosin and actin, and they can form even when the actin filament is in the "off" state (Weber and Murray, 1973). The rigor complex acquired its name because the stiffness of muscle in death—after all the ATP has disappeared from the cell—is due to the combination of nearly all the myosin molecules with actin in this kind of complex. The rigor complex also appears to be a normal intermediate in muscle contraction. The current view of this process (Fig. 11b, Huxley, 1969, Taylor, 1972) assumes that an activated myosin molecule first combines with the actin filament to produce tension followed by shortening. The rigor complex is formed at this point by the release of ADP and P_i. The complex is then dissociated by the binding of ATP, and the cycle is repeated.

To demonstrate that an actin filament has been switched on by rigor complexes, one must show that actin interacts with ATP-activated myosin and accelerates the rate of ATP hydrolysis. This requires conditions in which both rigor complexes and ATP-activated myosin are present, that is, low, nonsaturating ATP concentrations. Figure 12a shows that a high concentration of rigor complexes (low ATP) turns on the regulated actin filament to the same extent as does calcium; the rates of actin-activated ATP hydrolysis are as high in the absence of calcium as in its presence. When the level of ATP is increased, resulting in the gradual disappearance of rigor complexes, all of the actin filament returns gradually to the "off" state in the absence of calcium. Figure 12b shows the relationship between ATP concentration and hydrolysis in the absence of calcium that is expected

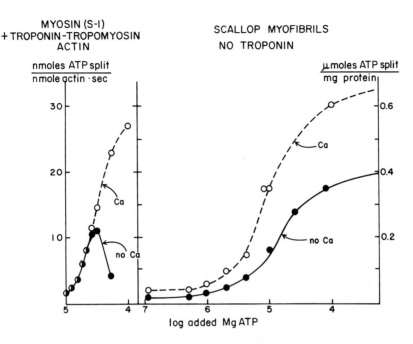

FIG. 12. Rate of actin-activated ATP hydrolysis as a function of MgATP concentration in the presence (0.1 mM) and absence (1.0 mM EGTA) of calcium. *Left:* Regulated (reconstituted) actin filaments and single myosin sites (S-1; proteolytic fragments); 1.0 mM free Mg. (From Bremel and Weber, 1972.) *Right:* Washed scallop myofibrils (kindly provided by A. G. Szent-Györgyi) that had aged considerably before use and therefore showed only partial relaxation; 5.0 mM free Mg.

when rigor complexes do not turn on the actin filament; this was observed with myofibrils from mollusc muscles that do not possess troponin-tropomyosin regulated actin filaments and in which calcium regulation takes place on the myosin filament (Kendrick-Jones, Szentkirályi, and Szent-Györgyi, 1972; Lehman et al., 1972). In such muscles, the removal of calcium inhibits the actin-activated ATPase activity equally at all ATP concentrations. Under conditions where rigor complexes turn on actin filaments, X-ray diffraction patterns of vertebrate skeletal muscle suggest that tropomyosin undergoes the same shift in position as that induced by calcium (Haselgrove, 1972).

When tropomyosin moves as the result of rigor complex formation, troponin undergoes a conformational change that expresses itself in an increased affinity for the last two calcium ions (Bremel and Weber, 1972). It is likely that rigor complexes — through a shift of the tropomyosin position — induce the same conformational state in troponin as does calcium. In that case, the calcium affinity should increase; that is, more binding energy should be released, because the energy for the conformational change of the troponin molecule would no longer come from calcium binding but from the formation of rigor complexes.

Turning on the actin filament by two different mechanisms is thus associated with a similar or identical shift in the position of tropomyosin and a conformational change in troponin. This supports the view that the movement of tropomyosin away from a site where it overlaps the active site of actin is the event responsible both for the transmission of information between actin and troponin and for the switching on of actin.

Not all of the cooperative interactions occurring on the actin filament can be described so plausibly by changes in the tropomyosin position, nor have they been demonstrated to be associated with such tropomyosin movements. Cooperative interactions that occur after the actin filament has been turned on by calcium can be demonstrated when the effect of rigor complexes on ATP hydrolysis in the presence of very little myosin (only one myosin active site for each 50 actin monomers) is compared to that when myosin is present in considerable excess over actin (Fig. 13; Bremel, Murray, and Weber, 1972). With a large excess of actin, it is improbable that active (between ATP-activated myosin and actin) and rigor complexes can occur close to each other on the filament—for example, that both kinds of complexes occur on actin monomers associated with the same tropomyosin molecules. Under these conditions the rate of ATP hydrolysis

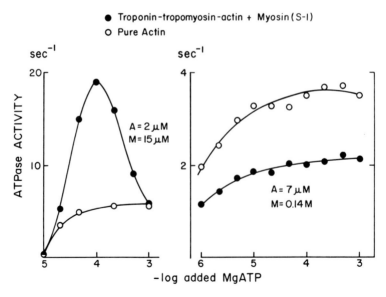

FIG. 13. The rate of ATP hydrolysis as a function of MgATP in the presence of calcium. On each part a comparison is made between the interaction of regulated and of pure (free of tropomyosin and troponin) actin with S-1. *Left:* Actin is present in 50-fold excess over S-1. *Right:* S-1 is present in sevenfold excess over actin. (From Bremel et al., 1972.)

is lower than with actin from which tropomyosin had been removed (Fig. 13*a*), suggesting that even in the presence of calcium, tropomyosin can still interfere somewhat with the access of myosin to actin. Rigor complexes do not appear to affect ATPase activity, since the rate of ATP hydrolysis increases smoothly with increasing ATP saturation.

In contrast, under conditions where active and rigor complexes are associated with the same tropomyosin molecule, that is, when myosin is in excess over actin, rigor complexes seem to induce strong cooperative effects (Fig. 13*b*). The ATPase activity is maximum at low ATP levels, when the ratio between rigor and active complexes is optimal; it falls when rigor complexes gradually disappear with increasing ATP saturation. Furthermore, the maximal rate of ATP hydrolysis is much higher in regulated actin than in actin from which tropomyosin had been removed. Cooperative interactions induced by rigor complexes appear to change the behavior of tropomyosin from that of an incompletely removed steric hindrance to a mediator for the enhancement of actin-myosin interaction, presumably by increasing the rate of active complex formation (Bremel, Murray, and Weber, 1972). X-ray diffraction patterns cannot be sufficiently resolved to determine whether the mediation of this cooperative interaction is associated with movement of tropomyosin. It can be suggested that the position of tropomyosin was altered to permit the addition of tropomyosin side chains to the active site of actin, thus improving its reactivity with myosin. However, sequence studies have not shown any sevenfold repeat in tropomyosin (Hodges, Sodek, Smillie, and Jurasek, 1972); therefore, each actin active site cannot be modified by the same amino acid side chain. An alternative explanation for these cooperative interactions is that the mediation of cooperative effects by tropomyosin occurs indirectly, by linking actin monomers together in such a way that conformational changes induced in one actin monomer by myosin may be transmitted to the other monomers associated with the same tropomysin molecule.

In summary, the regulated actin filament is a multicomponent system whose composition and topography have become well understood through the work of Hanson (Hanson and Lowy, 1963), Ebashi (Ebashi and Endo, 1968), and H. E. Huxley (Spudich et al., 1972). Its proteins are capable of cooperative interactions, the most noticeable physiological function of which is the switching on and off of the actin filament for contraction and relaxation, in response to changes in the calcium level of the immediate environment, that is, the cytoplasm. One of the subunits of troponin senses the calcium level, and the binding of four calcium ions by this subunit alters the conformation of the whole molecule and transmits its message to another protein, tropomyosin. Tropomyosin does not respond by a conventional conformational change, but by a shift in its position on the actin filament; this shift is postulated to be the event responsible for switching on seven actin monomers simultaneously. According to this view, the state of actin is determined by the equilibrium position of tropomyosin, which in turn depends on the conformational state of troponin, as described in the preceding section by Cohen. This concept is a plausible mechanism for switching actin on and off. Whether all changes in the state of actin, such as the enhancement of activity above that of tropomyosin-free actin, are caused by changes in the tropomyosin position has yet to be determined. While the cooperative interactions of the regulated actin filament are best understood, they may by no means be the only ones that control the behavior of the myofibrils.

APPENDIX: MITOCHONDRIAL CALCIUM TRANSPORT IN MUSCLE

Albert L. Lehninger

Three membrane systems in the cells of vertebrates can transport Ca^{2+} and participate in its segregation: the plasma membrane, which has an outward-directed ATP-dependent Ca^{2+} pump; the mitochondrial inner membrane, which has a highly efficient inward-directed pump dependent on electron transport; and the sarcoplasmic reticulum, which has an ATP-dependent Ca^{2+} pump directed inward into the cisternae.

Some time ago we suggested that mitochondria may play an important role in segregating Ca^{2+} in heart and other red muscles, on the grounds that heart has a sparse endoplasmic reticulum, especially in amphibia, but a very large number of mitochondria. Approximately 40% of the heart cell volume consists of mitochondria, suggesting that they may participate in Ca^{2+} segregation, in addition to or instead of the sarcoplasmic reticulum. Heart mitochondria have ample capacity to segregate Ca^{2+} during the relaxation phase of the cycle, but the question is whether they have sufficient affinity.

Under normal conditions the transport of a pair of electrons down the respiratory chain of mitochondria is accompanied by the accumulation of two Ca^{2+} ions at each of the three energy-conserving sites in the transport chain, to give a total Ca^{2+}/O ratio of about 6.0. However, under some conditions (high pH, very low phosphate, high KCl) the Ca^{2+}/O ratio increases to values exceeding 50 or more. This is the phenomenon of "superstoichiometry," which we first observed in 1965 but which has remained a mystery until very recently.

The basis for the superstoichiometry effect has just been elucidated in our laboratory. Superstoichiometry results from a very rapid, early burst of Ca^{2+} binding to the membrane, with ejection of H^+; both processes are dependent on the flow of electrons through the respiratory chain but are not stoichiometrically related to electron flow. This early burst of energy-dependent Ca^{2+} binding, when superimposed on the normal stoichiometric ratio of Ca^{2+} uptake ($Ca^{2+}/O = 6$), yields the superstoichiometric Ca^{2+}/O

ratios of 50 or more in the early phases of Ca^{2+}-induced respiratory jumps.

We have found that the binding of the first few molecules of Ca^{2+} induces the entire mitochondrial membrane to undergo a transition to a more active form, similar to the transition induced by ADP. As a result the entire membrane develops a strong affinity for Ca^{2+} and loses affinity for protons, which are ejected into the medium. This early phase is followed by a second phase of much slower Ca^{2+} uptake, during which Ca^{2+} uptake is stoichiometric with oxygen uptake.

The extent and rate of Ca^{2+} uptake is extremely high during the superstoichiometric phase of Ca^{2+} uptake. The mitochondria of liver and heart can bind Ca^{2+} at the rate of 1,400 to 2,000 ng-ions/mg protein/min; up to 80 ng-ions Ca^{2+}/mg protein may be bound during the superstoichiometric phase. The capacity of heart mitochondria to bind Ca^{2+} by the superstoichiometric process is some 40-fold greater than required for maximum relaxation of cardiac muscle. Moreover, the rate of Ca^{2+} binding is more than ample to segregate the Ca^{2+} released during excitation. On the other hand, the sarcoplasmic reticulum, as represented by microsomes, appears to have a greater affinity for Ca^{2+} than mitochondria, suggesting that in heart muscle the mitochondria may function as Ca^{2+} segregating organelle largely during the period of peak Ca^{2+} concentration, with the sarcoplasmic reticulum responsible for segregating Ca^{2+} when the Ca^{2+} level drops to about 1 μM. There is a sigmoid relationship between the concentration of Ca^{2+} and Ca^{2+} binding by the membrane of respiring liver mitochondria. We have no specific evidence as to the nature of the Ca^{2+} binding sites, but two different Ca^{2+}-binding glycoprotein fractions have been obtained for mitochondria which may be involved.

REFERENCES

Bremel, R. D., Murray, J. M., and Weber, A. (1972): Manifestations of cooperative behavior in the regulated actin filament during actin-activated ATP hydrolysis in the presence of calcium. *Cold Spring Harbor Symp. Quant. Biol.*, 37:267–275.

Bremel, R. D., and Weber, A. (1972): Cooperation within actin filament in vertebrate skeletal muscle. *Nature New Biol.*, 238:97–101.

Caspar, D. L. D., Cohen, C., and Longley, W. (1969): Tropomyosin: Crystal structure, polymorphism and molecular interactions. *J. Mol. Biol.*, 41:87–107.

Cohen, C., Caspar, D. L. D., Johnson, J. P., Nauss, K., Margossian, S. S., and Parry, D. A. D. (1972): Tropomyosin-troponin assembly. *Cold Spring Harbor Symp. Quant. Biol.*, 37:287–297.

Cohen, C., Caspar, D. L. D., Parry, D. A. D., and Lucas, R. M. (1971): Tropomyosin crystal dynamics. *Cold Spring Harbor Symp. Quant. Biol.*, 36:205–216.

Cohen, C., and Holmes, K. C. (1963): X-ray diffraction evidence for α-helical coiled-coils in native muscle. *J. Mol. Biol.*, 6:423–432.

Cohen, C., Lowey, S., Harrison, R. G., Kendrick-Jones, J., and Szent-Györgyi, A. G. (1970): Segments from myosin rods. *J. Mol. Biol.*, 47:605–609.

Crick, F. H. C. (1953): The packing of α-helices: Simple coiled coils. *Acta Cryst.*, 6:689–697.

Ebashi, S., and Endo, M. (1968): Calcium ion and muscle contraction. *Prog. Biophys. Mol. Biol.*, 18:125–183.

Ebashi, S., Kodoma, A., and Ebashi, F. (1968): Troponin. I. Preparation and physiological function. *J. Biochem.,* 64:465–467.

Hanson, J., and Huxley, H. E. (1953): Structural basis of the cross-striations in muscle. *Nature,* 172:530–532.

Hanson, J., and Lowy, J. (1963): The structure of F-actin and of actin filaments isolated from muscle. *J. Mol. Biol.,* 6:46–60.

Harrison, R. G., Lowey, S., and Cohen, C. (1971): Assembly of myosin. *J. Mol. Biol.,* 59:531–535.

Haselgrove, J. C. (1970): X-ray diffraction studies of muscle. Ph.D. Thesis, Cambridge University.

Haselgrove, J. C. (1972): X-ray evidence for a conformational change in the actin-containing filaments of vertebrate striated muscle. *Cold Spring Harbor Symp. Quant. Biol.,* 37:341–352.

Head, J. F., and Perry, S. V. (1974): The interaction of the calcium-binding protein (troponin C) with bivalent cations and the inhibitory protein (troponin I). *Biochem. J.,* 137:145–154.

Hitchcock, S. E., Huxley, H. E., and Szent-Györgyi, A. G. (1973): Calcium sensitive binding of troponin to actin-tropomyosin: A two-site model for troponin action. *J. Mol. Biol.,* 80:825–836.

Hodges, R. S., Sodek, J., Smillie, L. B., and Jurasek, L. (1972): Tropomyosin: Amino acid sequence and coiled-coil structure. *Cold Spring Harbor Symp. Quant. Biol.,* 37:299–310.

Huxley, A. F., and Niedergerke, R. (1954): Structural changes in muscle during contraction. *Nature,* 173:971–973.

Huxley, H. E. (1963): Electron microscope studies on the structure of natural and synthetic protein filaments from striated muscle. *J. Mol. Biol.,* 7:281–308.

Huxley, H. E. (1969): The mechanism of muscular contraction. *Science,* 164:1356–1366.

Huxley, H. E. (1971): The structural basis of muscular contraction. *Proc. Roy. Soc. B,* 178:131–149.

Huxley, H. E. (1972): Structural changes in the actin- and myosin-containing filaments during contraction. *Cold Spring Harbor Symp. Quant. Biol.,* 37:361–376.

Huxley, H. E. (1973): Muscle contraction and cell motility. *Nature,* 243:445–449.

Huxley, H. E., and Brown, W. (1967): The low angle x-ray diagram of vertebrate striated muscle and its behaviour during contraction and rigor. *J. Mol. Biol.,* 30:383–434.

Huxley, H. E., and Hanson, J. (1954): Changes in the cross-striations of muscle during contraction and stretch and their structural interpretation. *Nature,* 173:973–976.

Kendrick-Jones, J., Szentkirályi, and Szent-Györgyi, A. G. (1972): Myosin-linked regulatory systems: The role of the light chains. *Cold Spring Harbor Symp. Quant. Biol.,* 37:47–53.

Lehman, W., Kendrick-Jones, J., and Szent-Györgyi, A. G. (1972): Myosin-linked regulatory systems: Comparative studies. *Cold Spring Harbor Symp. Quant. Biol.,* 37:319–330.

Lowey, S. (1971): Myosin: Molecule and filament. In: *Biological Macromolecules. Subunits in Biological Systems. Part A,* edited by S. N. Timasheff and G. D. Fasman, pp. 201–259. New York: Marcel Dekker.

Lowy, J. (1972): X-ray diffraction studies of striated and smooth muscles. *Bollettino di Zoologia,* 39:119–138.

Margossian, S. S., and Cohen, C. (1973): Troponin subunit interactions. *J. Mol. Biol.,* 81:409–413.

Miller, A., and Tregear, R. T. (1971): X-ray studies on the structure and function of vertebrate and invertebrate muscle. In: *Contractility of Muscle Cells and Related Processes,* edited by R. J. Podolsky, pp. 205–228. Englewood Cliffs, N.J.: Prentice-Hall.

Moore, P. B., Huxley, H. E., and DeRosier, D. J. (1970): Three-dimensional reconstruction of F-actin, thin filaments and decorated thin filaments. *J. Mol. Biol.,* 50:279–295.

Potter, J., Seidel, J. C., Leavif, P., Lehrer, S. S., and Gergely, J. (1974): Interaction of calcium with troponin. In: *Symposium on Calcium-Binding Proteins,* edited by W. Drabikowiski and E. Carafoli. Amsterdam: Elsevier (*in press*).

Sodek, J., Hodges, R. S., Smillie, L. B., and Jurasek, L. (1972): Amino-acid sequence of rabbit skeletal tropomyosin and its coiled-coil structure. *Proc. Nat. Acad. Sci.,* 69:3800–3804.

Spudich, J. A., Huxley, H. E., and Finch, J. T. (1972): Regulation of skeletal muscle contraction. II. Structural studies of the interaction of the tropomyosin-troponin complex with actin. *J. Mol. Biol.,* 72:619–632.

Squire, J. M. (1973): General model of myosin filament structure. III. Molecular packing arrangements in myosin filaments. *J. Mol. Biol.,* 77:291–323.

Szent-Györgyi, A. G., Szenkirályi, E. M., and Kendrick-Jones, J. (1973): The light chains of scallop myosin as regulatory subunits. *J. Mol. Biol.*, 74:179–203.

Taylor, E. W. (1972): Chemistry of muscle contraction. *Ann. Rev. Biochem.*, 41:577–616.

Weber, A., and Bremel, D. R. (1971): Regulation of contraction and relaxation in the myofibril. In: *Contractility of Muscle Cells and Related Processes,* edited by R. J. Podolsky, pp. 37–53. Englewood Cliffs, N.J.: Prentice Hall.

Weber, A., and Murray, J. M. (1973): Molecular control mechanisms in muscle contraction. *Physiol. Rev.*, 53:612–673.

Wray, J., Vibert, P., and Cohen, C. (1974): Cross bridge arrangements in *Limulus* muscle. *J. Mol. Biol. (in press).*

Functional Linkage in Biomolecular Systems, edited by
F. O. Schmitt, D. M. Schneider, and D. M. Crothers.
Raven Press, New York © 1975.

TRANSDUCTIVE COUPLING IN
THE NERVOUS SYSTEM

As explained in the introductory section, this conference was planned
with the idea of drawing attention to the fundamental biological role of
functional linkage, primarily including phenomena of cooperativity, allosteric interaction, transductive coupling, and amplification. Applications
to conventional neuroscience are conspicuous throughout, particularly in
connection with transductive coupling in sensory systems. It was antici-
pated that a subsequent conference might deal with higher levels of organization, including neuronal circuits, brain cell assemblies, and brain regions, up
to the brain as a whole.

Over the years, informal and tentative discussions at this higher level
have been held among the Associates of NRP. W. R. Adey, in particular,
has for several years reported progress in his study of the striking neurophysiological and behavioral effects of weak electrical fields and of the
apparent ability of brain cells to sense field potentials modulated at EEG
frequencies. These findings imply the existence of a mechanism capable of
amplifying very weak electrical signals whose magnitude is far less than that
required for postsynaptic excitation or presynaptic release to a level that
influences neurophysiological events and behavior. Such facts and concepts
depart widely from conventional models that consider only synaptic mechanisms and spike-mediated waves in neuronal nets, and suggest hierarchies
of excitatory organization interacting in a highly functionally linked fashion.
In more detail, cooperative interaction of Ca^{2+} ions with membrane surface
macromolecules was considered, as well as glycoproteins that extend from
the extracellular surface of brain cells and are regarded as sensing trans-
ducers for weak electric fields.

The material in Chapter 15 was presented in the final session of the
conference, "Major Conceptual Issues: Outlook for Further Advances."
Whether this contribution will serve as the "functional link" to a possible
future conference featuring linkage at "higher" levels of organization remains to be seen.

Functional Linkage in Biomolecular Systems, edited by
F. O. Schmitt, D. M. Schneider, and D. M. Crothers.
Raven Press, New York © 1975.

Chapter 15

Evidence for Cooperative Mechanisms
in the Susceptibility of Cerebral Tissue
to Environmental and Intrinsic Electric Fields

W. Ross Adey

The cerebral cortex of all vertebrates and the cerebral ganglia of invertebrates produce a rhythmic electrical activity that arises in their closely
packed cellular elements. This activity has long been considered to be little
more than a "noise" in cerebral tissue, having no direct physiological role
in information processing, although the advent of sophisticated computer
analyses of the EEG combined with pattern-recognition techniques has
increasingly challenged this view. At the very least, it is now clear that fine
correlates exist between the EEG and a wide range of behavioral states
(Adey, 1974*b*). Nevertheless, adequate evidence has been lacking that
would assign a causal role in information processing to the EEG.

How may we proceed further to answer the question of whether the EEG
may have a physiological role in brain tissue? Do brain cells sense field
potentials such as the EEG, and do such potentials modify their excitability
in the genesis of propagated action potentials? What experimental paradigms
and criteria should be used in testing for possible interactions between brain
cells and extracellular fields? Very importantly, does the anatomical and
physiological organization of brain tissue possess properties that might make
possible interactions between weak intrinsic or environmental electric
fields and the aggregate behavior of a domain of elements, thus precluding
observation of these effects in so-called simpler systems?

Classical neuroanatomy and neurophysiology, particularly synaptic
neurophysiology, have drawn heavily on simple systems, including spinal
motoneurons, aplysian ganglion cells, and cerebellar Purkinje cells. It is
doubtful that these are appropriate models for the intrinsic processes unique
to cerebral tissue in transaction, storage, and recall of information. The
disappointing but inescapable conclusion that we are rapidly approaching an
impasse in following cerebral models that consider only synaptic mechanisms and axonal connectivity has invited investigation of all the possible
ways in which interactions might occur in cerebral tissue. By experimental
isolation of a tissue or its cellular elements, it was hoped to discern better
certain properties which may be miniscule in individual elements but sub-

stantive in systems as a whole. Complexity may be an inherent and essential quality of cerebral tissue. There is a kinship with Heisenberg's uncertainty principle, not so much in the effects of measurement on the system being measured, but rather in the effects of its experimental isolation, or in the functional limitations inherent in most simple systems.

We have observed effects of weak electric and electromagnetic fields on the behavior of both humans and animals, and have correlated these effects with altered neurophysiological activity and modified brain chemistry. One striking conclusion of these studies is that mammalian central nervous functions can be modified by electrical gradients in cerebral tissue that are substantially smaller than those known to occur in postsynaptic excitation, as well as those presumed to occur with inward membrane currents at synaptic terminals during the release of transmitter substances.

Neither these observations nor models of cerebral organization which arise from them are nihilistic to the impressive body of synaptic physiology. Rather, they suggest the existence of hierarchies of excitatory organization, in which synaptic mechanisms represent but one level.

BRAIN AS A TISSUE IN THE PROCESSING OF INFORMATION

Information processing in brain tissue no longer is considered to involve only the nerve cells. There are strong physiological interactions between nervous and surrounding neuroglial cells, including concurrent electrical changes (Karahashi and Goldring, 1966) and simultaneous and sometimes reciprocal changes in chemical measures. The latter include enzyme activity and protein synthesis (Hydén, 1972), differential accumulation of the putative transmitter substances GABA (Henn and Hamberger, 1971), glycine (Ehinger and Falck, 1971), glutamic acid, aspartic acid, and taurine (Ehinger, 1973). By light microscopy, staining for calcium is low in neuronal cytoplasm, but appreciable in neuroglia (Tarby and Adey, 1967; Adey, 1970).

These interactions occur across the intervening intercellular space, which has been shown by rapid freezing techniques to be approximately 20% of the cerebral volume (van Harreveld, Crowell, and Malhotra, 1965), a figure confirmed by biochemical estimates (Reed, Woodbury, and Holtzer, 1964). The space is occupied by highly hydrated macromolecular material, forming a loose "fuzz." Although polyanionic, this material binds strongly to acidic solutions of phosphotungstic acid (Pease, 1966; Rambourg and Leblond, 1967). Despite its loose structure, it appears to blend with other glycoprotein material to form the outer coats or "glycocalyces" of cell membranes (Bennett, 1963).

Only a small portion of any extracellular current penetrates either neuronal or neuroglial membranes (Cole, 1940). Weak electric currents in cerebral tissue preferentially flow through the extracellular space; tissue impedence measurements therefore appear to reflect primarily conductance in the extracellular space (Coombs, Curtis, and Eccles, 1959; Nicholls and Kuffler, 1964). Moreover, conductance changes in cortical and subcortical structures accompany a variety of learned responses, suggesting that the cell surface and intercellular macromolecular material may be one site of structural change during information storage and its retrieval (Adey, Kado, and Didio, 1962b; Adey, Kado, Didio, and Schindler, 1963; Adey, Kado, McIlwain, and Walter, 1966). As discussed below, these surface regions may have other quite special functions in the detection and transduction of weak chemical and electrical events at the membrane surface (Schmitt and Samson, 1969; Adey, 1972).

The hypothesis has been advanced elsewhere (Adey and Walter, 1963; Adey, 1974b) that the characteristic phenomenon of overlapping dendritic fields in the palisades of cells that characterize all vertebrate cerebral ganglia may be associated with the concurrent development of a rhythmic electric wave process. This in turn may be fundamentally related to the ability of these tissues to undergo permanent changes in excitability as a result of their prior participation in specified patterns of excitation. This dendritic organization appears to constitute a specific arrangement in cerebral tissue, and is discussed further below.

HOW MIGHT INFORMATION BE PROCESSED IN BRAIN TISSUE?

Although it is clear that fiber conduction and synaptic activation are essential elements in brain function, there are at least three other modes of information handling in cerebral neurons that merit equivalent attention. These include dendro-dendritic conduction, neuronal-neuroglial interactions across the intercellular space, and the detection of weak stimuli that modify the immediate environment of the neuron. The last would include sensitivity to weak electric (and perhaps magnetic) fields and to minute amounts of chemical substances, including drugs, hormones, and neurohumors. The susceptibility of brain tissue to drugs such as LSD in body fluid concentrations as low as 10^{-9} (Adey, Bell, and Dennis, 1962a) is well known and generally accepted, and hormone concentrations that predictably modify brain function are even lower.

It is therefore surprising that such scant consideration has been given to the possibility that brain tissue may be sensitive to field potentials in the environment of the neuron, including the intrinsic fields of the EEG. The EEG appears to be the summed contribution of waves from many neuronal generators, volume-conducted through the extracellular medium. This volume-conducted component will appear simultaneously at points quite distant from the original generators, including the brain surface and scalp. Unlike axonal spike conduction, it will not behave as a propagated disturbance with a measurable conduction velocity, but will exhibit a frequency-dependent attenuation of its high-frequency components. The extent of this attenuation will be determined by the impedance character-istics of the extracellular medium. Intracellular records from cortical neurons show waves with amplitudes up to 20 mV whose frequency spec-trum resembles that of the EEG from the same region (Creutzfelt, Fuster, Lux, and Nacimiento, 1964; Elul, 1964, 1967a, 1972; Fujita and Sato, 1964). Evoked field potentials have also been correlated with membrane potential deflections in intracellular records (Purpura, Shofer, and Mus-grave, 1964; Elul and Adey, 1965; Creutzfelt, Watanabe, and Lux, 1966). Approximately 100 μV of signal would be contributed to the volume-conducted signal by a neuronal wave 10 mV in amplitude in intracellular records.

How, then, could such a weak extracellular field influence neuronal excitability? With a membrane potential of 50 mV, a typical depolarization of at least several millivolts is necessary to initiate a propagated spike discharge. Nevertheless, field gradients comparable with the EEG alter firing thresholds in spinal motoneurons (Nelson, 1966).

We may consider a mechanism of "membrane amplification" to account for sensing these fields during the possible sequence of events activating a domain of cortical neurons, here considered to be a group of several hundred cells (Anninos, Beek, Csermely, Harth, and Pertile, 1970). Neu-ronal spikes would be generated in the axon hillock of the neuronal soma and then pass by short axons or axon collaterals to adjacent neurons in the same domain. In a similar fashion, interdendritic connections would provide paths for the spread of slower neuronal wave activity generated in the dendrites, which might sweep longitudinally toward the soma (Green, Maxwell, Schindler, and Stumpf, 1960). These processes would jointly generate an EEG in the extracellular space enclosing the cell. A system of macromolecular sensors on the membrane surface might transduce com-ponents of the extracellular fields by altered ion binding and an associated conformation change. This altered membrane surface would then trigger a transmembrane amplification of ionic movements, thus modifying both the initial events mediated by neuronal slow waves and concurrent membrane potential changes induced by synaptic activation.

We may summarize this working model:

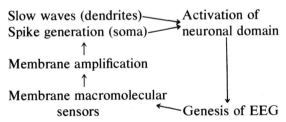

Such a model is hierarchically organized. Molecular events at the mem-brane surface would influence the excitability of a particular neuron, which in turn would influence others in its domain through conduction processes. The joint activity of other neurons would then produce a volume-conducted field through the domain, and this field would again modify the environment at each neuronal surface. This field is a remarkable "enchanted loom" when recorded at cellular dimensions, showing great differences in adjoining tripolar records along different electrical axes (Elul, 1962).

The following observations of central nervous interactions with weak electric and electromagnetic fields invite serious consideration of this type of model, since they occur at energy levels far below those required for classical synaptic activation, and will lead in turn to a more detailed consideration of membrane surface phenomena that might be involved.

EFFECTS OF LOW-LEVEL, LOW-FREQUENCY ELECTRIC FIELDS ON EEG AND BEHAVIOR

In 1960, Konig and Ankermüller reported altered human reaction times in response to low-level electric fields between 5 and 15 Hz; this was later confirmed by Hamer (1968) in our laboratory. Wever (1968) exposed human subjects to 10-Hz fields with an electric gradient of 2.5 V/m, and measured their patterns of circadian rhythms from sleep-wake cycles and from peaks and troughs in diurnal temperature cycles. After 7 to 10 days of control measurements, the fields were activated for an approximately equal period. Circadian rhythms were shortened by 1 to 2 hr in many subjects during field exposure.

After pilot studies in our laboratory suggested that subjective estimates of the passage of time were influenced by such fields, a detailed study was made of time estimation in the presence of weak electric fields in the pigtail macaque monkey (Gavalas, Walter, Hamer, and Adey, 1970).

Three monkeys were trained to estimate 5 sec between level presses. If the animals pressed with a 2.5-sec reward-enable interval, they were rewarded with apple juice. They were then exposed to the fields for 4 hr each day. In these initial experiments, the fields were generated between two large metal plates 50 cm square and 40 cm apart, and the field amplitude was 2.8 V peak-peak at 7 Hz. Each monkey was tested in two experiments of 20 exposures to 7-Hz fields and two comparable control experiments in the absence of any field. In summary, five of the six experiments showed a shift to significantly faster interresponse time in the 7-Hz fields compared with performance in the absence of fields; all mean differences were 0.4 sec or greater. Shifts in modal values also occurred in all five experiments, and were all 0.2 sec or greater. Although the total output of responses and the variability of those responses differed considerably from monkey to monkey (Fig. 1), the trend to shorter interresponse times in the presence of the fields was remarkably consistent, and the size of the shift was relatively large.

These initial findings have been confirmed and extended in five monkeys.

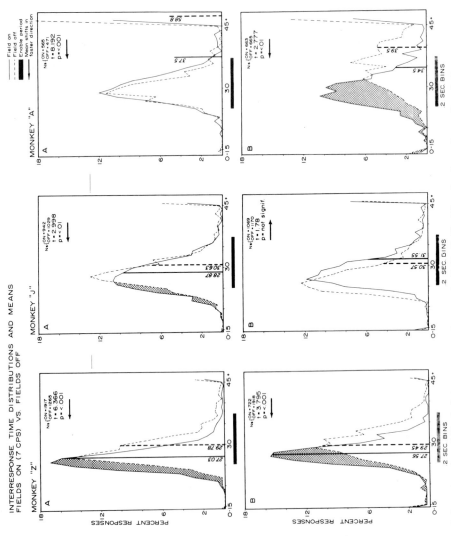

FIG. 1. Behavioral data showing shifts in interresponse time under 7-Hz fields. The abscissa shows time between responses in 0.2-sec bins; the ordinate shows percent of total responses at each interval. Note that only bins 15 to 45 are plotted; bins 0 to 144 were used in calculation of means and standard deviations. (From Gavalas et al., 1970.)

We have tested fields at 7, 10, 45, 60, and 75 Hz, at gradients ranging from 10 to 100 V/m. These later studies have indicated that higher voltage gradients decrease the variability in interresponse times.

Since questions of the possible production by implanted electrodes of antenna effects that might produce a focal field enhancement within the tissue have been widely raised, it is noteworthy that these thresholds and frequency differentials are similar for unimplanted and implanted subjects (Tables 1 and 2). Thus, it seems clear that the field is sensed directly by the organism without intercurrent effects attributable to an implanted electrode system.

TABLE 1. *Unimplanted monkey in a high-voltage field (56 V/m)*

Entire experiment			Hour 1			Hour 2			Hour 3		
Hz	V/m	x̄IRT	Hz	V/m	x̄IRT	Hz	V/m	x̄IRT	Hz	V/m	x̄IRT
7	56	5.347	7	56	5.440	7	56	5.697	75	56	5.659
75	56	5.576	75	56	5.498	75	56	5.922	60	56	5.784
60	56	5.756	60	56	5.698	0	0	5.976	7	56	5.819
0	0	5.960	0	0	5.883	60	56	5.987	0	0	6.121

* Rank-order weighted mean interresponse times (last bin excluded).

TABLE 2. *Unimplanted monkey in a high-voltage field (56 V/m)*

Entire experiment			Hour 1			Hour 2			Hour 3		
Hz	V/m	σ	Hz	V/m	σ	Hz	V/m	σ	Hz	V/m	σ
75	56	0.796	75	56	0.714	0	0	0.872	75	56	0.814
60	56	0.897	7	56	0.821	7	56	0.929	60	56	0.858
7	56	0.913	60	56	0.826	75	56	1.050	0	0	0.943
0	0	1.016	0	0	1.027	60	56	1.081	7	56	1.039

* Rank-order weighted standard deviations (last bin excluded).

EEG records during field exposure were not markedly changed by the fields. All of the monkeys in the initial study showed an altered EEG power output at 6 to 8 Hz in the hippocampus, with less consistent alterations in the amygdala and nucleus centrum medianum with the 7-Hz fields.

EFFECTS ON BRAIN ELECTRICAL RHYTHMS AND BEHAVIOR OF LOW-LEVEL, VERY-HIGH-FREQUENCY (VHF) RADIO FIELDS AMPLITUDE MODULATED AT EEG FREQUENCIES

In a search for more definite evidence that the membrane surface might transduce weak extracellular fields as a step in the excitation process, we have examined the effects of VHF electromagnetic fields, amplitude modulated at EEG frequencies. This approach was based on the strong asymmetry of the fixed charge distribution on membrane surface glycoproteins with respect to extracellular fluid and to deeper layers of the membrane. Such a phase partition would be expected to demodulate the envelope of a high-frequency carrier wave, as in a semiconductor, although remaining unresponsive to the carrier frequency itself. If this hypothesis were correct, low-frequency modulation on the carrier would be a prerequisite for central nervous effects, and differential effects at specific brain sites would depend on particular modulating frequencies.

This hypothesis was strongly supported by our findings in cats exposed to a 147 MHz, 2.0 mW/cm^2 field, amplitude modulated at 0.5 to 30 Hz. Field modulation at frequencies identical with EEG "signatures" in single brain structures sharply reinforced the occurrence of these rhythms, in both conditional and unconditional behavioral situations (Bawin, Gavalas-Medici, and Adey, 1973). Animals trained to produce a specific brain rhythm in the presence of the field (or receive an aversive stimulus) continued to produce the rhythm without aversive stimulation (extinction trials) for 25 to 40 days, but ceased to perform within a few days in the absence of the fields. The fields also increased the rate of occurrence of spontaneous rhythms at specific locations, but only when modulated at frequencies close to the dominant biological frequency of the selected intrinsic EEG rhythm.

Spectral analysis of EEG records showed a concentration of energy around the imposed modulated frequency. However, daily controls with field amplitudes modulated at different frequencies for short periods failed to produce any changes or any artifactual patterns in these highly stable responses. If, despite their shielding up to the head, antenna effects on the electrode leads had induced even small potentials at the tip of the electrodes, spectral analysis would be expected to reveal voltages so induced and rectified at the electrode-tissue contact. The EEG changes were anatomically localized, highly specific in terms of frequency and associated

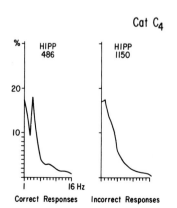

FIG. 2. Comparison of the EEG autospectra of hippocampal patterns in cases of correct and incorrect responses during exposures to VHF fields amplitude modulated at 4.5 Hz. Autospectra were calculated from averages of 20 epochs, each 2.5 sec in duration. (From Bawin et al., 1973.)

with transient patterns. Figure 2 compares the EEG autospectra in one animal accompanying correct and incorrect responses during irradiation with fields modulated at 4.5 Hz (the peak frequency of the response), and shows that the spectral peak shifted away from the imposed frequency when the animal was not performing. It therefore seems unlikely that the tissue effects can be attributed to direct injection of field voltages via the electrodes, a viewpoint strongly supported by the changes in chemistry induced in isolated brain tissue that are described below.

PARTICIPATION OF MEMBRANE SURFACE MACROMOLECULES IN EXCITATION; EVIDENCE FOR COOPERATIVE INTERACTIONS WITH CALCIUM IONS

Our studies strongly imply that the binding and release of calcium ions to membrane surface macromolecules is an important step in these field interactions. This surface glycocalyx greatly extends the effective membrane thickness, perhaps to as much as 2000 Å, and may play a role in the detection of hormones and neurohumoral substances that are effective in minute amounts. Initial conformational changes at the binding site may be followed by transmembrane effects, with molecular "switches" such as prostaglandins triggered in the presence of Ca^{2+} (Ramwell and Shaw, 1970), thus greatly "amplifying" the initial binding energies. We have followed three lines of related research.

The Role of Ca^{2+} in the Release of Ca^{2+} and GABA from Cat Cerebral Cortex

When cat cerebral cortex is equilibrated with $^{45}Ca^{2+}$ and ^{3}H-GABA in the absence of general anesthesia, a small increase in unlabeled Ca^{2+} in the solution bathing the cortex elicited a large release of labeled $^{45}Ca^{2+}$ and labeled GABA (Fig. 3). Moreover, the effect of a 1 mM increment in Ca^{2+} concentration was only slightly less than that of a 20 mM increment (Kaczmarek and Adey, 1973). Mg^{2+} did not trigger the release of either Mg^{2+} or Ca^{2+}. A possible mechanism for this highly nonlinear release of $^{45}Ca^{2+}$ may be the displacement of $^{45}Ca^{2+}$ bound to polyanionic sites on the membrane surface. To be consistent with the $^{45}Ca^{2+}$ efflux and net Ca^{2+} binding, this mechanism might take the form

$$Ca^{2+} + {}^{45}Ca\text{--}M^{n-} \rightarrow Ca\text{--}{}^{45}Ca\text{--}M^{(n-2)-}$$
$$Ca\text{--}{}^{45}Ca\text{--}M^{(n-2)-} \rightarrow {}^{45}Ca^{2+} + Ca\text{--}M^{n-}$$

where M represents a membrane anionic species. The efflux of Ca^{2+} ions from the membrane would then be proportional to a higher power of the bound Ca^{2+} ion concentration.

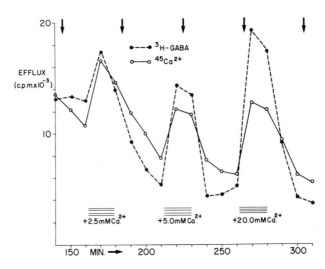

FIG. 3. The simultaneous efflux of $^{45}Ca^{2+}$ and ^{3}H-GABA from cat cortex in an experiment in which aminoxyacetic acid (AOAA), 5 mg/kg body weight, had been administered before incubation with ^{3}H-GABA. The superfusion medium contained 2.16 mM Ca^{2+} before increasing the Ca^{2+} concentration by the amount indicated. Time after the start of superfusion is shown on the abscissa, and the arrows indicate gallamine triethiodide administration. (From Kaczmarek and Adey, 1973.)

Effects of Weak Electrical Gradients on Ca ion and GABA Fluxes in Cortex

This sharp nonlinearity in the release of bound calcium by a small increase in extracellular Ca^{2+} suggested that Ca^{2+} release might be triggered by a weak electric gradient (Kaczmarek and Adey, 1974). Pulsed electrical stimulation of cat cortex with gradients in the range of 20 to 60 mV/cm increased the efflux of both $^{45}Ca^{2+}$ and ^{3}H-GABA (Fig. 4). The mean increase with a gradient of 50 mV/cm was a 1.29 ± 0.04 for ^{3}H-GABA, but these values may reflect larger changes in the rate of binding and release in the tissue.

Important questions may be raised by these findings in terms of classical processes of transmitter release. If a typical synaptic terminal is 0.5 μ in diameter, the extracellular gradient imposed by these fields is, at most, 2.5 μV across the terminal. It is unclear how such a weak stimulus would be able to modify a transmembrane potential of 50 mV sufficiently to influence transmitter release; the gradients in these experiments were more than four orders of magnitude less than the transmembrane gradient. Similar considerations apply to effects of the fields on postsynaptic excitability.

To what extent might the field generated by one cortical neuron influence a nearby cell? For the spinal motoneuron, extracellular gradients generated by the neurons exceed 50 mV/cm and do alter neuronal excitability (Nelson,

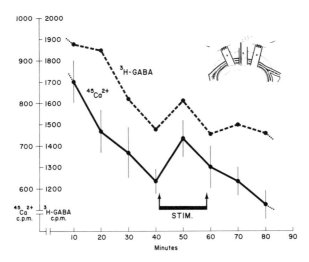

FIG. 4. Effects of low-level electrical stimulation with cortical electrical gradient of 50 mV/cm, 200 pulses/sec, 1.0 msec duration, on efflux of $^{45}Ca^{2+}$ and ^{3}H-GABA. (From Kaczmarek and Adey, 1974.)

1966). In our experiments, seizures induced by topical glutamate or intravenous thiosemicarbazide were as high as 37.5 mV/cm across a 1.0-mm dipole. Considerably higher gradients in the normal EEG can be recorded from microelectrode tips separated by cellular dimensions (Elul, 1962).

The applied fields in these experiments are therefore in the range of naturally occurring gradients, thus supporting the hypothesis that cortical neurons are sensitive to the natural electric field gradients which surround them.

Altered Ca Efflux in the Isolated Chick Brain with Modulated VHF Fields

The release of Ca^{2+} by weak electrical stimulation led us to test the effects of the modulated VHF fields described above on freshly isolated chicken brain (Bawin, Kaczmarek, and Adey, 1974). The cerebrum was placed in a $^{45}Ca^{2+}$ Ringer solution for 30 min and the efflux of Ca^{2+} subsequently observed for a 90-min period, with and without VHF field exposure. There was a remarkable "tuning curve" for different modulation frequencies, with increased Ca^{2+} efflux from the cortex at modulation frequencies between 9 and 20 Hz, but very little increase outside this frequency band (Fig. 5). Moreover, the results were identical in brains killed with 10^{-4} M potassium cyanide prior to equilibration with $^{45}Ca^{2+}$. Previous studies in our laboratory have shown the persistence of membrane fixed charges after cyanide poisoning of cultured neurons (Elul, 1967b), and it therefore seems reasonable to assume that the binding of Ca^{2+} and its subsequent efflux

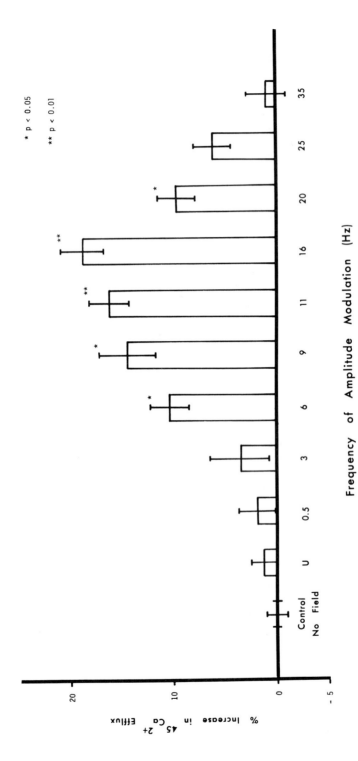

FIG. 5. Effects of amplitude-modulated VHF fields on the $^{45}Ca^{2+}$ efflux from the isolated brain of the neonate chick. The results, given ±S.E.M., are expressed as percent of increase of the calcium efflux, by comparison with control condition, in the absence of fields (From Bawin et al., 1974.)

relate to persisting properties of membrane surface polyanions. Identical exposures of isolated gastrocnemius muscle to these VHF fields have not elicited increased $^{45}Ca^{2+}$ efflux, suggesting that the phenomenon may be specific to brain tissue.

DISCUSSION

Three major points emerge from these studies. It seems clear that un-equivocal interactions have been demonstrated between the brain tissue of mammals and birds and a variety of electric and electromagnetic fields, with tissue electric gradients and associated transmembrane ion fluxes far lower than those known to occur in the classical processes of excitation. Indeed, behavioral effects seen in our studies and those of others occur with such low tissue electric gradients that they may be best modeled from a considera-tion of cooperative processes at the membrane surface. A second basic consideration is the emergence of the calcium ion as a strong candidate for an essential role in these interactions. Third, the evidence suggests a func-tional role for intrinsic electric gradients, including the electroencephalo-gram, since behavioral electrophysiological and neurochemical changes have all followed the imposition of external electric fields with tissue com-ponents at or below levels of these intrinsic gradients.

We may model these membrane events in certain sequences and at differing levels of organization. The effectiveness of these low-level fields suggests an initial interaction in the long axis of the membrane, perhaps involving macromolecular conformation changes attributable to altered calcium binding, and acting as precursors to transmembrane responses. The broad polyanionic glycoprotein surface sheet may be a sensor for these fields, binding cations as a "counter-ion" layer at their surface. Divalent cations are more powerfully bound than the monovalent, with the exception of hydrogen ions, and calcium is more powerfully bound than other divalent ions, including magnesium (Katchalsky, 1964). Bass and Moore (1968) have proposed that excitation involves displacement of Ca^{2+} ions from macromolecular binding sites by hydrogen ions. Although the ensuing local alkalosis would entail only a restricted movement of calcium ions to ad-jacent binding sites, and not their release in a major diffusional flow, the present studies invite consideration of a yet more fragile series of interac-tions, at the level of transient states of cooperative organization among fixed charges on surface macromolecules.

Our data on calcium release by these fields indicates that the tissue electric gradients are effective at levels of tenths of microvolts per micro-meter, and that the binding and release of calcium to membrane surface polyanions is probably in the class of "cooperative" processes, with a weak trigger at one point initiating macromolecular conformational changes over considerable distances along the membrane, and thereafter triggering metabolic energy release through transmembrane signals. Schwarz et al. (Schwarz, 1967, 1970; Schwarz and Balthasar, 1970; Schwarz, Klose, and Balthasar, 1970) envisaged the development of cooperativity in linear biopolymers, such as poly-L-glutamic acid, by assuming that immediately neighboring segments of the polymer are more likely to be found in like charge states than unlike ones. Grodsky (1974) has proposed a quantum mechanical model for the appearance of coherent membrane "patches" in the glyocalyx at 37°C. At the membrane surface, decremental dendritic conduction and the detection of perineuronal electric fields might then be based on a "virtual" wave of altered Ca^{2+} binding, traveling longitudinally on dendritic structures and leaving modified states of binding sites on the macromolecular sheet behind the advancing wave, but involving minimal displacement of Ca^{2+} ions to adjacent sites.

Ca^{2+} ions move grossly through cerebral tissue at rates around 0.3 μM/sec (Adey, 1971; van Harreveld, Dafny, and Khattab, 1971), a speed compatible with this hypothesis, but these observations do not address the question of small, focal displacements of Ca^{2+} to adjacent binding sites in the presence of a fixed charge field. Einolf and Carstensen (1971) have pointed out that lateral cationic movement along a porous surface having radially oriented fixed charges is associated with dielectric constants as high as 10^6 at frequencies under 1.0 kHz. Their model would offer an explanation for reactive components in cerebral impedance (Ranck, 1963) that alter with shifting physiological states (Adey et al., 1966; Adey, Bystrom, Costin, Kado, and Tarby, 1969), and have been attributed to properties of the electrode-tissue interface rather than to cerebral tissue itself (Gesteland, Howland, Lettvin, and Levine, 1959). These very high dielectric constants at low frequencies may also be relevant to the rapid attenuation of volume-conducted high-frequency components of neural activity in brain tissue.

Finally, interactions between cerebral tissue and fields whose frequency and intensity components mimic those of intrinsic natural gradients suggest a functional role for the latter. Although it is not yet possible to assign a clear role to them in information processing, the data do suggest that they can modify states of the neuronal surface, and thus modify thresholds of excitability for both spike propagation and dendro-dendritic interaction. In terms of the model proposed at the beginning of this paper, they would thus play an essential role in transductive coupling, with these first weak interactions relating in a hierarchical sequence to later well-known transmembrane events.

For imposed external fields, the observed behavioral thresholds appear to lie between 1 and 10 V/m. We have measured the component of a 7 V peak-to-peak 7-Hz field induced in a monkey's head as a current to ground of 0.8 nA through the electrode system. Although no precise measurement of the intracerebral electric gradient produced by the field has been feasible, it would be about 0.02 μV/cm in a brain having a conducting cross section of approximately 10 cm^2 and a maximum linear dimension of 7 cm in the axis of the field, based on a specific brain impedance of 300 Ω-cm at these frequencies (Ranck, 1963). That such a weak field should be an effective stimulus is baffling in terms of classical synaptic excitation, in which an action potential transiently abolishes a gradient of about 1 kV/cm, some ten orders of magnitude larger than these weak fields. A significant release of transmitter substances from within the membranes of presynaptic terminals is equally difficult to explain. This disparity between observed field effects on the central nervous system as a whole and the improbability of a direct synaptic action surely invites fresh consideration of more subtle membrane sensitivities.

ACKNOWLEDGMENTS

These studies were supported by National Science Foundation grant GB-27740, U.S. Air Force contract F44620-70-C-0017, and ONR contract N00014-A-200-4037.

APPENDIX: A POSSIBLE MECHANISM FOR CALCIUM STORAGE AND RELEASE

David A. Rees

The polysaccharide-Ca^{2+} associations described in Chapter 1 suggested that similar types of interaction might be involved in Ca^{2+} sequestering and release within the intercellular space. Although little is yet known about the polysaccharide content of the intracellular space of brain tissue, carbohydrates known to be present in the intercellular space of other tissue include hyaluronic acid, keratan sulfate, and chondroitin sulfate, all of which contain repetitive regions that are capable of forming extended helices. For example, hyaluronic acid has been thought to form stable structures similar to those of the carrageenans (Dea, Moorhouse, Rees, Arnott, Guss, and Balazs, 1973).

The carbohydrates that are more intimately associated with cell membranes, particularly those that are covalently attached to polypeptide or lipid moieties anchored in the membrane bilayer, do not have regular sequences of sugar residues (Kiss, 1969; Hughes, 1973; Spiro, 1973), and are therefore unlikely to form regular structures such as the helix or ribbon. However, the conclusions that have emerged from studies with the long-chain repetitive molecules do suggest the possibility that certain kinds of interactions might have biological significance. For example, sialic acid is found in abundance as the terminal residue of the glycolipids and glycoproteins that are anchored in the bilayer. The disposition of carboxylate and other oxygen functions within this sugar carboxylic acid residue suggests an analogy with the sugar carboxylate residues that form egg-box structures and cooperatively bind Ca^{2+} (see Chapter 1). In addition, sialic acid residues have been shown to be involved in important calcium binding sites on the external surfaces of some cells (Long and Mouat, 1971).

Gangliosides are major components of many cell membranes, and these glycolipids are particularly abundant in neuronal membranes. Since Ca^{2+} is intimately involved in nerve excitability, it is tempting to speculate that these gangliosides might interact specifically with Ca^{2+}. The covalent structures of many gangliosides are well known, and it was possible to derive tentative conformations for them using principles of conformational analysis that were recently developed for carbohydrate polymers (Rees, 1973; D. Thom, *personal communication*).

The conformations predicted for several of the gangliosides that contain consecutive sialic acid residues linked to position 3 of an interior galactose residue were of particular interest. The conformations predicted for these molecules contained an extensive system of long-range hydrogen bonding. This supported the plausibility of the structures, because the models were built only from a consideration of short-range interactions. In these models, a cavity is present that matches the ionic radius of Ca^{2+}, and that is lined with about nine oxygen atoms within a suitable distance for coordination, including one oxygen from each of the two carboxylate groups. The region opposite this site is a hydrophobic basin formed by the C—H bonds of the sugar rings and of the N-acetates; binding of an apolar species at this site might be coupled to Ca^{2+} binding and release.

REFERENCES

Adey, W. R. (1970): Cerebral structure and information storage. *Prog. Physiol. Psychol.*, pp. 181–200.

Adey, W. R. (1971): Evidence for cerebral membrane effects of calcium, derived from direct-current gradient, impedance, and intracellular records. *Exp. Neurol.*, 30:78–102.

Adey, W. R. (1972): Organization of brain tissue: Is the brain a noisy processor? *Int. J. Neurosci.*, 3:271–284.

Adey, W. R. (1974a): Extracellular microenvironment. In: *Dynamic Patterns of Brain Cell Assemblies. Neurosciences Res. Prog. Bull.*, 12:80–85.

Adey, W. R. (1974b): The influences of impressed electrical fields at EEG frequencies on brain and behavior. In: *Behavior and Brain Electrical Activity*, edited by H. Altshuler and N. Burch. New York: Plenum Press.

Adey, W. R., Bell, F. R., and Dennis, B. J. (1962a): Effects of LSD-25, psilocybin, and psilocin on temporal lobe EEG patterns and learned behavior in the cat. *Neurology*, 12:591–602.

Adey, W. R., Bystrom, B. G., Costin, A., Kado, R. T., and Tarby, T. J. (1969): Divalent cations in cerebral impedance and cell membrane morphology. *Exp. Neurol.*, 23:29–50.

Adey, W. R., Kado, R. T., and Didio, J. (1962b): Impedance measurements in brain tissue of animals using microvolt signals. *Exp. Neurol.*, 5:47–66.

Adey, W. R., Kado, R. T., Didio, J., and Schindler, W. J. (1963): Impedance changes in cerebral tissue accompanying a learned discriminative performance in the cat. *Exp. Neurol.*, 7:259–281.

Adey, W. R., Kado, R. T., McIlwain, J. T., and Walter, D. O. (1966): The role of neuronal elements in regional cerebral impedance changes in alerting, orienting and discriminative responses. *Exp. Neurol.*, 15:490–510.

Adey, W. R., and Walter, D. O. (1963): Application of phase detection and averaging techniques in computer analysis of EEG records in the cat. *Exp. Neurol.,* 7:186–209.

Anninos, P. A., Beek, B., Csermely, T. J., Harth, E. M., and Pertile, G. (1970): Dynamics of neural structures. *J. Theor. Biol.,* 26:121–148.

Bass, L., and Moore, W. J. (1968): A model of nervous excitation based on the Wien dissociation effect. In: *Structural Chemistry and Molecular Biology,* edited by A. Rich and C. M. Davidson, pp. 356–368. San Francisco: Freeman.

Bawin, S. M., Gavalas-Medici, R. J., and Adey, W. R. (1973): Effects of modulated very high frequency fields on specific brain rhythms in cats. *Brain Res.,* 58:365–384.

Bawin, S. M., Kaczmarek, L. K., and Adey, W. R. (1974): Effects of modulated VHF fields on the central nervous system. *Ann. N.Y. Acad. Sci. (in press).*

Bennett, H. S. (1963): Morphological aspects of extracellular polysaccharides. *J. Histochem. Cytochem.,* 11:14–23.

Cole, K. S. (1940): Permeability and impermeability of cell membranes for ions. *Cold Spring Harbor Symp. Quant. Biol.,* 8:110–122.

Coombs, J. S., Curtis, D. R., and Eccles, J. C. (1959): The electric constants of motoneurone membrane. *J. Physiol.,* 145:505–528.

Creutzfelt, O. D., Fuster, J. M., Lux, H. D., and Nacimiento, A. (1964): Experimenteller Nachweis von Beziehungen zwischen EEG-Wellen und Activtät corticaler Nervenzellen. *Naturwiss.,* 51:166–167.

Creutzfelt, O. D., Watanabe, S., and Lux, H. D. (1966): Relations between EEG phenomena and potentials of single cortical cells. II. Spontaneous and convulsoid activity. *Electroencephalogr. Clin. Neurophysiol.,* 20:19–37.

Dea, I. C. M., Moorhouse, R., Rees, D. A., Arnott, S., Guss, J. M., and Balazs, E. A. (1973): Hyaluronic acid: A novel, double helical molecule. *Science,* 179:560–562.

Ehinger, B. (1973): Glial uptake of taurine in the rabbit retina. *Brain Res.,* 60:512–516.

Ehinger, B., and Falck, B. (1971): Autoradiography of some suspected neurotransmitter substances: GABA, glycine, glutamic acid, histamine, dopamine, and L-DOPA. *Brain Res.,* 33:157–172.

Einolf, C. W., Jr., and Carstensen, E. L. (1971): Low-frequency dielectric dispersion in suspensions of ion-exchange resins. *J. Physical Chem.,* 75:1091–1099.

Elul, R. (1962): Dipoles of spontaneous activity in the cerebral cortex. *Exp. Neurol.,* 6:285–299.

Elul, R. (1964): Specific site of generation of brain waves. *Physiologist,* 7:125 (Abstr.).

Elul, R. (1967a): Statistical mechanisms in generation of the EEG. In: *Progress in Biomedical Engineering,* edited by L. J. Fogel and F. W. George, pp. 131–150. Washington, D.C.: Spartan Books.

Elul, R. (1967b): Fixed charge in the cell membrane. *J. Physiol.,* 189:351–365.

Elul, R. (1972): The genesis of the EEG. *Int. Rev. Neurobiol.,* 15:227–272.

Elul, R., and Adey, W. R. (1965): The intracellular correlates of gross evoked responses. *Proc. 23rd Int. Cong. Physiol. Sci.,* Tokyo, p. 434 (Abstr.).

Fujita, Y., and Sato, T. (1964): Intracellular records from hippocampal pyramidal cells in rabbit during theta rhythm activity. *J. Neurophysiol.,* 27:1011–1025.

Gavalas, R. J., Walter, D. O., Hamer, J., and Adey, W. R. (1970): Effect of low-level, low-frequency electric fields on EEG and behavior in *Macaca nemestrina. Brain Res.,* 18:491–501.

Gesteland, R. C., Howland, B., Lettvin, J. Y., and Levine, S. (1959): Comments on microelectrodes. *Proc. Inst. Radio Eng.,* 47:1856–1861.

Green, J. D., Maxwell, D. S., Schindler, W. J., and Stumpf, C. (1960): Rabbit EEG "theta" rhythm; its anatomical source and relation to activity in single neurons. *J. Neurophysiol.,* 23:403–420.

Grodsky, I. T. (1974): Possible physical substrates for the interaction of electromagnetic fields with biological membranes. *Ann. N.Y. Acad. Sci. (in press).*

Hamer, J. R. (1968): Effects of low level, low frequency electric fields on human reaction time. *Commun. Behav. Biol.,* 2(A):217–222.

Henn, F. A., and Hamberger, A. (1971): Glial cell function: Uptake of transmitter substances. *Proc. Nat. Acad. Sci.,* 68:2686–2690.

Hughes, R. C. (1973): Glycoproteins as components of cellular membranes. *Prog. Biophys. Mol. Biol.,* 26:191–268.

Hydén, H. (1972): Macromolecules and behavior. In: *The Arthur Thomson Lectures* (University of Birmingham, England), edited by G. B. Ansell and P. B. Bradley. London: Macmillan.

Kaczmarek, L. K., and Adey, W. R. (1973): The efflux of $^{45}Ca^{2+}$ and $[^3H]$-γ-aminobutyric acid from cat cerebral cortex. *Brain Res.*, 63:331–342.

Kaczmarek, L. K., and Adey, W. R. (1974): Weak electric gradients change ionic and transmitter fluxes in cortex. *Brain Res.*, 66:537–540.

Karahashi, Y., and Goldring, S. (1966): Intracellular potentials from "idle" cells in cerebral cortex of cat. *Electroencephalogr. Clin. Neurophysiol.*, 20:600–607.

Katchalsky, A. (1964): Polyelectrolytes and their biological interactions. In: *Connective Tissue: Intercellular Macromolecules. Proceedings of a Symposium sponsored by the New York Heart Association*, pp. 9–41. Boston: Little, Brown.

Kiss, J. (1969): Glycosphingolipids (sugar-sphingosine conjugates). *Adv. Carbohydrate Chem. Biochem.*, 24:381–433.

König, H., and Ankermüller, F. (1960): Über den Einfluss besonders niederfrequenter elektrischer Vorgänge in der Atmosphäre auf den Menschen. *Naturwiss.*, 47:486–490.

Long, C., and Mouat, B. (1971): The binding of calcium ions by erythrocytes and "ghost"-cell membranes. *Biochem. J.*, 123:829–836.

Nelson, P. G. (1966): Interaction between spinal motoneurons of the cat. *J. Neurophysiol.*, 29:275–287.

Nicholls, J. G., and Kuffler, S. W. (1964): Extracellular space as a pathway for exchange between blood and neurons in the central nervous system of the leech: Ionic composition of glial cells and neurons. *J. Neurophysiol.*, 27:645–671.

Pease, D. C. (1966): Polysaccharides associated with the exterior surface of epithelial cells: Kidney, intestine, brain. *J. Ultrastr. Res.*, 15:555–588.

Purpura, D. P., Shofer, R. J., and Musgrave, F. S. (1964): Cortical intracellular potentials during augmenting and recruiting responses. II. Patterns of synaptic activities in pyramidal and nonpyramidal tract neurons. *J. Neurophysiol.*, 27:133–151.

Rambourg, A., and Leblond, C. P. (1967): Electron microscope observations on the carbohydrate-rich cell coat present at the surface of cells in the rat. *J. Cell. Biol.*, 32:27–53.

Ramwell, P. W., and Shaw, J. E. (1970): Biological significance of the prostaglandins. *Rec. Prog. Horm. Res.*, 26:139–187.

Ranck, J. B. (1963): Specific impedance of rabbit cerebral cortex. *Exp. Neurol.*, 7:144–152.

Reed, D. J., Woodbury, D. M., and Holtzer, R. L. (1964): Brain edema, electrolytes, and extracellular space. Effect of triethyl tin on brain and skeletal muscle. *Arch. Neurol.*, 10:604–616.

Rees, D. A. (1973): Polysaccharide conformation. *M.T.P. Internat. Rev. Sci. Org. Chem.*, 7:251–283.

Schmitt, F. O., and Samson, F. E., Jr. (1969): Brain Cell Microenvironment. Neurosciences Res. Prog. Bull., 7:277–417.

Schwarz, G. (1967): A basic approach to a general theory for cooperative intramolecular conformation changes of linear biopolymers. *Biopolymers*, 5:321–324.

Schwarz, G. (1970): Cooperative binding to linear biopolymers. 1. Fundamental static and dynamic properties. *Eur. J. Biochem.*, 12:442–453.

Schwarz, G., and Balthasar, W. (1970): Cooperative binding to linear biopolymers. 3. Thermodynamic and kinetic analysis of the acridine orange-poly(L-glutamic acid) system. *Eur. J. Biochem.*, 12:461–467.

Schwarz, G., Klose, S., and Balthasar, W. (1970): Cooperative binding to linear biopolymers. 2. Thermodynamic analysis of the proflavine-poly(L-glutamic acid) system. *Eur. J. Biochem.*, 12:454–460.

Spiro, R. G. (1973): Glycoproteins. *Adv. Protein Chem.*, 27:349–467.

Tarby, T. J., and Adey, W. R. (1967): Cytological chemical identification of calcium in brain tissue. *Anat. Record*, 157:331–332 (Abstr.).

van Harreveld, A., Crowell, J., and Malhotra, S. K. (1965): A study of extracellular space in central nervous tissue by freeze-substition. *J. Cell. Biol.*, 25:117–137.

van Harreveld, A., Dafny, N., and Khattab, F. I. (1971): Effects of calcium on the electrical resistance and the extracellular space of cerebral cortex. *Exp. Neurol.*, 31:358–367.

Wever, R. (1968): Einfluss schwacher elektro-magnetischer Felder auf die circadiane Periodik des Menschen. *Naturwiss.*, 55:29–33.

SUBJECT INDEX

A

A1 protein of myelin, 108-112
ACTH, 204
ADP
  and contraction, 301, 312-318
  in mitochondria, 168-180
  regulation of phosphofructo-
    kinase, 55
AMP
  regulation of phosphofructo-
    kinase, 55
ATP, 4, 301
  and contractile tissue, 297-321
  in mitochondria, 168-180
  regulation of aspartate trans-
    carbamylase, 53
  regulation of phosphofructo-
    kinase, 55
ATPase
  of kidney, 113
  of sarcoplasmic reticulum, 97,
    299-301
Acetylcholine receptor, 142, 215-
  228
  allostery of, 223-227
  isolation and characterization of,
    215-223
  movement of, 142
Acetylcholinesterase, 215
Actin, 4, 297-321
Adenylate cyclase, 157, 203-213
Alginates, 35-37

Alpha-bungarotoxin, 216, 219
Allosteric interactions, 3-8, 43-56,
    171, 192-193, 223-227, 297-321
Amphotericin B, 112
Amplification and functional linkage,
    4, 28, 231-252, 328-329
Aniline napthalene sulfonic acid (ANS),
    105, 177
Antibody production, 181-192
Anticodon of mRNA, 30-31
Antisystems of mitochondrial trans-
    port, 173, 175
Aspartate transcarbamylase, 53
Assymetry of erythrocyte membrane,
    106-107
Atractyloside, 178
Auxotrophic bacteria, 123-136

B

B-cells (bone marrow derived cells),
    181-201
Benson model of membrane structure,
    103
Beta-galactosidase, 64, 132-135
Beta-hydroxybutyrate system, 112
Bohr effect, 5, 177
Bombykol, 263-270
Bombyx mori, 263-270
Bromostearic acid, 134-137